Readings

in Science and Spirit

PRENTICE-HALL INTERNATIONAL, INC., *London*
PRENTICE-HALL OF AUSTRALIA, PTY., LTD., *Sydney*
PRENTICE-HALL OF CANADA, LTD., *Toronto*
PRENTICE-HALL OF INDIA (PRIVATE), LTD., *New Delhi*
PRENTICE-HALL OF JAPAN, INC., *Tokyo*

EDITED BY

CAMILLUS D. TALAFOUS, O.S.B.

Readings
in Science and Spirit

Prentice-Hall, Inc.   Englewood Cliffs, New Jersey

Nihil obstat:
  John Eidenschink, O.S.B.
  CENSOR DEPUTATUS

Imprimatur:
  ✠ Peter W. Bartholome
  BISHOP OF ST. CLOUD

St. Cloud, Minnesota
July 31, 1965

Current printing (last digit):

10 9 8 7 6 5 4 3 2 1

LIBRARY OF CONGRESS CATALOG CARD NUMBER: 66-10611

PRINTED IN THE UNITED STATES OF AMERICA [76109-C]

CONTENTS

INTRODUCTION

Many Americans are offended by the blunt assertion of French novelist and essayist François Mauriac that the American and Communist philosophies of life offer little real choice to a third party. Nevertheless, the stance of American philosophy and also of much popular feeling does suggest strongly that our contemporary milieu is, if not antispiritual, at least aspiritual. Such an environment is characterized by an indifference to the presence of anything transcending matter or empirical investigation. In general, the problems created by the prevalence of this aspiritual conviction underlie the choice of essays in this collection. But having said this, there still remains much to explain in the apparently diffuse character of the collection.

We hope here, first of all, to present an ensemble of problems relating to a scientific world which is largely the creation of men who would either ignore the notion of spirit or, at times, oppose it openly. Secondly, we mean to provide a provocative springboard for thought and reflection on the problems the scientific world presents to the thinker, especially the thinking believer in spirit. The book makes no attempt to review the classic texts or the history of the problems treated. It aims rather to cast light on the matter in the context of our own time and thought. The resultant collection is neither all-inclusive nor intended, in sum, as a definitive *answer* to the varieties of positivism and materialism. Communism, for example, is not treated explicitly since that requires works of much greater length and these are easily available.

The ideas and views presented in the essays that follow are not necessarily those of the editor. In instances where the selection attempts to give an *answer*, we hope that the *answer* is at least given in terms dictated by today's statement of the question. For many, the traditional responses seem to have lost their edge because they are so often repeated in overly generalized terms or without sufficient critical thought as to their meaning. Such responses are well known, but fewer and fewer men listen to them.

While trying to avoid mere restatement of traditional arguments and problems, we have also tried to avoid excessively technical scientific treatment and approaches. In a few instances a page here or there may seem out of the range of the liberally trained student. In general, however, such pages should offer no insuperable obstacles, and they are, at the same time, necessary to keep the selection relevant to contemporary developments.

Some will be troubled by the difficulty in classifying the material in this book. It is certainly not, at least not all of it, either theology or philosophy or psychology or natural science. The editor's choice was dictated, not by the limits of a particular category or discipline, but by the current problems of college students. Obviously not all the current problems of college men and women will be embraced in this one fairly brief book. Certain areas were explicitly excluded because they often receive fuller treatment in other books. Among the excluded areas are communism (mentioned previously), the ecumenical movement, moral problems, and the apologetic problems surrounding the gospels or the person of Jesus.

The editor's commitment to Christianity should be apparent early in the selection of the essays. The pieces collected here are, however, first of all concerned with the reassertion of spirit, or in some way impinge on it; only insofar as acceptance of spirit (whether in a hylomorphic or Cartesian or Teilhardian context is another question) is a condition of religious faith are the essays concerned with Christianity.

The introductions to each part of the volume attempt to relate the essays to the whole and to what precedes or follows each part. Useful here is a short survey of the entire volume. Treated first is the problem of evil, since this most rudely challenges those who see man as more than merely a machine or an animal. For those who previously have not been much given to reflection on the matters treated in this book, the problem of evil is the most existential place to begin. This problem seems to demand of all men either thought or defiance or weeping. Part Two focuses on the problems related to the origin of life itself and of contemporary man. These problems are more patently germane to the theme of the collection, and they are intrinsically bound up with some notion of what constitutes man, of how he is like the animal creation, and of how he is different. In Part Three,

Lovell and Tillich pose questions about the purpose of the universe and about man's place in the awesome context of the universe. Following this, Walshe and Allport discuss from physiological and psychological viewpoints the inner constitution of man. De Lubac surveys the favorite modern-day analyses of religion as one great expression of spirit. In Part Six, Vann speaks of the essential character of myths and symbols, their nonconceptual or supraconceptual nature, and the witness they give to something not to be caught in numbers, words, or tools. Zaehner draws some enlightening comparisons between Christian religion and Hinduism and Buddhism, an undertaking toward which Vann's more general essay naturally draws the mind. The final section suggests a way, largely through existentialist thought, to spirit and from it to *the Spirit*, God. Daniélou's essay, the concluding one, touches, in a compelling way, on a number of other matters all related to Christian faith, matters which, as we have noted earlier, are treated more completely elsewhere.*

* We have appended to each part a selected bibliography for further reading. The books included represent a variety of viewpoints and were chosen for accessibility to the college student, pertinence to today's situation, and intrinsic interest to college students.

Readings

in Science and Spirit

PART ONE   The Problem

and Mystery of Evil

*And don't tell me God works in mysterious ways. . . . There's nothing
so mysterious about it. He's not working at all. He's playing. Or else
He's forgotten all about us. That's the kind of God you people talk
about—a country bumpkin, a clumsy, bungling, brainless, conceited,
uncouth hayseed. Good God, how much reverence can you have for
a Supreme Being who finds it necessary to include such phenomena
as phlegm and tooth decay in His divine system of creation? What
in the world was running through that warped, evil, scatalogical mind
of His when He robbed old people of the power to control their
bowel movements? Why in the world did He ever create pain?* *

In these words Joseph Heller has captured in all its crudity and
concreteness the problem which, no matter how nonmetaphysical
the mind, hardly ever fails to awaken at least some bit of wonder
or reflection. Placing the essay by Yves Congar on the problem of
evil at the beginning of this book is the result of experience in
teaching college classes. Students vetoed a more logical order by pointing out how Congar's essay manages so well to engage the individual
in one of the most immediate problems of life, that of the simul-
taneous existence of evil and a good purpose in this universe. It
readily happens that thinking about this fundamental problem opens
the mind more to the need of thinking about the other problems
which follow. The issue of evil raises a host of problems about man
and God. For example, Elie Wiesel in *Night* records that his belief
in God ceased the day he saw God stand by and allow children to
be hanged in a Nazi concentration camp.

* Joseph Heller, *Catch-22* (New York: Dell Publishing Co., Inc., 1955), p. 184.
Reprinted by arrangement with Simon and Schuster, Inc., N. Y.

1

Congar gives a number of representative statements of the problem of evil and surveys well the best-known solutions offered in philosophy and in revealed religion. Even apart from this invaluable service, Congar has shown himself a master of this kind of thought, the nettling concerns which leave us no rest. After many years of opposition and misunderstanding, he received some much-deserved recognition when he was made a *peritus* at Vatican II.

CHAPTER I

The Problem of Evil

YVES CONGAR

A solution at last? Hardly that: we are under no delusion that any arguments of ours will succeed in answering all the difficulties; but at least we can explain why no such solution is to be expected, or is even possible. On the problem of evil—on the question, that is, insofar as it admits of a solution—much that is cogent has already been said; probably everything. Like others before us, we shall bring forward arguments that are not without force. But it is not so much the problem itself we propose to deal with—or rather, not the metaphysical problem—as the problem in its human aspect, as man actually encounters it; and more particularly as he encounters it when he takes it into his head to reflect on his own destiny, on the meaning of himself and of everything else. For it is then he runs up against evil as an obstacle masking the face of God. When we take into consideration the dimensions of the problem, and where it really lies, we shall see that fundamentally what man needs most is to perceive in a true light the *meaning* of evil and of the scandal it presents.

The Dimensions of the Problem and Where It Lies

There is evil in nature. So many living things destroyed, so much seed that perishes! Animals devour one another; natural catastrophes destroy harvests and life itself. . . . And above all there is evil in man: not only is the course of his life marked by painful effort, by a perpetual reversal of all that would make him happy, but he bears within himself an inclination to do evil, to spoil his own happiness, and still more that of others.

Yves Congar, "The Problem of Evil," *God, Man, and the Universe*, Jacques de Bivort de la Saudée, ed. (New York: P. J. Kenedy & Sons, 1953) pp. 393-421.

3

All this presents a problem, the intellectual problem of evil: how, in such circumstances, can one believe that God is Providence, that He personally concerns Himself with each and everything, that He is just and wise and all-powerful? We would ask Him to explain Himself, just as Job did (Job 23:2-9), but like Job we have no idea where He is to be found; we ask our questions, but all the time He remains shrouded in silence.

Again, to us evil is more than a problem; it becomes a scandal. It is not just a question we ask ourselves, it is a cry from our very heart, torn from us by all the wrong we observe in the universe, by the contradictions present in the nature of things, and (very much more) by the harsh experience of life itself. What we are concerned with here is not only the problem of evil but the problem of suffering. We confront evil not simply as a reality we observe, but as a thing we experience directly, sometimes with a violence that spurs us to revolt. Everyone, unhappily, has known tragic tests of his faith in Providence: war ("if there were a beneficent God, there would be no wars"), the suffering of children (cf. Dostoevsky's *Brothers Karamazov*), the death of little ones, painful diseases, the misfortunes of life that drive some to despair, whereas the unscrupulous so often succeed and prosper. This latter consideration was the one most disturbing of all to the Jews, to whom the Mosaic Law promised happiness as a sure return for fidelity: the subject recurs time and again in the Bible.[1] How can God do such things, or allow them to be done? As M. Guyau exclaims:[2] "What tears would I weep if I were a God like that!"

Deep down in his consciousness, man has an obstinate instinct for justice; alienists tell us it is the last strictly human sentiment to be retained by the mad. It is liable, when frustrated, to turn to resentment and revolt. And so to refusal. "It's not that I rebel against God," says Ivan Karamazov, "only I decline to accept his universe." The man who refuses the universe is getting pretty near to refusing its God. Here in fact we have precisely the position—the religious, or rather areligious position—of so many of our contemporaries. Strictly speaking it is not atheism, at any rate not speculative atheism. No one ever proved the nonexistence of God. As far as proofs and reasons go, one might say the chances of God's existence are incomparably greater than the chances of His nonexistence, and men suspect as much. Their atheism is not of the speculative sort, but (as Jules Lagneau observes [3]) a practical atheism, an atheism of conduct, justified very often by that curtain of mystery interposed between the invisible God and His creation as we experience it; and that not merely at the phenomenal level but in life and sensibility: it is the mystery of suffering. Here every argument, however speculatively valid, seems somehow to lose its force; the testimony of the intellect, even where this has been obtained, is (so to speak) clouded by the more immediate datum of evil experienced.

We must be careful to bear these facts in mind. They will enable us to define where the problem of evil is precisely located.

It is not in nature. Nature, in itself, is good; in the conditions in which it has to function, it always does what is best. Hack a tree, set a heavy stone on a young shoot, and it is astonishing how the tree remakes its protective tissues, the plant contrives to evade the obstacle, recovers the conditions necessary to live; and invariably it does so by the best possible means. There are few things so interesting as the way a scab forms over a wound, the way an animal will behave when something hampers its instinctive impulse. Dam a mass of water, and it will get around the obstacle in just the same way. Nature, in every field, does whatever it should; in itself it is good. Man, too, with that side of him which is one with nature, does what he should in the conditions imposed on him, and what he does in these conditions is good. If he too could be reduced to a series of linked causes, of operations and results, the latter would always conform as they should to what was given initially. No doubt this is the reason why simple people—those who live very close to nature, primitives, or even those who in various ways assume an attitude of resignation, sometimes not far removed from fatalism—probably suffer less, and in any case never regard evil as a scandal. And all this seems to suggest the following conclusion: the problem of evil, regarded as a scandal, lies in man as something more than a mere part of nature, in man appreciating his own destiny and himself constructing it.

The problem of evil is certainly not bound up with existentialism, than which it is scores of centuries older. Indeed there is a whole aspect of the problem of evil, an entire ontological groundwork, which is wholly outside the scope of existentialism. But as scandal, as occasion of revolt or refusal, the problem seems to me to be pretty closely linked with man as the existentialists like to define him: that is, not as merely *being*, like an animal, but *existing*, which means thinking, interpreting the world as a totality, and so giving a significance both to the world itself and to his own situation within that world. Man as a purely natural being would be at every moment what he is capable of being. He would ask no questions. As a mere spectator of nature and of himself, he would encounter evil as a purely speculative question. Provided he were enough of a metaphysician to grasp their import, he would be satisfied with the explanations the philosophers have to give him. And these explanations are far from being nugatory: we shall find room for them later. But they stop short, I think, of the field where the human protest occurs: the protest of the man for whom evil is no mere intellectual problem but a suffering that can become a scandal and eventually a revolt. The man who reaches this stage is one who adds to the problem an 'interpretation and a meaning, a meaning corresponding to that which he gives to his own existence. It is man facing the task of his self-realization in accordance with a certain quality of existence. The problem of evil amounts to a scandal not so much in the intellectual sphere, as calling for explanations, as in the world of freedom, in respect of the particular way man conceives of his own existence and his own self-realization.

It should be noted that where man realizes himself most, is not, where nature does, in a world of certainty, clarity, and determinism; it is in a world of hazards, of darkness shot with lights, a world of free choice. It is there we encounter evil, in that world of faith where we use our frail liberty. Man, according to Proclus, is situated at the horizon where heaven and earth meet; [4] he participates in both but belongs wholly to neither. It depends on the direction in which he realizes himself, whether he falls below or rises above his ontological level. It is an ambiguous world, the world of freedom and self-realization. As Dostoevsky saw and suggested so well, freedom is the condition and root of both evil and good. You find Dostoevsky himself, in *The Legend of the Grand Inquisitor*, asking the question which is the knottiest of all in our problem: in creating us as we are, did God show less love than He would have done by making us mere things? We are reminded of the Grand Inquisitor's reproach to Christ: By setting on men the burden of freedom you made them unhappy; you acted as though you were without any love for them!

Can we be surprised, after this, that the question of evil is expressed differently at different levels? It must depend on how man himself is situated and on the use he makes of his faculties. To one who takes up a purely intellectual position, that of a spectator of the world—including himself as an object in it—to the person who is merely seeking explanations, the question of evil is a problem. But for the man at grips with his destiny, who seeks in this perspective the meaning of himself, of the world, and of the evil in the world with regard to himself, the question is primarily that of the *meaning* of what he feels to be evil. It presents itself either as a mystery inspiring reverence, or else as a scandal: as a mystery, if the idea we pursue in realizing our self has full respect for the sovereignty of God; as a scandal, if the idea we pursue is that of a being who would realize itself quite autonomously, allowing no submission to Him who gives and takes away, puts to the trial and heals, exalts and reduces to impotence. Clearly the more a man is (believes himself or wishes to be) in control of the game he plays, the more he is apt to resent those mysterious trials due to the interference of his divine Partner. We noticed just now that the question of evil is no great worry to simple folk, to primitives and believers. In antiquity and the Middle Ages (but especially in antiquity) men seem to have given it very little attention, and when they did it was as an intellectual problem much more than as a scandal. The question, it would seem, has presented itself as a scandal only insofar as man has realized, in thought and action, his demiurgic capabilities. It is when he has been more aware of his own creative powers that he has considered creation and the Creator critically and ventured to set himself up as their judge.

This short analysis of the dimensions and the true situation of the problem of evil has made us rather more conscious of its urgency, and it has also provided us with the major divisions of the question. We shall now examine in turn, first evil as a problem, then evil as it presents itself, as either scandal or mystery, to man at grips with his fate.

Evil as Problem

This is how it presents itself to the philosopher, who seeks, behind the phenomena perceived by science, a reconstruction, intellectually satisfying, of the totality of what is. Here it is a question of reconciling the existence of evil with the existence of God; of justifying God in respect of evil ("theodicy"), not (as we shall see later) at the level of the concrete meaning of evil in our existence, but at the level of the metaphysical notions of cause and being. Such an approach may seem too abstract to some, without any immediate bearing on the difficulty as they actually feel it, and therefore rather pointless. But for those engaged with the problems of speculative philosophy it is necessary. Moreover theories, sooner or later, enter into consciousness and life; they may be unable to satisfy all that consciousness and life ask, but at the deepest level they condition the validity of all that can be said and claim to have value in the way of ideas. Ultimately, therefore, the philosophical approach is necessary and indispensable. For more detailed elaboration there are plenty of excellent works the reader may consult; all we shall do here is to sketch the main lines of a philosophical justification, showing that (1) God is not the cause of evil; and (2) if He permits it, the fact that He does so is not irreconcilable either with His wisdom or His omnipotence, with His justice or His goodness.

1. Evil is certainly real, but it is not itself a thing; it simply affects a reality which, in all that it has of being, is positive and good. If, when jumping a ditch, I miss the further side, break my leg, and am lame ever after, it doesn't follow that my leap as such was not good, merely that it was short by a few inches; my leg, as a leg, is good, only the joints want something of perfect articulation. Similarly war is an evil, yet the things that go to make it are all good in themselves. The men who engage in it, the intellectual and physical actions that enter into its operations, the airplanes and bombs, as sources of energy, are all good. The same explosives and combustibles, used for the making of war, are also useful for the extraction of minerals. It is simply that they are not being applied constructively to the ends of human life. They have no business to be used to cause destruction and sorrow.

So there are things that are bad, but evil as such has no existence. And things are bad, not in respect of their being, but in respect of their not being what they rightly ought to be. The reality of evil is not that of what is; it is that of what is not (negation), or rather more exactly, of what is not when it ought to be (privation). What was bad was the fact of not reaching the other side of the ditch; so the jump was bad, not insofar as it was successful up to a point, but insofar as after that point it was a failure. And so with all the rest. Evil is not being; it is a hole in being, a lack.[5]

That is why there can be no absolute evil: evil can exist only in what is itself good. However unhappy we are, we *are*; and the fact of existing is for us a very great good. A crime is morally and socially harmful only through some positive action, and this action, as an action (for example, a blow with a knife as such), is good; in certain circumstances it may be signally so. There is nothing—even the devil himself, considered in his angelic nature—which is not endowed with goodness and beauty. At first sight the case of death is more obscure. Sentiment, in practice, hinders reflection; it makes a cold appreciation of things impossible. Yet to anyone who is willing to examine the question, it is evident that death is an evil only to the living: to him who must submit to it, for the fear and horror it inspires; to those who lament it after the event, for the sadness it leaves behind. But for all this, there is perhaps nothing that shows more clearly than death how the question of evil has an aspect other than the metaphysical aspect and calls for some other answer than one that can be formulated analytically in terms of being.

2. Yet these considerations are not without value. They are directly connected with this other, which goes to the heart of the question: evil does not involve God's causality like good. Since good is something *being* it requires a First Cause which is absolute Good and perfect Being; to be realized it requires the positive causality of the Creator. Evil as such, being limitation and lack, requires no causality of being, only a reason for nonbeing; all that is necessary to account for it is the natural limitedness and frailty of the creature. Fundamentally there could be only two ways of obviating evil altogether: either by things not existing at all (but their existing is a great good), or by their being positively infinite, which is impossible. From the fact of their being creatures, they are bound to be finite,

and so carry in themselves—not evil (finitude itself is not an evil) but—a tendency to result in evil and an explanation of the evil by which they are liable to be affected.

The relation of our native poverty to divine perfection may be compared to that between an ignorant pupil and a learned master. One who is ignorant can acquire learning only by way of his teacher; all he contrives to learn must be attributed to the teacher whose learning he will have shared. But if you ask to see the pupil's notes and there discover—what teacher has not had this devastating experience?—the grossest misunderstanding of the instruction given, then the shortcomings of the pupil himself are at issue: they alone are enough to account for the lamentable gaps in the treatment of the subject. But supposing the master, it will be said, had given the pupil more help, taught him still more, then the mistakes might have been avoided. At the present stage of our examination of the matter, it is sufficient to consider things as they are actually given and to know that they suffice, metaphysically speaking, to account for all the evil that affects them. For the moment we need not inquire whether God might not have done more or perhaps something else. What He does, that of which He is truly the cause, is good. The "cause" of evil is not creative power.

3. Permitting evil, as He does, within a design that is generally good, exerting His causality only in what is positive in this design, God applies Himself, when evil occurs, to preserve and enhance the value of the good that still remains.

Metaphysically speaking, it is in the light of this principle that we have to regard hell. Metaphysics may not here shed the best possible light, but it does shed some.[6] Through taking sides, by sin, against God, the spiritual creature introduces into the world the worst possible evil. It is not the evil to which we are most sensitive: physical pain hurts us more, and Joinville was very much one of ourselves when he declared he would rather have committed thirty mortal sins than suffer from leprosy once. Yet, for all that, mortal sin is the gravest evil, the supreme disorder in regard to the supreme good. It is a turning away of the human will from God. If man's will is still such when the time of choice has gone by—what Scripture calls the time of repentance—what good is there left for the divine power to call forth? Only the good of nature and its permanence in being, and the good represented by a return of the spiritual person into an order that proclaims the sovereignty of God. There can be no such return by the way of mercy; our refusal has closed that. It must be by the way of justice, and therefore pain. Such at least is the conclusion we must draw in the light of what is given us. Whether, beyond the range of that light, every creature may not be enfolded in a new outpouring of mercy is something we are denied the means of knowing. Here again we must confine ourselves to the order of things given. This, interpreted metaphysically and in terms of being, suggests that God seeks to realize every good that is permitted by the limited nature of things themselves, by the interferences set up as they react on one another, and by the abusing of the various freedoms He has created.

4. God is not properly the cause of evil. But as the First Cause of finite and fallible being in which evil does exist, He certainly accepts or permits it, and so in some sort assumes responsibility. How is this to be justified? We may say, if we will, that evil is permitted by God by reason of its relation to an ulterior good, because it serves indirectly the achievement of some work that taken as a whole is good. Here evil is justified as far as God's wisdom and goodness are concerned. But the difficulty, for us, lies in the fact that we would see immediately *what* good is in view when God permits *this* particular evil. The trouble is that the more we are painfully affected by some evil, the more elusive seems its connection with the resultant good. But at any rate what we can infer, from considering the principal classes of evil, suggests some promising lines of thought and inclines us to the view that there is more in the optimistic statement of the case than a blind guess or a mere trifling with the issue. So we will sketch out the lines of such a reasoned inference and we can afterwards summarize the considerations they suggest.

It can hardly be said that pain *does* evil: it is surely rather the feeling of evil. But could one say that it is itself an evil? This would be to assert that awareness of evil is itself something bad; but in practice it serves as a warning; it is the reaction of a living organism when called upon to counteract some injury to itself. "Pain," writes Father Sertillanges,[7] "has a useful function; it cannot be regarded as an evil except by isolating it from the injury of which it is the sign and warning, and from the general sensibility of which it is evidence. Granted these antecedents, it can be said to be good. . . ."

For a passing pain, yes. When I have a decayed tooth it aches; it is a warning to have it attended to. So far so good. When I have a secret aversion to someone, I am inwardly ill at ease; or if I have been guilty of forgery, I have a persistent feeling of remorse. That too is well enough. Here, fundamentally, pain is signally a factor of order and good. But what of those states of perfectly devastating suffering and disease, such as we have all of us witnessed and sometimes close at hand—how to justify these, how to value these as positively good? The answer is: also as factors of order and good; but in a higher key, one, unhappily, that few of us ever contrive to appreciate.

In the first place this applies, at any rate for trials that are not superhuman, for a very ordinary degree of self-realization. Woods grown on the plain are notably softer than mountain timber, and many prefer them as easier to work and less blunting to the saw; but they are not so good and not so serviceable. Similarly wine from vineyards on the plain has never the same bouquet as that produced by the hillside vines. It is the same with human beings. Those who have had no great difficulties to overcome, whose life has flowed (as it were) over low-lying ground, have less resistance, less *savor*, shall we say. On the other hand, it is when suffering and hardships rob us of all our resources that we are offered the chance of becoming truly great.[8] "Suffering passes," it has been said, "having suffered does not": an indication, this, of the kind of human quality that suffering can produce. It is even truer if we go beyond such values, out of reach of some but still merely humanist, and consider values, fundamentally human, but formally spiritual and even religious. "Man," said Léon Bloy, "has places in his heart that as yet have no existence; pain has to enter before they can *be*." [9] As a reality in that universe of "existence," in the sense we have suggested above and shall return to presently, suffering can be the occasion, in quite an exceptional way, for a man's realizing himself either below or above the line (or horizon) where he finds himself situated. It is the privileged occasion for realizing a humanity more closed or more open to others and to God; according as the one choice is made or the other, suffering will turn out to be useless or profitable, a waste of time or a means of advancement.[10] It is in suffering that we are withdrawn from the bright superficial film of existence, from the sway of time and mere things, and find ourselves in the presence of a profounder truth. We are given the opportunity to have a spiritual clean-up, to make a true assessment of the goods of life, of those that pass and those that endure, of those that enlarge and deepen and build up, and of those that have a shrinking and parching effect even on him they at first seem to refresh. In suffering, a man is emptied (as it were) of his false appreciation of what are really vanities, everything appears small and of little importance except the inner joy that is sent by God. Such was the happy experience of Francis of Assisi, and with him of that multitude, uncounted and unknown, of those who have received illumination from suffering.[11] Pastor Adolphe Monod, condemned to a long agony of nearly six months, told the friends who assembled every Sunday about his bed: "The thing to keep in mind above everything else is that we do not belong to ourselves; nothing belongs to us, not even our time. Our time is God's; it is from Him we must learn how to use the time He gives us, how to turn to good purpose the opportunities we are offered. And here illness, I can assure you, provides the best of all lessons. The heart is naturally prone—and this is the root of all sin— to set itself up as the center and goal of its life. But when you are ill and in pain, what consolation can you get out of seeking the goal of your life in yourself? . . ."[12] Thus illness, suffering—something, that is, very different from mere momentary pain—has a value of its own if a man accepts it: it can teach the highest possible self-realization. It is the threshold of a very high spiritual good, one of the true, divine, and universal order. This is a spiritual order, certainly, but there is no denying that it is one of the highest realities, the highest of all, perhaps, that have to do with man's good. That is why so many of our fellows, who are by no means insensitive, addicted to gloom, or in any way subhuman, have experienced, sometimes throughout their lives, the truth proclaimed by Baudelaire:

> Soyez béni, mon Dieu, qui donnez la souffrance
> Comme un divin remède à nos impuretés.[13]

There is no grief that cannot acquire this value: not even the cruelest, the death of a little child. Frederic Ozanam's parents lost eleven of their fourteen children; St. Thérèse of Lisieux's, four out of eight. Can we believe that the way they bore such a trial, the way they accepted it from God, did not contribute something to the sanctity they gave the world, a sanctity which for fruitfulness makes the most brilliant worldly careers seem insignificant? Not that Christianity is a religion of suffering, or implies any desire to multiply suffering. Suffering is there, and the Church has never ceased to alleviate it; it has always been conspicuous in its care of the sick and the orphaned, of prisoners and lepers. But it has also opened to all an understanding of the supreme good—a Christian but also a human good—which suffering makes possible; to say nothing of even greater goods, hidden behind the veil of faith, which are a mysterious but very real association in the world's redemption by Christ.

The theme of suffering, though only glanced at superficially, has taken us already into the existential field which concerns itself primarily with suffering as a mystery; we shall have to return to this. Yet all we have said about it has its place in the actual order of evil as a problem, since it shows how God can permit evil as the condition of a greater good.

We know the difficulties presented to the Jewish mind by the fact that the wicked prosper. The Jews had grown accustomed to the idea that God's blessing was translatable in terms of abundance of worldly goods. Hence we find the question arising as far back as the Old Testament, and we shall see the answer given to it by the Book of Job. But God, as we have now been taught by the Gospel, makes His sun rise on the evil and equally on the good: here lies the novelty of the Sermon on the Mount (Matt. 5:45) and of the Gospel generally. Hence the Christian order, which is also the order of salvation, is dissociated from all material questions, such as those of place, nationality, and observance, of eating and drinking, or not eating and not drinking.[14] It is not in any of these things that God is served, nor by means of these things; *nor is it for any of them that He is more loved, or less.* The Gospel distinguishes between the spiritual and temporal order, between a Cosmos and a Church. There is an independent physical world where everything, in a sense, takes place just as if there were no God at all—no living God, that is, as the Bible understands Him, intervening directly in the course of our lives. A trainload of pilgrims can be run into and wrecked as well as a trainload of skiers or ordinary travelers. A Christian father, with two daughters who are nuns, may be financially ruined as well as another; a pious child may fail his examinations. . . . Nature as a whole is ordered, but it follows its course according to laws and consequences that are generally unrelated to the moral order. Holiness and power, in this world, don't necessarily go together, and the will to make them do so, the secret ambition of theocracy or clericalism, leads quite as much to chaos as to order. Their perfect reconciliation is reserved to the Kingdom of God: not only because that will be the time of retribution, but because the Kingdom, fundamentally, will be the bringing into harmony of the cosmic and the spiritual by an order that is perfect in the eyes of God and by the setting up of His sovereign rule.[15]

Where, ultimately, lies the answer to the difficulty? Once again in the fact that an immediate evil, felt very keenly, is the condition of a higher but remoter, less immediately felt, good: the freedom and purity of the spiritual. If God had a worldly recompense for the just, He would be loved for His gifts and not for Himself. The friend who loves us only when our hands are full is neither worthy of us nor truly our friend: he treats us as a means. The trials of the just, like voluntary sacrifices, establish (or re-establish) the true relationship between means and end. They are the condition of a higher justice and—even in us—of a higher spirituality. Just when I am in a hurry the doors of the underground slam in my face. The business I have in hand is important; I chafe impatiently during the ten minutes' wait and am sorely tempted to question Providence. . . . Or say I am a prisoner of war. I have planned my escape carefully, I am clear of the barbed wire, then I run into a patrol. . . . They are good examples, but one could think of a hundred others perhaps more impressive. And then again, apart from the human world which is so often one of accidents and frustrations, what lamentable interferences, what disasters and destruction! The lion eats the gazelle, the hurricane levels forests, the mountainside streams overflow and cause floods. . . .

All this serves to illustrate what was said just now about that fatal determinism, so regardless of life. It also illustrates another principle, one that seems on the whole beneficial: the origin of many particular evils can be found in the simple plurality and inequality of forces. But this plurality and inequality are necessary if things are to share more abundantly in the divine perfection, if they are to represent it less feebly; they are the condition of order, a good incomparably greater than the evil they involve.[16] There is more in popular sayings than is commonly thought, and one of them is that "it takes all sorts to make a world"; or, shall we say, to enhance its beauty, a cosmos? It is good that there should be both lions and gazelles, but this makes it inevitable that the lions should eat the gazelles. We ourselves eat plenty of ruminants, which in turn eat grass, which feeds upon the earth. . . . I dare say it all involves lamentable destruction; but this is the way, in this marvelously varied universe of ours, that mineral nature must serve animate nature, animate sensuous, then sensuous spiritual—that spiritual nature which without loss of identity is destined to become united with God Himself. . . . True, I failed to escape, but the sentry who caught me had a very good day; I missed the underground and cursed my ill-luck, but the person who fifteen seconds earlier slipped through the doors just at the moment they were closing was (I am perfectly sure) delighted at having done so! Ignore the frustration immediately experienced; then, if you reason it out, it is impossible not to see that behind the partciular evil there is a more general good, which cannot exist without making its victims. "Always consider the whole" [17]—a golden rule, proclaimed long ago by Plotinus and Marcus Aurelius. When humanity was in the throes of the last war's horrors, Pope Pius XII translated it in terms, not of the cosmic order, but of the order of Providence and God's designing:

In God's eyes all men are merely children, even the profoundest thinkers, the most experienced leaders of nations. They judge events by the short view, that of time that passes, flees away never to return; but God regards them from the heights, from the immovable center of His own eternity. All they can see is the restricted panorama of a very few years; God has before Him the whole panorama of all the ages. They weigh human events by their proximate causes and immediate effects: God sees them all in their remotest causes, measures them all by their farthest effects.

They are content to unravel the particular responsibilities of this or that hand: God sees, as a single whole, a complex and mysterious collection of responsibilities, although His high Providence never deprives human choice, good or bad, of its freedom.

They would have immediate justice; they are scandalized at the ephemeral power of God's enemies, at all the humiliations endured by the good. But the heavenly Father, who in the light of His eternity absorbs and penetrates and rules time's vicissitudes, as He does the serene peace of ages without end, God, the Blessed Trinity, full of compassion for the frailties of men, for all their ignorance and impatience, but loving them too much to allow even their wrongdoing to affect the course of His wisdom and love, continues, and will ever continue, to cause His sun to rise on the evil and equally on the good, to make His rain fall on the just and equally on the unjust (Matt. 5:45), to guide their childish footsteps with firm tenderness, asking only that they let themselves be led by Him and have confidence in the power and the wisdom of His love for them.

Have confidence in God. . . .[18]

. . . [Men] are the cause of many evils. We often hear it said: If God existed there would be no wars. But it would be truer to say: If God's laws were observed there would be no wars. Nor would there be any quarrels, nor hatred in hearts, nor the evils due to drunkenness and misconduct, nor any crime at all. . . . All these things come from the abuse of our freedom. But freedom itself is a great good, the greatest of all the natural goods created.

So great, indeed, that it actually makes us "God's counterpart and rival, His seconder and His only redoubtable adversary." [19] Whether it be the iniquities unleashed by the will of a Hitler or the petty malignities of our immediate neighbor, their possibility is a condition of man's supreme distinction: that of being a minor god, the carrier of his own destiny. Dostoevsky, whom we refer to with good reason since of all men of genius he was the one most tormented by the problem of evil, was also a thinker who well understood our condition as free agents and exalted it as highly as any. Few reflected more deeply on the problems of crime and human suffering and the spurious superman, with no belief for God or respect for other men's freedom, who for the better asserting of his own brings destruction upon himself. Against freedom such as this, Dostoevsky sets the freedom that looks to God, the freedom of the true superman, which is submission to the divine and communion with all things in a humble love at the service of all.

But it may still be insisted: could not God, while creating us free, have seen to it that we used our freedom for order and good alone? Péguy's metaphysics were unsound when he made God say of man:

Si je le soutiens trop, il n'est pas libre,
Si je ne le soutiens pas assez, il tombe. . . .[20]

St. Augustine saw more deeply into the problem when he recognized the possibility of a higher freedom, so enlightened by the spirit, so much in love with true good, that it would no longer be capable of sinning.[21] But that being the case, are we not justified in asking again: could not God have created a world of freedom without sin; and if not, why not?

If we take up an intellectualist stand, on the ground of the purely possible and conceivable, it is correct to say that God might have made a human world without sin. But once we are on the concrete ground of the world as a reality, we leave the order of what is purely *conceivable* for that which is *willed*. Here, to the simple idea of what is possible, there is added a deliberately chosen intention and end. What we have to consider in this case is more than the possible hypothesis, the object of pure intelligence: it is the set of concrete conditions involved by the choice made in view to the chosen end. Ideally I can conceive a profession in which I might keep my hands clean and always remain my own master; but *if* I single out a particular end and choose to succor the miseries of humanity, I thereby limit and condition my existence and can never avoid being soiled and frustrated. This is the field in which we must think out our question: not in the ideal and the possible, but in the concrete hypothesis in which a man setting out to realize his aim finds his situation delimited by the actual end he is pursuing, without which end, or ignoring which, he would never be able to realize anything.[22]

Now it must have seemed to God—insofar as we may speak of Him so and attempt to interpret what He does—that if a sinless world was worthy of His wisdom, a world-with-sin-plus-the-redemptive-Incarnation would realize His goodness even more, would satisfy His wisdom still more fully, in that His wisdom itself is at the service of His goodness (God *is* love). Once we ask the question, not in the sphere of the purely possible (an abstraction from which a world could never have come forth), but in regard to a world that is real and therefore realized, it is impossible to leave out the end, the final cause which made the world emerge from the possible into the real. But the action of God is conditioned by this end and the question of what He might have done in its absence is meaningless.

By asking the question thus it has been impossible to avoid introducing Christ: the uniting of God with our human flesh in order to heal and restore it, to lead it past all evil and sin to communion with Himself and with all things, to a state of final perfection and glory. Whatever, in the realm of concrete being, God has done or permitted is inseparable from all that. Hence the principle that when He created a sinful world He willed at the same time the remedy for sin: He willed both things together. His wisdom, even His wisdom as Creator, was a wisdom of the Cross and the Resurrection. His justice and His goodness, which we are tempted to call in question, were those which themselves included the Cross, where His justice acquires its meaning, His goodness finds its perfect consummation.

This last, the most decisive of all evils, is itself illuminated and finds its justification in the good for which it is willed or permitted by God: assuming, of course, we view it in the Christian perspective, which is essentially in the light of Christ. Like sin, with which it is linked (so we are told by St. Paul), like the wages we receive from the master we serve (Rom. 6:23), death in the universe is to be regarded as God willed it, from the triple point of view of physics-cum-chemistry, ethics, and theology. But we may reasonably see in death some reference to a greater good and so show that it is not in itself a total evil.

In the first place, surely it is the human condition of succession and multiplication of the vast mass of wealth accumulated by history and civilization. And because, paradoxically, it affects an immortal being, it is impossible to consider it as a yawning darkness by which all things are engulfed, but as a simple passing of the threshold by which we enter, or shall enter, a higher state. As we sing in the Preface for the Dead: *Vita mutatur, non tollitur:* "Life is but changed, not ended. . . ." [23] To us, who see but this side of the veil, it is natural that all should seem to be lost. But for those of us who are believers, whose vision pierces beyond the veil, death's sting is blunted; the victory is not to death but to Life (1 Cor. 15:54)! And there is another thing. Man is the only creature who can make a sacrifice of his death. The angel cannot, for he has no mortal life; nor can the animal, for it has only that and no consciousness of its self. But man is at once mortal and immortal. Since he has a body, he can die; but having consciousness of self, knowledge of God, and the power to judge his own actions, he can offer up his death and give it a meaning. This is the point emphasized by the Epistle to the Hebrews (2:14-18); God took on the likeness, not of the angels, but of men; and the reason He did so was to share their sufferings and be able to offer up His death, namely, the totality of His life. It is to this level we must rise, if we are to see how God can permit death with a view to good.

In all the principal kinds of evil with which we have just been dealing our reply has always been to look for a higher and more general good behind the evil which necessarily conditions it. Turning from the part to the whole, we see very much more clearly.[24] Unfortunately—and it is only natural—we are more sensitive to the immediate than we are to the remote, to the exceptional shock than to the normal harmony. "Philosophy," said La Rochefoucauld,[25] "triumphs easily enough over past and future ills, but it is itself vanquished by ills that are present." And St. Thomas observes that if hatred is not so strong as love, it is felt more keenly; this is because of the loss of balance it involves and the contrast it makes with the general current of life.[26]

What is rather helpful here is the idea, so often used by Lecomte du Noüy, of *scale*.[27] He shows how much the appreciation of facts depends on our scale of measurement (of space and time) and on the scale of values we use. "What is 'quick' to us, in relation to the rhythm of our life, of the sensory and mental mechanisms conditioned by the structure of our brain, will be 'slow' to the insect that lives but one or two days. To an imaginary being, with a life lasting ten thousand millions of years, the process of evolution would seem very rapid indeed. . . ." Even in regard to objections drawn from particular evils, Lecomte de Noüy makes the idea provide grounds for optimism: life ultimately succeeds. At any rate his argument makes it easier to understand how certain things, when seen in the short scale of partial or immediate experience, appear simply as evils, yet have aspects that are perceptibly good if we are willing to look at them in the long-scale whole, inserted in the total process in which they occupy no more than an instant.

This idea of scale, if we take a sufficiently wide and qualitative view of it, explains why reasons objectively good have very little force for us. Restricted as we are to the senses and the sensible, and in

practice being extremely sensitive to the immediate, we are condemned by our situation [28] to know things from below; we reach
the soul only by way of the body, spiritual realities by way of sensible realities; we see things from below, and also (as it were)
through the wrong end of the telescope. But God sees them—and
wills them—from above. He sees the body by way of the soul, as an
irradiation of the soul, and the soul ultimately, with everything else,
in Christ, in whom and for whom, in His effective will as Creator,
He both willed and created them (Col. 1:16). Thus God sees evil
only in the sovereign good, which compensates for it abundantly
and also serves to redeem and repair it.[29] We, on the other hand,
see everything from below, and it is there we feel the gnawing of all
those painful ills. Hence our fellow-feeling for Joinville, with his
thirty mortal sins in preference to leprosy. . . .

Yet with St. Louis it was just the opposite: he preferred leprosy
thirty times to a single mortal sin. Why? Because he had more than
the faith of an ordinary Christian sinner like Joinville; he had a
sense of the spiritual, developed within him by that true kind of
conversion which consists in closing the eyes to the flattering entice-
ment of carnal goods and opening them to the splendor of spiritual
good. This is the lesson we are taught by Holy Scripture,[30] by all the
saints and spiritual writers: the truth of things and their real order
of value is discovered only at the cost of conversion. And it is one
of the fundamental conditions of such a conversion that a man should
so mortify his lower instincts that his selfish ego ceases to be the
center of his world and the goal of all else, his sensations the measure
of every judgment he makes.

So much for evil as a problem that calls for explanation. And as we
reach the limits of this aspect of the question we are brought once
more to its other aspect, that of evil as a mystery calling for reverence,
requiring to be given some meaning.

Evil as Mystery

In the middle of the eighteenth century, an age that was already
rationalistic but still deist and even religious, the Academy of Berlin
offered a prize for an essay on the problem of evil. A number of
philosophers competed, undertaking the defense of Providence just

as we have been doing. But as the Academy was in the act of re-warding the successful competitor,[31] there occurred the Lisbon earth-quake of 1755. Whereupon the whole question took on a wholly new urgency; the simple problem had become a scandal for all the Voltaires of the day. To all those well-meaning mortals who had sought to justify Him, it was as though God had replied with the voice of His own thunder: none should justify Him, He seemed to say; His will must remain a mystery. But, like all other mysteries, this too has its light to bestow; a light not of the order of rational explanations, but no less humanly reassuring for that; reassuring to the heart *and also to the mind*.

Yet this light is presented, and can only be perceived, in certain conditions of which account must be taken. There is a time for rea-soning, and this is the time for argumentative apologetic: here man meets evil as an object he must explain. That is all there is to it. But there is another time than this, one for revealing the values of existence; here man is engaged in choosing, in seeking out the spirit-ual standpoint he is to adopt for the accomplishing of his destiny. What he meets with here are the answers *of God*; man's part is simply mediatory and suggestive; he acts as a living transparency through which, by the testimony of words and still more of life, a third and personal element is introduced: the presence of the living God and the recognition that He is holy and true in all His ways. "How unerring are the awards which the Lord makes, one and all giving proof of his justice!" (Ps. 18:10).

In the Judaic-Christian revelation the question of evil is expressly raised and discussed. In the Old Testament it is raised more particu-larly in connection with the way God deals with the good and the wicked, whether people or individuals (cf. note 1); but it is also discussed in its wider aspects, especially in the Book of Job (c. 500–450 B.C.), which is, so to speak, the *locus classicus* for our subject.

Job is in rebellion against the evils that overwhelm him. He declines to accept his lot. Conscious of his innocence, he protests (chap. 6); strong in a sense of his own righteousness, he would defend himself, argue with God; but God and ourselves are not on equal terms; He crushes us without giving us the chance to explain (chaps. 9-10). There is no putting Him in the dock, no calling Him to account (9:27-35; 23:2-9).

First there come three of Job's friends to console him, and more especially to reason with him. Eliphaz, the first of them, develops the following arguments: None is just in God's eyes; therefore Job has no grounds for complaint (4:12ff.); God is wise and just, but also merciful, which is a reason for retaining hope (5:9ff.); Bildad follows (chap. 8): God is just, he says; if He punishes us, it is because we have done wrong. If Job is really just, God will restore him. Then it is the turn of Sophar, who continues the same line of argument, hinting that evils are a punishment and a mystery of justice, for God reads the guilty depths of our souls (11:5ff.). One after the other, Eliphaz, Bildad, and Sophar return to rub in this lesson in humility: none is pure; God punishes impiety.

Then a fifth character appears, the young Elihu. The answers he gives are more philosophical; they go deeper into the question. Disease, he says, is a message from God (33:14ff.); God is our master and He is certainly just in the sovereign exercise of His power (34:10ff.); moreover, even if Job is innocent, he cannot use his righteousness to exact anything of God, for God needs nothing; what He gives is gratuitous (34:5-6); He is also all-powerful, His "deeds are so great and so unsearchable" (37:5), we cannot call Him to account (36:22-37:24). . . . So whereas Job's three friends had adopted what was primarily a moral point of view (saying: you are wrong to protest, for God sends ill to none but the sinner), Elihu is more philosophical in his standpoint: God's right is so sublime and so sovereign that He is absolute, wholly above man's questioning.

Thus the sages of antiquity. They could proclaim that we learn from suffering (as Aeschylus declared); that the enduring of suffering has value as testimony; that God employs it to make trial of the faithful.[32] Except that we find them somewhat tedious, we can easily recognize ourselves in Job's friends, as we can in Job himself—according as our role is that of consoler, or of one who is himself overwhelmed by trials. What his friends have to tell him—so like the rhetoric and generalizations we use ourselves—Job would have said too, if he had been in their place and they in his (16:1-5). There is nothing that can be called "existential" in all this, nothing that goes to the heart of the scandal. Job is equally convinced by all the undoubted truths, theoretical and general, they are pleased to offer him. He is intellectually persuaded, and continues to remain so, that

God is master and does what He wills; it is this that checks him in his revolt and stops him short on the threshold of blasphemy (cf. chaps. 9-10, and 17:1ff.): proof enough that these ideas in themselves have value. Fundamentally—as it is so often with us in our moral life: in the matter of chastity, for instance, or patience or brotherly love—Job knows quite enough to resolve intellectually, insofar as that is possible, the problem raised: God's almighty power, His wisdom, and so forth (cf. 12:9, 16, and others). But there we are: what Job knows intellectually he has to learn to *live*, to adhere to existentially.

It is because God wishes to bring him to this, that after the speeches of Job's friends, and Job's own answers as he continues to protest, He intervenes Himself (in chap. 38). For poetic beauty the passage is perhaps unsurpassed in the Bible. The answer given is philosophical; but it is not this that is most remarkable about it, for in all essentials what is said in this respect can already be found in the speech of Elihu. Apart from any answer to the "problem," it is to question Job himself that God addresses him: "Strip then, and enter the lists; it is my turn to ask questions now, thine to answer them" (38:3). The parts are reversed. Job was for arguing with God, for calling Him to account and seeking His reasons; but here he is, directly and personally questioned himself. You, says God, would have put me to the question; now it is you who must make reply. What do you know? What do you know even of the simplest things that take place at your side every day? What causes the movements of the sea, how come the birds to be made? Come, tell me!

Will he who would criticize God venture to make any answer? (40:2). God's own "answer," in theory, is simple. How, He asks Job, can you question and judge me? You know nothing. Every being, everything created, is a mystery: and so are the evils that come about. . . . This appeal to mystery Job had heard already and rejected (cf. 9:32-35, 23:2-9). After all, it may be precisely the mystery that gives scandal—scandal, that is, in the etymological sense, as the thing that causes us to trip and fall down. But it may also, as Pascal said, be something to be reverenced. The parting of the ways between revolt and worship lies very deep down, at the secret center of the heart, where we make the choice either to be ourselves the supreme arbiters or frankly to admit that God infinitely transcends us. What it comes to, ultimately, is that our frank acceptance of our condition as creatures must be more than intellectual; it must also be existential. As the Creator's partners by virtue of our freedom, we have to realize our condition as unequal partners of the living God and so voluntarily submit to be led where He wills.

For this it is necessary that we encounter Him personally, not to argue with Him any more, but to be ourselves questioned and freely submit. God's whole treatment of souls that He seeks to draw to Him aims at getting them to say "yes" at an ever deeper level: first by conversion and faith, then by entering upon the successive stages of the spiritual life. But conversion is effected by putting oneself in the presence of the living God at an existential point, a point where there is nothing but Him and our true selves, from which He has brushed away (as it were) the various "havings" that serve us as alibis and lead us to evade the decisive issues of "being." It is the story, not only of Job, but of the woman of Samaria (John 4), who at every attempt by Jesus to make her realize that "it is a question of us and of our whole self," starts off at a tangent, making irrelevant "diversions," and each time Jesus leads her back to herself till the moment comes when she feels herself in the Master's presence and is at last ready to listen: It is I—"I who speak to thee. . . ."

It is the point when Job says: "I acknowledge it, Thou canst do all Thou wilt, and no thought is too difficult for Thee. Here indeed is one that clouds over the truth with his ignorance! I have spoken as fools speak, of things far beyond my ken [. . .]. *I have heard Thy voice now; nay, more, I have had sight of Thee*" (42:2-5).

The blows of misfortune had aroused Job's *attention*, to use the word employed so profoundly by Claudel about the Japanese earthquake of 1923. They have led him from the moral and even the religious plane to a mystical plane of veritable presence. He had not, like the woman of Samaria, to be converted; or at any rate his was not that initial conversion which gives access to faith. He was a man "true and honest; ever he feared God, and kept far from wrongdoing" (1:1). But did he love God for Himself or for His gifts? "Job fears his God, and loses nothing by it." So Satan sneered, and was given leave to try him (1:9 and 12).

So in the same aspect of an arousing of attention—a yielding to be led to that edge of the well of life where we become truly ourselves and truly meet God—evils have value for us as a purifying test of faith and of our love for God.[33] God wills that those souls which He would draw wholly to Himself should cease to reason and consider, to weigh their motives or seek extraneous support, but yield to Him in utter consent and self-surrender; He would lead them to the point where they believe in Him, serve Him and love Him *for no other reason than that He is what He is.* And because, for so many, this work of purifying and disencumbering is not achieved in this world, He continues it after their bodily death in those, His elect, who are to escape that other and "second death," the death of the soul. Thus purgatory, stripped of the gratuitous and deplorable imagery of torture with which preachers still occasionally see fit to embroider it—purgatory itself would seem to be an evil that is willed by God with a view to a good incomparably greater.[34]

Even the answer given by the Book of Job has led us beyond metaphysics into the order of existence, the order of personal relationship to a living God. The answer given by the Gospel (including all the apostolic writings) sets us in an order of facts undiscoverable by reason alone but received by faith as representing God's plan, *His* solution to the problem. To raise the question of evil outside this perspective, on the plane of metaphysical principles alone and from the point of view of creative goodness, is not by any means to invite an erroneous answer. The Creator and the Redeemer are one and the same Lord: it is simply that God is first (if we may so express it) Creator, before He is our Redeemer. But it would be to ask a question which is not *the* question of evil—evil in the concrete as God permits it—for it would be to fall into the mistake, pointed out above, of asking a question about the work of God without considering the real ends He pursues in this work. It would also be to invite an incomplete answer which would not be purely and simply *the* answer of God. True, it is legitimate and necessary to see question and answer in that abstract partial order, since it is thus that the question does in practice arise and it is the only way that many minds ever envisage it. But in so doing we are not confronting fairly and squarely the universe where God has set us, together with the evils we suffer there—the concrete universe which is that of the fall and salvation, of the devil and Christ, of the Cross and the Resurrection. It is by looking at it in this perspective that we now intend to hear God's own answer, the total answer.[35]

The Revelation of the New Testament considers evil solely in the light of God's intention and design, and that means in an economy of sin and salvation. Evil? It would be better to say *evils*, for it considers them under no abstract principle, to be explained by metaphysics, but as realities belonging to a historical order to which it supplies two keys: the one that closes, the other that reopens. The evils spoken of in the New Testament are those of a world that no longer belongs to God, a world seemingly given up to a power hostile to its Creator and therefore fallen into a state in which it is no longer fully in possession of itself. St. Paul expresses this by the ideas of slavery and enmity; similarly we talk of the wounds and conflicts that lead the world in painful search of a state of integrity and reconciliation (see note 15). Instead of submitting to God and so finding harmony and integrity in its various parts, creation is out of joint (a "broken world") and disordered, a victim to corruption, to diminutions of every kind. What we see in the Gospels is a sick humanity. One of the great works of Jesus is healing, sometimes even the restoring of life itself (many of the Gospels for the Sundays after Pentecost have reference to this particular messianic activity). St. Paul prefers to show us man as subject to sin and death, subject also to the malign influence of the flesh and the world: tendencies, within and without us, that turn us away from submission to God.

Both St. Paul and the Gospels set all these evils in relation to the fact that other created freedoms, far more powerful than ours, revolted against God before ever we did, drawing after them a world which has become their own kingdom. Concerning this there are statements in St. Paul and in the Gospels—especially in St. John, wholly dominated as he is by the dramatic spiritual and cosmic struggle between the forces of darkness and light [36]—which cannot be set aside by any who profess to be seeking, and willing to accept, the standpoint of the Christian Revelation. The ills with which this is concerned, those which threaten to cut across God's design, are all related to the Evil One, the Adversary (which is the meaning of the word Satan), "from the first, a murderer" (John 8:44).

But here is God's answer: one might even call it—since we are talking of a combat—His riposte. This evil that threatens to cut across His design is assumed by God into the design itself. It is the wisdom of the Cross. The Word of God, His Wisdom, which at the beginning of the cosmos was found beautiful and good, which perfected that cosmos in beauty and goodness, by taking flesh became the prince of this groaning creation, assumed the quality of its slave, and took upon Him at last its supreme evil, death. More than this, He entered the lists against the usurper, the false prince of this world; submitted to be tempted by him; felt, in some sort, the breath of his foulness; overcame him and destroyed his kingdom: "Now is the time when the prince of this world is to be cast out" (John 12:31; cf. Matt. 8:29). If God willed the world as it is with its evil, with the fall of the rebellious angels and the slavery they impose on us—sin and death—we know that He did so only while willing at the same time the Incarnation of His Son, who, taking on Himself evil, save only sin, became the vanquisher of evil and showed creation the way to the full consummation of its own harmony and good. In the New Testament, and in the Fathers, this design is constantly affirmed and lauded: it is the subject of wondering praise addressed to God.[37] The resurrection of Christ as the first-born of many brethren, and ultimately of all creation (Rom. 8:29; Col. 1:18), gives the refrain its full meaning. By faith we are given the unique certitude of being ourselves beneficiaries, ourselves sharers, in this total restoration. Yes, we shall ourselves be part of it: and that means the whole of us, not only our souls but our bodies as well, mortal today but destined to be incorruptible! "I regard myself," wrote the Communist leader Jacques Decourt when about to be shot by the Nazis, "as a leaf that falls from the tree to form mold. The quality of the mold will depend on the quality of the leaf." [38] There is something moving in these words, expressing as they do such a love for humanity; but in our eyes the outlook offered by the Faith is still more inspiring: while taking nothing from the duty and fruitfulness of sacrifice, it adds to it the certainty of final triumph, of rediscovering ourselves whole, soul and body, in our immortal personalities. It will be a final and also a total restoration. "God will wipe away every tear from their eyes, and there will be no more death, or mourning, or cries of distress, no more sorrow . . ." (Apoc. 21:4; 7:17). Nothing momentarily bad is permitted but what must be assumed by Life and absorbed in His triumph—nothing save sin, for which there is no healing but only pardon and expiation. By expiation, the suffering that proceeds directly from sin serves to efface and restore the order sin destroys.[39] And by pardon God's goodness is made manifest most of all.

There lies the ultimate explanation of all that design of goodness which even includes evil. A creation without evil would certainly manifest God's goodness and wisdom, but it would not be a complete manifestation of His pity. Theology seeks in the nature of God, who *is* Love, the principle of all He produces; thus there can easily be traced, from inorganic creation to life, from life to personal consciousness, from consciousness to grace, an ever-deepening continuity of God-imparted goodness.[40] But in the goodness of God there is a certain gratuitousness: it is revealed in a creation that is gratuitous through and through, and most of all in the exercise of pity. A. Nygren's *Eros and Agape* has notably emphasized this fundamental of Christian love we know as *Agape*, the love which St. John made the very name of God (1 John 4:8, 16): "But here, as if God meant to prove his *agape* for us, it was *while we were still sinners* that Christ, in his appointed time, died for us" (Rom. 5:8); "God is *agape*. What has revealed the *agape* of God, where we are concerned, is that He sent His only-begotten Son into the world [. . . .] That *agape* resides (*precisely*) *not in our showing any love for God, but in His showing love for us first*, when He sent out His Son to be an atonement for our sins" (1 John 4:8-10). One could quote numerous other texts to illustrate this specific feature of God's goodness, His love; that gratuitousness in pity which consists in loving someone who has neither beauty nor goodness. It is this that realizes to the full the *sovereign* aspect of God's gracious giving.

Yes, "sovereign" in the fullest sense of the word. Goodness shown in the exercise of pity is in fact the proper attribute of a sovereign, one who is himself above all wants and can therefore truly *give*, having nothing to receive in return. That is why it is pity that manifests most clearly the mystery of God's goodness in its sovereign character.[41] Thus the concrete world, willed by God in pursuance of what His wisdom requires but also in pursuance of the finalities of His goodness, is a world in which pity is exercised and made manifest to the utmost. A world of piteousness and pity, each needing the other. . . .

Conclusion

The metaphysical problem is not to be ignored, nor is the light that metaphysics is capable of shedding; but the decisive question is not metaphysical, any more than the decisive question about God is that of His existence as First Cause and eternal Axiom. The latter is an important truth, the recognition of which is invaluable for all else; but it is one which men are little concerned with and very few deny. No: the decisive issue is that of God's dealings with the world, His design, the intention He has of drawing all our destinies to Himself.

That is why the question of evil is profoundly existential; epistemologically it belongs to apologetics rather than to philosophy pure and simple. Or so it seems in the matter of these three characteristic points:

1. There is an apologetic of demonstration and argument, another of what might be called "monstration," revealing the values of existence; and in leading people to faith the second is more decisive than the first. In just the same way, there is a treatment of evil as a problem, at the level of explanations, and a treatment of it as a mystery, at the level of choice of destiny and values of existence. But they are not alien to one another, these two different ways of tackling the question. We have seen this above, where in the first part of the chapter we already had to anticipate religious consideration; and in a sense these considerations, as Father Sertillanges has already pointed out, have apologetic value only when combined with a satisfactory metaphysical solution.

2. As in apologetics, what really counts is the totality of the answer. Firstly, because any partial difficulty puts in question (so to speak) God's indivisible honor. But chiefly because we are not concerned with this or that explanation so much as with a view of the total design; indeed without this view of a total design no particular explanation can be completely valid. Evil exists in the world, and it is chiefly a matter of providing a view of things in which this

existence of evil is seen to harmonize with the wisdom and goodness of God. Such a view is provided by Christianity. Of course a man may reject that view *en bloc*. But if he ignores this view put forward by Christians—a view that embraces their God and the world and the evil that exists in the world—he cannot argue that the existence of evil in any way implicates the Christian God.

And here one might insert a general remark worth bearing in mind. Christianity is to be taken as a whole, and it is only within that whole that the solutions it has to offer are valid. Take, for instance, the subject of purity. What it has to say about this is true and practicable; but not if isolated from prayer, from faith, and the sacraments. Its social doctrine is also true and applicable; but it is bound up wth its whole conception of man and with the means it offers for putting it in effect. So Christianity justifies God in regard to evil; but not without providing a complete theology, and the concrete means of passing from a state of hostility and indifference to a filial attitude of communion with God. The vestibule of Christianity stands wide open, and there are plenty of doors that give access to it; but its vision of things is to be seen only from within.

3. If we take the problem of evil as a whole—and this is also the concrete problem—we have to recognize that its law of light and obscurity is like that which governs the order of faith. Pascal defined it unforgettably: "It was not fitting," he says, "that Jesus Christ should appear in a divine fashion, carrying total conviction; but neither was it fitting that He should come in a manner so hidden that He could pass unrecognized by those who honestly sought Him. He willed to be perfectly recognizable to these. And so, willing to appear openly to those who sought Him with all their hearts, He tempered men's knowledge of Him in such a way that the signs He gave, of who He was, were visible enough to those who sought Him, but invisible to those who did not. *There is enough light for those whose only desire is to see, enough obscurity for those who have no such desire.*" [42] What touches God and our destiny is always a mingling of light and shadow. It is the field of self-realization, of the paradoxical play of freedom and grace.

One might say that here, if the justifications in themselves are stronger, the difficulties are more acutely realized. They derive from all that is most sensitive in us, all that is most immediate. The lights, on the other hand, come from the metaphysical relation of the Created to the Uncreated, from the nature of God or His design. But this last is also a mystery; when revealed to us, it is known only by faith, and even then much more in its general lines than in the details of its working. Unlike the soldier in battle, Stendahl's Fabrice at Waterloo, the faithful know their General's broad plan of campaign, they are certain of the issue, but the detail escapes them; and it is in the matter of detail that so many of the evils occur that they experience most cruelly.

Moreover, as so often happens in apologetics, the objection is very much easier than the answer. To present a difficulty in all its force, all I need is a short sentence and half a minute's experience. But to work out the answer and perceive all its bearings calls for a lengthy discourse, mental poise, and years of preparation. After all, it is easier to knock a man down than to lift him up; a few ounces of lead are enough to lay him out. . . .

It depends on the heart: by which we mean something entirely different from a mere sentimental choice, made more or less blindly. "Heart" must be understood here in the biblical sense, which is near enough to the Pascalian sense. It means man insofar as he adopts with his whole self, and primarily with his mind, a standpoint that is fundamentally one of refusal or acceptance. It is there that we begin to be either carnal or spiritual—again in the biblical sense, in which it is possible to be spiritually carnal, and in one's bodily life spiritual. How closely Pascal's thought is here in line with Scripture can be seen in texts like the following: "Good men see a light dawn in darkness" (Ps. 111:4); "The man whose life is true comes to the light" (John 3:21). Those whose hearts are inclined toward God recognize—beneath His dealings with the world, so mysterious to us—a wisdom comparable to that which is revealed in nature, where so many processes, equally impenetrable to us, work out ultimately for good.[43] Even in the midst of great suffering, such souls have no difficulty in justifying Providence.

Occasionally they are criticized. They may seem to some to have a kind of arrested animist mentality, seeing intentions everywhere, explaining everything that occurs by the direct intervention of some higher spirit. Or again those who do not look at things in such a light of loving confidence may perhaps discern a kind of will to be deceived in the imperturbable calmness with which such souls, re-solved beforehand to see an adorable Providence wherever they turn, find always some means of detecting good in evil.

Such criticism raises the question of every good founded on faith. It would be possible to answer it by reasons and explanations: the whole of this chapter provides the elements of such an answer. After all, if we ourselves put so much intention into what we do, why should not infinite Intelligence, the Creator and Governor of the universe, put an infinite amount of intention into His work? But fundamentally, here again, the objection lies at the existential level, where we choose the highest values of our life. It introduces no new intellectual arguments; it simply challenges the application of a principle that is dependent entirely on the Christian choice. It is to be hoped that the foregoing pages have furnished some serious motives for this choice. But at such a level what is really worth most of all is testimony. Such a testimony is provided, for those whose hearts are inclined towards God, by the experience they have had of the total truth of St. Paul's words: "We are well assured that everything helps to secure the good of those who love God." [44]

Since we are all, even the most religious of us, carnal as well as spiritual, and since both believer and unbeliever, alternately or simul-taneously, take possession of our hearts, for us evil is always both a scandal and a mystery, a scandal that provokes rebellion or a mystery we are bound to revere in faith. The very mingling of the two things is typical of this ambiguous world of freedom where the question of evil is practically encountered. The believer, when he has silenced the voices that prompt him to refuse and is in the very act of adoring, cannot but say: "Lord, I do believe! Succor my unbelief . . ." (Mark 9:24).

References

1. Temporal goods allied to fidelity: Leviticus 26; Deuteronomy 28. Problem of the happiness of the ungodly: Habakkuk 1:12-17; Psalms 36, 48, 72; Ecclesias-tes *passim*, especially 7:13-18; Jeremiah 12:1-6; Malachi 3:13-18, 8:9-15, 9:1-10; Job 21:7-15, 24:2-12; and so forth.

2. *Esquisse d'une morale sans obligation ni sanctions*, 2nd ed. (Paris: Alcan, 1890), p. 12.

3. "There are only practical atheists. Their atheism consists, not in denying

the truth of God's existence, but in failing to realize God in their actions. . . ."
Célèbres leçons et Fragments (Paris: Presses Universitaires, 1950), p. 229.

4. An idea often revived in the early thirteenth century (William of Auxerre; William of Auvergne) and by St. Thomas (IV *Sentent.*, d. 50, q. 1, a. 1), *Contra Gentiles*, II, 63, 81; in *librum de Causis*, lect. 2; and so forth.

5. On evil as privation, cf. St. Thomas, *Contra Gentiles*, III, 7-9; *Compendium Theologiae*, 115; *Summa theologica*, 1a, q. 48, a. 1; *De Malo*, q. 1, a. 1. Very few thinkers have admitted evil to be something positive in origin; Jacob Boehme was one of the exceptions: cf. A. Koyrè, *La philosophie de Jacob Boehme* (Paris: Vrin, 1929), pp. 72ff., 142, 166, 183.

6. Cf. T. Deman, *Le Mal et Dieu* (Paris: Aubier, 1946), pp. 69ff., 117ff.

7. *Le problème du mal*, Vol. II (Paris: Aubier, 1951), 15.

8. An example that suggests itself in the case of Roosevelt, who suffered . . . from infantile paralysis: cf. E. Ludwig, *Roosevelt* (p. 100 of the French edition).

9. Quoted by L. E. Halin, *A l'ombre de la mort*, Cahiers de la Revue nouvelle (Tournai-Paris: Casterman, 1947), p. 183.

10. See, for example, Péguy, *Mystère de la charité de Jeanne d' Arc* (Paris: Gallimard), pp. 80-81, 86.

11. See J. Joergensen, *S. François d' Assise, sa vie et son oeuvre* (Paris: Perrin, n.d.), chap. i.

12. *Les adieux d' Adolphe Monod* (Paris: Fischbacher, 1929), p. 137.

13. Ah, blessed be thou, my God, who givest suffering,
To be a heavenly cure for our impurities.

14. See, for example, apart from the Sermon on the Mount (Matt. 5-8) and the conflict of Jesus with the Pharisees (Matt. 21:23-23:39), St. Paul: Romans 14:6ff., 19; 1 Corinthians 6:12, 7:17-24, 7:6ff., 10:23; Colossians 2:16-23.

15. See chap. iii of my *Jalons pour une théologie du laïcat* (Paris: Editions du Cerf, 1951).

16. The answer given here might be applied in the field of social inequalities. Nature makes men equal as to the dignity of their *being*, but not in their various resources that might be described as *having*. Justice demands that all should be given a chance analogically (namely, an equal chance, taking into account the inequality of their initial endowments), but not that all should come to possess exactly the same. Human selfishness, which leads the "haves" to cloak their advantages under pseudo-principles drawn from religion, leads the "have-nots" to feel bitter that others should possess what they do not; it makes social inequalities a source of rancor or contempt. Providence is in question here simply for the two following reasons: (1) because it bestows different initial resources and different opportunites, and this involves general questions about the resulting inequality and the destiny Providence assigns to each individual; (2) because it allows the evils of oppression, envy, misery, conflict between man and man; and this is bound up with the general meaning of the question of evil in the concrete world where the responsibility of God is involved, a world which is one of sin and redemption.

17. Cf. A. M. Festugière, *La sainteté* (Paris: Presses Universitaires, 1942), p. 61. The consideration of the whole as the key to so many difficulties is a common theme with both pagan and Christian thinkers. See, among the former, Plato's *Laws* X, 903; among the latter, St. Irenaeus (*Adversus Haeres*, II, 25) or St. Thomas Aquinas (in II *Sentent.*, d. 32, q. 1, a. 1; *Contra Gentiles*, III, 71; *De Potentia*, q. 3, a. 6, ad. 4; *Summa theologica*, 1a, q. 22, a. 2); and so forth.

18. Message of June 29, 1941: *Acta Apost. Sedis*, 1941, p. 322.

19. A. Jouhandeau, *Algèbre des valeurs morales* (Paris, 1935), pp. 215, 229. Cf. H. Gohde, *Der achte Tag* (Innsbruck, 1950), p. 242: God prefers our freedom to the assertion of his own mastery.

20. If I hold him up too much, he is not free,
If not enough, he falls. . . . (*Mystère des saints Innocents*, pp. 71ff.).

21. Cf., for example, *Enchiridion*, c. 105 (P.L., 40, 281): an idea hereafter common in theology.

22. Cf. Sertillanges, *Le problème du mal*, II, 56-57 (with an interesting reference to Bergson), and 66.

23. *Ibid.*, pp. 11-12: "When we see a caterpillar so perish as to dissolve into seemingly formless matter, one might well suppose this is the caterpillar's ultimate evil, bordering on the absolute evil of death. Later, when we observe its metamorphosis, we shall continue to say that its previous decrepitude was an evil for it; but not an evil and nothing else, for by nature's will this humble creature was a butterfly from its very birth. The lofty application of the example is obvious. A human being too, a caterpillar crawling the earth, is destroyed by what we call death. But if he survives, as the Christian believes, in a higher definitive form, his death may still be called an evil, even the sovereign evil of *man upon earth*; but not of *man*, for man as such is immortal."

24. *Ibid.*, pp. 47ff., with the fine quotation from Lamartine, p. 51. See also note 17 above.

25. Gilbert, ed., Vol. I, p. 39; maxim 22.

26. *Summa theologica*, i-ii, q. 26, a. 3.

27. *L'homme et sa destinée* (Paris: La Colombe, 1948), cf. especially chap. i and pp. 161ff.

28. M. Merleau-Ponty defines the human situation as: "Being in the world by way of the body." *Phénomenologie de la perception* (Paris, 1945), p. 357n.

29. On all this see Garrigou-Lagange, *La Providence et la confiance en Dieu* (Paris: Desclée de Brouwer, 1932), pp. 152-153, 165.

30. "Eyes have I none for vain phantoms; let me find life in following thy way" (Ps. 118:37). "Though the outward part of our nature is being worn down, our inner life is refreshed from day to day. This light and momentary affliction brings with it a reward multiplied every way, loading us with everlasting glory; if only we will fix our eyes on what is unseen, not on what we can see. What we can see lasts but for a moment; what is unseen is eternal" (2 Cor. 4:16-18).

31. A. Fr. von Rheinterd. Cf. P. Hazard, *La pensée européenne au XVIIIe siècle, de Montesquieu à Lessing*, Vol. II (Paris: Boivin, 1946), 59-60.

32. Cf. Festugière, *La sainteté* (Paris, 1942), pp. 53ff., 58ff., 63ff.

33. The New Testament is full of this idea: "Then you will be triumphant" (in the joys promised and awaited). "What if you have trials of many sorts to sadden your hearts in this brief interval? That must needs happen, so that you may give proof of your faith, a much more precious thing than the gold we test by fire. . . ." 1 Peter 1:6-7; cf. Romans 5:3ff.; James 1:2ff.; Apocalypse.

34. Cf. *Le Purgatoire*, in *Le mystère de la mort et sa célébration* (*Lex orandi*, 12) (Paris: Editions du Cerf, 1951), pp. 279-336.

35. For what follows, see particularly L. Bouyer, *Le problème du mal dans le Christianisme antique*, in *Dieu vivant*, fasc. 6 (1946), pp. 15-42. A wealth of scriptural references will be found there. On humanity as sick, and the messianic activity as a work of healing, see also E. Peterson, *Qu'est-ce que l'homme?* in *Vie intellect.*, July 10, 1937, pp. 9-22.

36. This throws light on many of the Johannine texts. Cf., for example, M. F. Berrouard, "Le Paraclet, défenseur du Christ devant la conscience du croyant" (John 16:8-11), in *Rev. des Sciences philos. et théol.* (1949), pp. 361-389.

37. "Blessed be that God, the Father of our Lord Jesus Christ, who in His great mercy has begotten us anew, making hope live in us through the resurrection of Jesus Christ from the dead. We are to share an inheritance that is incorruptible, inviolable, unfading. It is stored up for you in heaven [. . .]. Then you will be triumphant. What if you have trials of many sorts to sadden your hearts in this brief interval? [. . .] Bow down, then, before the strong hand of God; He will raise you up when the (appointed) time comes to deliver you. Throw back on Him the burden of all your anxiety; He is concerned for you [. . .]. And God, the giver of all grace, who has called us to enjoy, after a little suffering, His eternal glory in Christ Jesus, will Himself give you mastery. . . ." (1 Peter 1:3, 6; 5:6, 10.) Quoted by Pius XII, Message of June 29, 1941.

38. Quoted in *La Pensée*, No. 3 (1945), p. 4.

39. A profound development of this point may be found in J. Guitton's *La Pensée moderne et le Catholicisme*: IX. *Le developpement des idées dans l'A. T.* (Aix-en-Provence and Paris: Aubier, 1947), pp. 75, 123.

40. Cf. St. Thomas, *Summa theologica*, IIIa, q. 1, a. 1. V. Heris, *Le Mystère de Dieu* (Paris: Editions Siloé, 1946).

41. See St. Thomas, *Summa theologica*, IIa-IIae, q. 30, a. 2 and 4; q. 67, a. 4; IIIa, p. 46, a. 2, ad. 3. Bossuet, *Sermon de Noël*, 1656, introd. (Lebarcq, Vol. II, 1891, pp. 99-100), *La Conception de la Ste V.*, December 8, 1656 (p. 248), *l'Annonciation*, 1662 (Vol. IV, 1892, p. 187). Cf. also, in systematic theology, M. A. Ciappi, *De divina misericordia ut prima causa operum Dei* (Rome: Angelicum, 1935). Holy Scripture often notes how pity is the proper characteristic of God's activity: cf., for example, 2 Kings 24:14; Hosea 9:9; and so forth.

42. *Pensées*, Brunschvicg, ed., n. 430; cf. n. 223, 485, 556, 558, and so forth.

43. Also a fundamental theme in the Book of Job: cf. A. Feuillet, "L'énigme de la souffrance et la réponse de Dieu" in *Dieu vivant*, No. 17 (1950), pp. 77-91.

44. Romans 8:28. Or according to another version, justified by certain MSS. [of the New Testament], "We are well assured that God helps in every way to secure the good of those who love Him." From our present point of view it amounts to the same thing.

PART TWO   The Origin of Life

Our otherwise hard and blasé age retains a bit of curious reverence where the origin of life itself is involved, and popular and scholarly magazines continually anticipate a breakthrough to the creation or laboratory origination of life. Current progress is reported in the essay by Leonard Engel. Obviously the terms used to describe the origin of life are equivocal: *origin, creation, life*. Do we mean a very proximate or an ultimate kind of origin? Do we expect a creation before our eyes or a long, barely perceptible process? Do we mean *human* life or some very primitive form of living matter? What *is* life? Do kinds of life differ qualitatively?

William J. Schmitt probes the actual avenues toward the creation of some elementary form of life and some of the philosophical and theological implications. Anthropologist Loren Eiseley writes a thoughtful essay taking us from the origin of life to the problem of the more proximate origin of *man*. While we shall leave to the weekly magazines and the daily newspapers the ever-changing picture of man's ancestry, we do have in Eiseley's essay a far-ranging picture of the evolutionary scheme as it looks today. Eiseley shows us clearly the paradox of man's likely origin "in some ratty insectivore upon a branch . . . [in whom] quivered there . . . in one frail body—Socrates, Confucius, and Gargantua, along with the organ-grinder's monkey," and his oft-demonstrated ability today to "dilate evil by drawing upon the innocent powers constrained in nature" or to "hold the world well lost for sake of such intangible things as truth and love."

The evolutionary picture both answers many questions and raises many more. Is evolution always *up*? Is man's history a pure continuum? Is Julian Huxley correct in saying that purposes are made, not found, in evolution? Does or should evolution have any function in the ordering of man's ethical and public life? Does evolution destroy any static notion of man's identity? Is the future direction of

37

human evolution at man's discretion and, if so, who is to determine which is the better direction? Are there means available for answering these questions? Does human evolution suggest or deny anything about the presence of spirit in man? Is a process so vast and complex as evolution purely fortuitous? Can the human mind or revealed religion situate evolution in an even broader context?

Many find in the highly controverted Pierre Teilhard de Chardin the most satisfying answers to these questions or, at least, the most fruitful approach to these problems. His originality and boldness make him unique among Christian thinkers in this area. In the selection we present here, his thought as found in *The Phenomenon of Man* is summarized. Noteworthy is Teilhard's conception of spirit or consciousness as present to some degree in all creation. In some ways Teilhard seems to transcend the traditional distinction of matter and spirit. Is he leading us to some kind of qualified monism or very limited dualism? (A rich commentary on these problems is given in R.C. Zaehner's remarkable book *Matter and Spirit*.) Finally, Teilhard's relation of man's evolution to Christ and His cosmic completion provides further, almost dizzying, perspectives for the thinker. The glorious harmony in his exposition certainly has an innate appeal for the Christian who by faith expects to find Christ at the heart and end of all God's creation. Is he justified in surrendering to Teilhard's vision? Teilhard seems destined to be at the beginning of a daring and almost limitless journey toward a cohesive view of man and his destiny which combines the findings of science with the data of revelation. In Part Three Paul Tillich comments further on man's place in the cosmos.

CHAPTER 2   **The Race**

to Create Life

LEONARD ENGEL

For the past several years, a number of the world's ablest biochemists have been striving to create living matter in the test tube. Many will deny that they are competing; their own work, they will point out, is only indirectly related to the possible synthesis of living matter. Nevertheless, research on the chemistry of life is heading in that direction with a rush that can be described only as a race, and the result could be even more portentous than the lighting of atomic fire.

In perhaps as little as a year or two, someone in some laboratory will fashion a bit of the unique chemical called DNA, which is found in the nuclei of all living cells and also in many viruses. DNA contains the genes, the fundamental units of heredity, and is the "mother molecule" that shapes and directs the machinery of life. If man can fashion DNA in the laboratory, he will create a chemical agent capable of initiating living processes and building up living tissue. In short, man will be creating life.

Until recently, the synthesis of living matter in the test tube was regarded as an idea for science fiction rather than science. What has made the artificial creation of living matter a genuine possibility is a remarkable new field of science, the chemistry of heredity. This is very different from the genetics most of us studied in biology classes, where we learned the chances, say, of a blue-eyed mother and a brown-eyed father having a blue-eyed daughter. The chemistry of heredity asks a deeper question: How do genes carry the message of heredity, and how is the message translated into living tissue? In

Leonard Engel, "The Race to Create Life," *Harper's Magazine*, Vol. CCXXV, No. 1349 (October, 1962), 39.

hardly more than a dozen years, many answers have been found. Research on the chemistry of heredity has revealed in impressive detail how genes make and shape life and has also shown how man on his own can go about creating the gene-bearing DNA, and hence living matter. The challenge has already been taken up in several centers. At least one team has come close. So before very long man will have gained nearly godlike power to interfere with nature and change it to suit his whim.

The first man-made living matter will almost certainly be a copy of a natural DNA, probably from a virus. Then natural DNA's will be modified in various ways, and finally there will be wholly artificial DNA's with no counterpart in nature. It is conceivable that they will be capable of generating wholly new forms of life. More importantly, they will provide a powerful new means of controlling heredity, not only in plants and animals, but in man himself. Once the scientist knows how to fabricate DNA, he will learn how to fashion *human* DNA containing *human* genes and how to use the test-tube product to alter human characteristics—to offset inborn defects, to produce children of specified sex and with other specified characteristics, perhaps with entirely new characteristics. Scientists themselves are awed by the prospect.

"Most of us can agree that it is all right to alter the heredity of plants and animals," says Alfred E. Mirsky of the Rockefeller Institute:

> After all, man has been doing that by selective breeding for a long time. Many of us can also agree that it will be good to alter human heredity to eliminate congenital defects.
>
> But what about altering human heredity for other purposes? That is a different proposition altogether. Before long we will have to decide whether we want chemical control of human heredity—chemical eugenics—and if so, how it should be exercised. And we will all have to take part in the decision as citizens. There are problems that are much too important to be left to scientists alone. This is one of them.

CHAPTER 3   **Spontaneous Generation**

and Creation

WILLIAM SCHMITT

The possibility of life arising from nonlife is once again the subject of much discussion. Universities noted for their scientific accomplishments are sponsoring symposia; scientists of outstanding reputation are undertaking serious research programs dealing with spontaneous generation. Unfortunately, a great deal of the literature on this subject, especially in book form, is unscholarly sensationalism. There are some also who, exhuming a long-dead line of argumentation, claim that spontaneous generation does away with any need for "the hypothesis of God."

For these reasons an outline of the modern hypothesis of spontaneous generation is of interest. A brief history of the question will be given, followed by a somewhat detailed outline of current thought. The theological implications will then be considered.

History

Spontaneous generation is a very old idea. Ancient man, unable to differentiate certain plants and animals into two sexes and at a loss to explain their origin, observed that these insects, shellfish, eels, and plants seemed to arise from the earth and putrid matter, and therefore concluded that they arose spontaneously from the nonliving matter. The earliest evidence we have of this belief is from two Mycenaean vases dated between 1500 and 1100 B.C.[1] Anaximander (560 B.C.) gave us one of the earliest written accounts and Aristotle taught spontaneous generation with such persuasiveness that it re-

Wm. Schmitt, "Spontaneous Generation and Creation," *Thought*, Vol. XXXVII, No. 145 (1962), 269-287.

mained part of our "common knowledge" for centuries.[2] Theophrastus, Lucretius, Pliny, and Ovid [3] accepted the common teaching. Virgil, with his usual eloquence, gave a celebrated recipe for making bees.[4] Among the ancient Chinese and in the Indian holy books we find a parallel Eastern belief.[5]

Coming to the Christian era, we find the theologians and writers of the Church accepting spontaneous generation as something almost obvious. Perhaps the earliest witness is that of Origen. The pagan, Celsus, had used spontaneous generation as an argument against the Christian religion. Origen freely admitted that serpents might come from the spine of a man, bees from dead oxen, and beetles from a dead ass. But he added that this was no argument that these creatures are independent of God.[6] St. Augustine made the interesting observation that only the higher animals were taken into the ark by Noah because there was no need to preserve those that normally were born out of corruption.[7] St. Thomas Aquinas also accepted the "fact" of spontaneous generation.[8]

Considering the evidence of their eyes, it is entirely understandable that man could come to such a general belief in spontaneous generation. Certainly the idea was no more beyond belief than that the sun "travels around the earth once a day."

In 1668, Francisco Redi, priest and scientist, delivered a severe jolt to belief in spontaneous generation. In an experiment that was to become classical he put meat in a jar, the mouth of which was protected by a covering of gauze. No flies or maggots came from the meat, although he did find eggs deposited by flies on the gauze. Thus he showed that maggots and flies do not arise spontaneously from rotten meat, but are the natural offspring of the flies which are attracted by the food.[9]

When Anton van Leeuwenhoek discovered bacteria in 1683, the hypothesis of spontaneous generation was again employed, this time to explain the appearance of "bugs" visible through the microscope, which apparently arose spontaneously from nonliving matter. This position was much disputed in the eighteenth century, but no really clear light was evident until the brilliant experiments of Louis Pasteur, beginning in 1858.

Pasteur's genius lay, to a large extent, in his ability to devise and carry out decisive experiments. His greatest achievement was to show that sterilized broth, even when in contact with air, did not produce bacteria as long as dust-carrying germs could be excluded from the broth.[10] The germ theory was vindicated. But it is important to note the precise conclusion from Pasteur's experiments. What he proved was that under normal circumstances the dictum *omne vivens e vivo* applied to the microscopic world of yeasts and bacteria. In other words, he demonstrated that the existence of spontaneous generation had never been proved; he did not prove that it was impossible.

After Pasteur there were those, like Thomas H. Huxley, who still held to the discredited hypothesis of spontaneous generation. While admitting the validity of Pasteur's work, Huxley nonetheless professed his belief by an act of philosophical faith that, at least in some remote period, life had arisen out of inanimate matter. He held this though there was admittedly no scientific evidence to support his belief.[11] It is easy to find in his writings the reason for this. Agnostics commonly believe that there is a necessary antagonism between the findings of science and the doctrines of the Roman Catholic Church.[12] The notions of creation and God are repugnant to them. A belief in primordial archebiosis, therefore, was for Huxley a sort of *deus ex machina*, one that would satisfy his agnostic prejudices. It was Huxley, the agnostic, and not Huxley, the scientist, who professed this belief. Other scientists of the turn of the century, less discerning than Huxley, claimed as a "scientific fact" the then completely discredited hypothesis of spontaneous generation.

The Modern Hypothesis

The Chemistry of Living Compounds

In 1828, more than twenty years before the brilliantly conceived experiments of Louis Pasteur destroyed belief in spontaneous generation, the chance discovery of Friedrich Wöhler, a relatively unknown chemist, laid the foundations for the resurrection of that same hypothesis.[13] In Wöhler's time scientists knew the difference between elements and compounds, and they divided the latter into two classes: organic and inorganic. In the former group were all those substances which were found to be produced only in living organisms. Sugar and indigo and other organic compounds, they thought, required a mysterious "vital force" for their preparation. Inorganic substances, salt and ammonia for example, could be produced without the intervention of this biological *élan*.

The historical experiment which forever discredited this artificial distinction between compounds which were thought to have their origin only *in vivo* and those which were amenable to laboratory synthesis, was, in restrospect, extremely simple. By merely heating a sample of ammonium cyanate, recognized by all as belonging to the category of inorganic compounds, Wöhler converted it into urea, an entirely different substance, but having exactly the same molecular formula as the starting material. The significance of the discovery lay in the fact that the organic compound urea, a product of animal metabolism, was produced for the first time outside of the living organism and in the absence of that "vital force" so gratuitously postulated by the chemists of an earlier period. A new era of science had begun.

Since then chemists have learned how to synthesize thousands of compounds that are usually produced in living plants and animals from such simple starting materials as alcohol, urea, and acetic acid. As early as 1883, Adolf von Baeyer announced the laboratory synthesis of indigo, a relatively complex plant dye.

Following the footsteps of Baeyer, Wöhler, and other pioneers, chemists have made magnificent progress in their understanding of the chemical compounds associated with life. Sugars, fats, vitamins, and the extremely complex steroid hormones have been studied to the extent that they can be synthesized in the laboratory.

Proteins and protein-like materials have long been considered as a sort of ultimate substratum of living material. Beginning with the work of Emil Fischer in 1900, we have come to know that protein material is not something mysterious, beyond the study of man. It is a wonderfully complex, but understandable, organic chemical. It is a very large molecule which is built up of many small units called amino acids. There are about twenty-five of these amino acids that can be used in the construction of a protein. They are strung together in chains hundreds to thousands of units long. The great variety of proteins results from the fact that these twenty-five building blocks can be used in the construction of a protein molecule in different proportions, in different sequences, and with a great variety of branchings and foldings. In 1958 Frederick Sanger of Great Britain won the Nobel Prize for his proof of the structure of the well-known protein, insulin. This is the first complete elucidation of the structure of a natural protein.[14]

Although we know the structure of insulin and other simple proteins, none of these has yet been synthesized. However, the chemist has had increasing success in starting with amino acids and synthesizing protein-like materials.[15] Nobel-laureate Du Vigneaud has successfully imitated nature by synthesizing the protein-like hormones, oxytocin and vasopressin. Theoretically we should eventually be able to synthesize the most complex of proteins.

Similarly, chemists have studied and often learned to duplicate many of the processes and compounds associated with life. We now know a great deal about nucleic acids,[16] although complete synthesis is still far off. The puzzle of photosynthesis is gradually being solved, the total synthesis of chlorophyll being the latest triumph in this area.[17]

Organic chemistry has come far in these one hundred and thirty years. We have had so much success in understanding the various life processes, in finding out the structures of important life chemicals and even in synthesizing these, that no one can say where the limit should be put. If and when we learn the nature of all the pieces, will we be unable to put them together?

A Chemical Theory

It is in the light of our increasing knowledge and ability to imitate and manipulate the chemistry of living things that scientists today are seriously studying the possibility of spontaneous generation. One distinction between the modern hypothesis and that held prior to Pasteur should be noted. The older hypothesis might be called "Biological Spontaneous Generation" because it envisioned the daily spontaneous appearance of fully formed living beings as we now know them. Pasteur demonstrated that all previous reports of such an occurrence had been the fruit of errors of method, incorrect design of experiments, or superficial interpretation of them. The modern approach relies heavily on the basic vision of Charles Darwin, more recently expanded and extrapolated by Teilhard de Chardin.[18] The appearance of life is thought of as merely one step in the prolonged development or evolution of higher forms from lower forms. "Chemical Spontaneous Generation" postulates a gradual evolution of non-living molecules according to the laws of nature. The term of the evolutionary process is a simple, primitive organism which then continues up the Darwinian scale. The modern view stresses the gradualness of the appearance of life. It is not a sudden cataclysm, but a hardly discernible change from a complex aggregation of nonliving molecules to the rudimentary living forms. The whole process is termed "spontaneous" only in the sense that it follows the ordinary workings of nature.

In outlining the modern concept of spontaneous generation, two points must be borne in mind. First, as with most hypotheses, there are differences of opinion among scientists on various points. Some of these differences will be pointed out here, but we will generally follow the hypothesis as conceived by Oparin and published in his monumental book, *The Origin of Life*. Secondly, the hypothesis is a chemical one and can be understood fully only by those trained in this field. The conclusions, however, can be presented in a significant way to all interested in this important question.

Primeval Conditions

The first step in the construction of the hypothesis of spontaneous generation of life on this planet is to consider the conditions under which life could have arisen. Paradoxical as it might seem, the absence of life is one of these conditions. The very statement of the question supposes this but, in addition, we find it a necessary condition for any spontaneous generation. Considering the fate of complex organic molecules in the world today, which is to be rapidly broken down by bacteria and other living organisms, we know that only in the absence of life could the postulated evolution of molecules take place, for only on an earth still sterile would they be safe from the devouring hordes of organisms.[19]

As regards temperature, moisture, pressure, and illumination, it is accepted by many that the conditions on the primitive earth were much what they are today. The atmosphere, however, was made up primarily of methane, ammonia, water vapor, and hydrogen. Another difference was in the solar radiation. It was probably richer in high-energy ultraviolet radiation, at present screened out by layers of ozone in the upper atmosphere. Other sources of energy would be electrical discharge and radioactive decay.

The Evolution of Organic Molecules

The first step in the proposed evolution of life must be the formation of simple organic molecules. Without these life as we know it is impossible and inconceivable.

The simplest organic compounds, the hydrocarbons, are readily formed by the action of minerals called carbides on water, which minerals could easily have arisen from the action of carbon on metals. The initially formed hydrocarbons could evolve into more complex ones under the influence of ultraviolet energy or electrical storms. Oxygen-containing compounds would also form, the oxygen coming from the dissociation of water.[20] The reactions involved here are simple and well known. They are not mere speculation. Thus we can be sure that, in the conditions described, the primitive earth would have a supply of alcohols, aldehydes, acids, amines, and other simple organic substances.

Let us consider, as an illustration, the manner in which the amino acids, the building blocks of proteins, might have been formed under the primeval conditions. Various approaches have been suggested, the most striking that of Stanley Miller. He exposed a mixture of ammonia, methane, hydrogen, and water vapor (the primitive atmosphere) to a spark discharge for several days. At the end of this time he found a number of amino acids, as well as other organic compounds.[21] From analogous experiments, it can be shown that even the more complex substances such as sugars and polyenes could have arisen naturally under the conditions of the primitive earth.

The problem of explaining the primordial generation of proteins presents more difficulty, though not insurmountable. We have seen that the amino acid building blocks could easily have existed on the primitive earth, but the vastly more complex proteins are another matter. Various mechanisms of protein synthesis have been suggested, but much more important for our consideration is the very statement of the problem. On this point there is a marked difference of opinion between Oparin and most other writers.

Chance, Protein, and Life

The proponents of what may be termed the "lucky protein" theory give most of their attention to the problem of protein synthesis. Admitting the very serious nature of the obstacles to spontaneous protein synthesis, they solve this difficulty by an appeal to time. Calvin points out that the period of chemical evolution probably occurred between 2.5 and 1 billion years ago. In this "great deal of time . . . many improbable events can occur. . . . This, of course, is one of the saving graces of the problem." [22] The argument is based on the fact that a statistically improbable event (the spontaneous synthesis of a protein), given a sufficient number of tries, can become statistically very probable. It is argued that the billions of years available for chemical evolution permitted many attempts and thus enabled a statistically improbable event to take place.[23]

The proponents of the "lucky protein" hypothesis feel that, having explained the origin of one protein molecule, they have explained the origin of life. They argue that once such a complex material as a protein, even one molecule of it, was formed, it would guide and direct the synthesis of like molecules. This reproduction would be the first manifestation of life.

Oparin attacks this solution [24] by denying that the "lucky protein" approach has any experimental verification whatever, a point that his opponents are willing enough to admit when hard pressed, but a point which they often conceal when they boast that their position is "virtually certain."

Oparin further directs a very logical attack on the basic assumption of the "lucky protein" hypothesis. He focuses attention on the specificity of proteins rather than on their complexity, on their function rather than on their structure. The enzymes and other body proteins are tailored for one operation and one operation alone. One cannot substitute for another. They are excellently adapted to their own job, but useless for any other. For this reason Oparin feels that it is useless even to consider the spontaneous synthesis of proteins as we know them today.[25] He furthermore thinks it highly unlikely that such compounds would, once formed, guide and direct the synthesis of like molecules. His reason is the same: they are not adapted to that function. And even granting such an ability of self-reproduction, this would merely mean that the primary organic material would be converted into uniform layers of protein in deposits similar to mineral formations. This is not life.

To hold the opposite view is tantamount, in Oparin's view, to returning to the position of Empedocles: "Out of it [Earth] many foreheads without necks sprang forth, and arms wandering unattached, bereft of shoulders, and eyes strayed about alone, needing brows." [26] Later these members joined to form animals and people. Now just as it is absurd that an eye exist alone, so it is absurd that a protein molecule exist alone. Both are too specific, too well adapted to their special function. Hence, any reference to "happy chance" is irrational, since it does not explain the purposeful specificity of the molecules.

Mechanism Refuted

Oparin takes a still more fundamental position of disagreement, based on the very conception of life:

> Quite large numbers of scientists now take the view that an understanding of life in general involves no more than a very thorough knowledge of physics and chemistry and a very thorough explanation of all vital phenomena in terms of physical and chemical processes. According to this view there are no specifically biological laws, and the rules which prevail in the inorganic world also govern all the phenomena taking place in living organisms. But this amounts to denying all the essential differences between organisms and the objects of the inorganic world, which is fundamentally unsound. Certainly life is material in nature, but it is not inherent in every sort of material. It is a manifestation of a special form of motion which we only find in organisms and which is absent from the objects of the inorganic world. This form of motion of matter, in addition to obeying the general physical and chemical laws, also has its own specific laws.[27]

Just what the "essential differences" between life and nonlife are he makes clear in another place:

> From a purely chemical standpoint . . . metabolism is a complicated association of . . . reactions. These are well known to chemists and are easily carried out outside the living organism under laboratory conditions. . . . There is nothing specific to life about any one of

these reactions. What is specific about the organization of biological metabolism seems to be that in protoplasm the reactions are strictly coordinated and harmonious, that they follow one another in a definite regular order and not at random, forming long series, branching chains, and closed cycles of chemical reactions.[28]

In other words, he argues that even if the scientist can explain the reactions and formation of a protein or nucleic acid or other biological chemicals, and even if he can duplicate the various individual processes associated with life, he has not explained life, for he has failed to explain the harmony of the various reactions. It is this harmony and teleology that make the difference between life and nonlife.

Oparin's Hypothesis

Having set such rigid standards, Oparin then proceeds to give what he considers a valid scientific explanation of how life might have arisen from nonlife on the primitive earth. He relies on points we have already considered: the absence of life, an atmosphere of ammonia, hydrogen, water vapor, and methane, the presence of electric discharge and strong ultraviolet radiation. Under these conditions, following the ordinary chemical laws there arose simple organic compounds which reacted further to form more complicated compounds.

The next step postulated by Oparin, the details of which we shall not go into, was the aggregation of some of the bigger molecules into associations called coacervates.[29] This part of his hypothesis is based on fairly well-known phenomena. It does, however, involve much extrapolation. The coacervate system is pictured as evolving toward specialized forms of greater stability characterized by nonvital growth through the intake of organic compounds.

Finally, Oparin postulates that there arose systems with closed cycles of reactions in which the reactions always followed the same circle and branching occurred only at definite points on the circle. This would lead to the constantly repeated formation of certain metabolic products. This process, he postulates, led to self-reproduction, and this point may be taken as the origin of life. These latter steps in the hypothesis seem to be possible, from a scientific point of view, but there is no experimental evidence to support them.

It was in the course of this evolution, and in the later evolution of living things, that the original catalysts developed into what we now know as enzymes. Later these individual molecules developed greater reactivity and specificity and became coordinated into the vast complex we now know as metabolism.

Oparin feels that this process of evolution of life can take place anywhere in the universe where the conditions are proper. He also believes that life will be created in the laboratory of the future.[30]

Oparin is, in turn, attacked by his colleagues. Some feel that his hypothesis is thermodynamically impossible. Perhaps, also, he has failed to explain the very thing he considers crucial: the harmony of activity that is the distinguishing mark between life and nonlife. The objection here is not that experimental verification is lacking, but that this or that "must have happened" does not give us sufficient explanation.

Indirect Evidence
for Spontaneous Generation

We find in living systems even today a number of nonspecific compounds. Diabetics are grateful that their bodies can make use of the insulin obtained from animals. Similarly, Butenandt has isolated a hormone that can be utilized by many insect species.[31] Such compounds can be considered relics of an early period of the evolution of life. The existence of such nonspecific compounds seems to support Oparin's idea that primitive vital activity involved many nonspecific compounds and that the highly specific substances of today are the result of prolonged evolution.

Comparative biochemistry also supports the Oparin view. In the many different organisms alive today we find certain aspects of metabolic chemistry that are very similar despite differences of species. To take a concrete case, chlorophyll, the green pigment of plants which is so important in their life chemistry, has the very same basic structure as hemin, the red pigment that is vitally concerned with animal respiration. Thus, just as Darwin concluded to the notion of a common ancestor from similarities in morphology, so we can find evidence for a chemical evolution in the similarities found in comparative biochemistry.

A final piece of indirect evidence resulted from fundamental research in virus chemistry. Heinz Fraenkel-Conrat has been able to separate the tobacco mosaic virus into two parts, neither of which shows virus characteristics. He has then successfully re-formed active virus from these parts. Furthermore, he has united the parts of different varieties of this virus in such a way that he has created new viruses.[32] Although most scientists tend toward the position that viruses are not living, they are certainly close to exhibiting the manifestations of life. Being able to synthesize them is very close to being able to synthesize life.

Summary

The present hypothesis of spontaneous generation postulates the evolution of elements and simple organic compounds to the highly obscure point where the nonliving becomes living. This study is a legitimate pursuit of scientists, since they use their particular tools and can reach conclusions in their own field. Some remarkable experimental results have already been obtained. It would be false, however, to say that the road is clear, that it is only a matter of performing certain experiments. Most scientists working on this problem admit to a hope that their efforts will be successful, but there is no certainty; and this is generally admitted. This much, perhaps, can be said: if life did arise spontaneously on the earth, the feat can probably be duplicated in the laboratory.

Theology and the Origin of Life

Any explanation of the origin of life on earth is also of theological interest, since it would have a relation to the teaching of the Church on creation and conservation. We have already seen how, even in Origen's time, the concept of spontaneous generation had been used by atheists. We are not surprised, therefore, to find modern authors who preface their writings on this subject with a sly reference to the "myth of creation." [33]

As will be shown, the Church has taken no official stand on the hypothesis of spontaneous generation. Individual theologians, of course, have discussed the question and should continue to do so. In such discussions, it would seem proper to avoid any hasty or over-strong reaction of either joyful acceptance or horrified rejection. Both extremes can do a disservice to theology.

Yet both extremes have existed. Because certain atheists and agnostics have used spontaneous generation as an argument in their favor, we have not lacked those who completely reject this hypothesis as incompatible with Catholic teaching.[34] On the other hand, one theologian has gone so far as to "prove" from Holy Scripture and from the writings of the Fathers of the Church that evolution and spontaneous generation are part of Catholic doctrine.[35] Such whole-hearted endorsement of a scientific theory which later may be discarded is, to say the least, imprudent, and it has rightfully brought severe criticism.[36]

The Teaching of the Church

Nowhere does the Church officially discuss the hypothesis of spontaneous generation, but we can get some idea of the mind of the Church by considering her teaching on the doctrine of creation.

The whole Christian attitude toward the world is that it resulted from the activity of God. In the early ages of the Church this was affirmed against the errors of Gnostic and Manichean dualism, which attributed the material world to the evil principle. The dogma of creation was considered so important that it was incorporated into most creeds.[37] It has been discussed and defined in various ecumenical councils.[38] In our own time this dogma is opposed to materialism in its many forms, all of which deny the existence of a transcendent God Who is distinct from the world and Creator of the world. Catholic dogma teaches that the material universe is completely dependent on God, that all things were created either mediately or immediately by Him, the true and only efficient cause of the universe taken as a whole.

Nowhere in these sources do we find either a condemnation or an approbation of spontaneous generation.

The only time an official pronouncement touches our question, it does so indirectly. This we find in the encyclical *Humani Generis* where direct reference is made to the theory of evolution. The Church very wisely points out that, since we are dealing with theory rather than fact, and since the evolutionary concept can be so mis-employed as to lead to serious philosophical and theological errors, prudence is required when dealing with the subject. We are further cautioned not to express as facts conclusions which go beyond the evidence. This, however, is merely one of the principles of the scientific method and is recognized, at least in principle, by all scientists.

But, after giving voice to these words of caution, the stand of the Church remains clear: "Thus, the teaching of the Church leaves the doctrine of evolution an open question. . . . In the present state of scientific and theological opinion this question may be legitimately canvassed by research, and by discussions between experts on both sides." [39]

Certainly, therefore, the theologian should be careful not to espouse too heartily a mere hypothesis. Nor should he forget that often the doctrine of the Church is merely a negative norm. The fact that the Church does not teach spontaneous generation does not make it untrue. Furthermore, where a scientific hypothesis leads men into error, it is necessary to examine whether the hypothesis does this per se or only because of improper application of the hypothesis.

Turning to the Holy Scriptures, we again find the absence of any statement which can be understood as either approving or condemning spontaneous generation. Today we realize more clearly than ever before that the message of Genesis is spiritual and theological; the Bible is not trying to teach science. Furthermore, science can neither affirm nor deny the answer to the religious questions contained in the Bible. Therefore, no matter how far back science can push its investigations of the origin of life, it will never reach the level of the message of Genesis.[40]

With regard to the testimony of the Fathers of the Church, certain distinctions must be made. The Fathers, like the authors of the various books of the Bible, were not attempting to teach science. At best they accepted the teaching of the philosophers (scientists) of their day to illustrate theological doctrine. Therefore, along with their contemporaries they did accept spontaneous generation, not the chemical theory of today but the crude biological theory that was held in some form until the work of Pasteur. But it is not proper to cite them except to show that the general concept of spontaneous generation is not inimical to Catholic teaching.

In all the official sources of Catholic doctrine, therefore, we find neither condemnation nor approval of spontaneous generation. On the other hand, the Church recognizes the validity of scientific theories which attempt to give a more proximate explanation of facts concerning which theology gives us more fundamental information. Only those hypotheses which per se oppose revealed truth must be rejected.

A Theological Speculation

Revelation is complete, but our understanding of it is ever growing. Scientific facts and hypotheses have assisted this understanding in the past and they can do so now. In particular, the theory of spontaneous generation can illumine and broaden our understanding of the creative activity of God.

God's purpose in creating the world is to manifest and communicate His perfections.[41] Or, to look at it from the viewpoint of the created world, the whole purpose of the world, its *rationale*, is to show forth the perfections of God.[42] It would seem reasonable to conjecture that the perfections of God are manifested more splendidly and to a greater extent by the spontaneous origin of life than by a mechanism which requires a special intervention of God.

In our human lives we are quite familiar with the concept of "making." When someone makes something, we attribute the object to the maker. The more elaborate, useful, beautiful, and pleasing the object, the more we admire the one who made it. In general, the more perfect the object, the more it manifests the skill and perfection of its maker. Thus we admire Michelangelo for his magnificent "Moses." We also admire the skill of the glassblower who turns out a crystal goblet. These products certainly manifest the perfections of the one who made them. But for Michelangelo to have invented a machine that would have done the entire sculpturing for him would certainly have been a greater feat and would have manifested more perfection in the artist. For the same reason, Michael Owens, the inventor of the first automatic bottle-blowing machine [43] might be thought worthy of greater tribute than the glassblower who turns out individual bottles which vary in uniformity.

The more God has given to creatures the power of causality, the more they can reveal the dignity and power of His creative act. When we contemplate the world God has made, we see a magnificent spectacle. This magnificence is enhanced when we consider that God does not "make" in the same way that man does. Among other things, it is not sufficient that God once and for all creates the world and then leaves it alone. Since He is the cause not only of the essence of things, but of their very existence, His creative activity must endure in a positive manner. Without this conservation the world would simply cease to exist. Hence we say that God continually creates the world. His activity never ceases and the products of this creative activity continually manifest the divine perfections.

Since God is the cause of the creatures' existence and perfections, He is also the cause of all created activity. Therefore, whenever a creature "makes" something, it is manifesting, in a limited way, God's creative activity. The creature-action is an image of the Creator-action. When molecules react according to the design and plan of God, they also manifest the perfections of God. The more perfect their activity, the more perfectly they manifest the divine activity.

Since molecular evolution that would result in a living organism is more perfect than the common molecular activity, such a process would more perfectly manifest the divine perfection. Indeed, it would manifest not only the creative activity of God, but also His very life. Vegetable life is an admittedly weak image of the perfectly immanent activity of God, but it is an image and hence cries out the perfections of the Living God.

All of this is said, not to prove the existence of spontaneous generation from theology, but to show that it is more compatible with Christian theology than its opposite postulate. Spontaneous generation manifests more perfectly the divine perfections of creative activity and life than does the postulate that God had to intervene in a special way to bring life on the earth.

In our daily life we become quite used to the process whereby a living organism takes nonliving matter and transforms it into its living self by the process of anabolism. Theologians do not postulate a special intervention of God in this wonderful process. Under the ordinary conservative power of God, Who keeps in existence both the food and the living being's active nature, the nonliving becomes living. It would seem that only our imagination [44] is in the way when we accept the fact that life from nonlife is possible under the directive influence of a living being, yet refuse to accept the same possibility under the directive influence of normal material activity which operates under God's provident care.

Spontaneous generation in this context can never substitute for creation, since the entire course of it is within the created sphere. But it can enhance creation and make clearer God's perfections. Charles Darwin, it seems, had the vision of this, for he concludes his great work as follows:

> It is interesting to contemplate a tangled bank, clothed with many plants of many kinds, with birds singing on the bushes, with various insects flitting about, and with worms crawling through the damp earth, and to reflect that these elaborately constructed forms, so different from each other, and dependent upon each other in so complex a manner, have all been produced by laws acting around us. . . . There is grandeur in this view of life with its several powers, having been originally breathed by the Creator into a few forms or into one; and that, whilst this planet has gone cycling on according to the fixed laws of gravity, from so simple a beginning endless forms most beautiful and most wonderful have been, and are being evolved. [45]

Such a concept of God's activity can bring us very close to the Creator. In the climax of his spiritual teaching, St. Ignatius presents his "Contemplation to Obtain the Love of God." After pointing out that love ought to manifest itself in deeds rather than in words, and that love consists in a mutual sharing, he turns to consider the blessing of creation and redemption. He reflects how God dwells in creatures, giving them existence and sometimes life, and how He works in creatures. [46] The contemplation of these truths can help prepare a man to make an act of love of God. The more wonderful God's ways, the more His perfections are manifest to us, the easier is that love. We do not know whether God is the author of life by a special act of His Almighty power or by the intrinsically more perfect way of His ordinary creative causality; but the latter seems more in keeping with His dignity and providence: "By his providence God watches over and governs all the things that He made, reaching from end to end with might and disposing all things with gentleness." [47]

References

1. Eugene S. McCartney, *Transactions and Proceedings of the American Philological Association*, Vol. LI (1920), 101-115.

2. Aristotle, *Historia Animalium*, VI, 15.

3. Theophrastus, *Enquiry into Plants*, III, 5; Lucretius, *De Rerum Natura*, II, 871-873; *ibid.*, V, 797-800; Pliny, *Naturalis Historia*, XI, 117-119; Ovid, *Metamorphoses*, XV, 368.

4. Virgil, *Georgics*, IV, 281ff.

5. E. O. von Lippmann, *Urzeugung und Lebenskraft* (Berlin, 1933). Quoted by Oparin; see below.

6. Origen, *Contra Celsum*, IV (PG 11 1123), 57.

7. Augustine, *De Civitate Dei*, XV, 27.

8. E. C. Messenger, *Evolution and Theology* (London: Burns, Oates & Washbourne, Ltd., 1931). The extreme position propounded in this book, however, is not accepted by scholars today.

9. René Vallery-Radot, *The Life of Pasteur* (1900), R. L. Devonshire, trans. (Garden City, N. Y.: Garden City Publ., 1910), p. 89.

10. *Ibid.*, pp. 107-109.

11. Leonard Huxley, *The Life and Letters of Thomas Henry Huxley*, Vol. II (London: Macmillan & Co., Ltd., 1913), 15ff.

12. *Ibid.*, Vol. I, 443.

13. Henry M. Leicester, *The Historical Background of Chemistry* (New York: John Wiley & Sons, Inc., 1956), p. 173.

14. *Chemical and Engineering News* (November 10, 1958), p. 102.

15. *Ibid.* (April 18, 1960), p. 68.

16. *Ibid.* (May 9, 1960), p. 38.

17. *Ibid.* (July 11, 1960), p. 20.

18. Teilhard de Chardin, *Phenomenon of Man*, Bernard Wall, trans. (New York: Harper & Row, Publishers, 1959).

19. A. I. Oparin, *The Origin of Life on the Earth*, 3rd ed., Ann Synge, trans. (New York: Academic Press, 1957), pp. 78-79.

20. *Ibid.*, p. 182.

21. Stanley L. Miller, *Science*, Vol. CXVII (1953), 528; *Journal of the American Chemical Society*, Vol. 77 (1955), 2351.

22. M. Calvin, *American Scientist*, Vol. XLIV (1956), 248.

23. George Wald, *Scientific American*, Vol. CXCI, No. 2 (1954), 45-53.

24. Oparin, *op, cit.*, pp. 217, 233, 260, 284, 287-289, 298, 347; Melvin Calvin, *Chemical and Engineering News* (January 27, 1958), p. 58.

25. Oparin, *op. cit.*, p. 233.

26. Quoted by Oparin, *op. cit.*, p. 260.

27. Oparin, *op. cit.*, p. 347.

28. *Ibid.*, p. 332.

29. *Ibid.*, p. 302

30. *Ibid.*, p. 489.

31. A. Butenandt, *Die Naturwissenschaften*, Vol. XLII (1955), 141.

32. H. Fraenkel-Conrat, *Journal of the American Chemical Society*, Vol. LXXVIII (1956), 882-883.

33. Wald, *op. cit.*

34. Felix Ruschkamp, "The Origin of Life," in *God, Man, and the Universe,* Jacques De Bivort De La Saudée, ed. (New York: P. J. Kenedy & Sons, 1953).

35. Messenger, *op. cit.*

36. E. C. Messenger, ed., *Theology and Evolution* (London: Sands and Co., 1949).

37. Henricus Denzinger, ed., *Enchiridion Symbolorum,* Edition 29 (Freiburg: Herder, 1953), No. 6; *ibid.,* No. 86.

38. *Ibid.,* No. 428; *ibid.,* No. 706; *ibid.,* No. 1805.

39. *Humani Generis,* translation appearing in *The Church Teaches,* prepared by St. Mary's College (St. Louis: Herder Book Co., 1960), p. 154.

40. John L. McKenzie, S.J., *The Two-Edged Sword* (Milwaukee: Bruce Publishing Co., 1956), pp. 73-75.

41. Denzinger, *op. cit.,* No. 1783

42. *Ibid.,* No. 1805

43. Freda Diamond, *The Story of Glass* (New York: Harcourt, Brace & World, Inc., 1953), p. 85.

44. It has often been objected that spontaneous generation goes contrary to the principle that the effect cannot exceed its cause. Since the philosophy of spontaneous generation will be published elsewhere, it will suffice for now to point out that the principle quoted applies only to the field of *efficient* causality and presupposes that you are dealing with the *adequate* efficient cause. It can be shown that spontaneous generation does not conflict with this principle.

45. Charles Darwin, *The Origin of Species.*

46. Ignatius of Loyola, The Spiritual Exercises, Fourth Week.

47. Denzinger, *op. cit.,* No. 1783.

CHAPTER 4

The Time of Man

LOREN EISELEY

* * *

If I write this history in brief compass it is because, on the scale of the universe, it is but an instant, shot with individual glory and unimaginable shame. Man is the only infinitely corruptible as well as infinitely perfectible animal.

The story I here record contains many gaps and few names. Most of what has gone into the making of man is as nameless as the nothing from which he sprang and into which, by his own hand, he threatens to subside. He has wandered unclothed through earth's long interglacial summers; he has huddled before fires in equally millennial winters. He has mated and fought for a bare existence like earth's other creatures. Unlike these others, however, he has clothed his dreams in magic that slowly became science—the science that was to bring him all things. And so, because of the dark twist in his mind, it has; it has brought him even unto death.

There are innumerable detailed questions of dating and of detailed anatomical analysis and interpretation of those scant human remains which through gaps of hundreds of thousands, even of millions of years, enable us to secure brief glimpses of our nameless forerunners. For a hundred years—ever since the theory of evolution became biologically demonstrable—these facts have been accumulating. To catalogue them, to debate their several arguments, would require volumes. It is my intention in this article merely to select for discussion a few key items which continue to intrigue the educated layman, and which may help him to comprehend not alone a few of the mileposts of his long journey but which may give him as well a better comprehension of his own nature and the built-in dangers it contains. The moment is topical, for it is within the past

Loren Eiseley, "The Time of Man," *Horizon* (March, 1962), pp. 4-11. Published by American Heritage Publishing Co., Inc.

year that discoveries have been made which may drastically change our ideas about our earliest past.

We will begin with a warning: more than 90 per cent of the world's animal life of past periods is dead. Though it flourished in some instances longer than the whole period of human development, somewhere along its evolutionary path one of two things happened. It vanished without descendants or was transformed, through still mysterious biological processes, into something else; just as man is now something quite different from what he was ten million years ago. This leads to the inescapable conclusion that, contrary to popular impression, evolution is not something "behind" us—the impression we may get while staring into museum cases.

So long as life exists on the planet, it is still changing, adjusting, and vanishing as natural forces—and among them we must now count man—may dictate. Thus life is never really perfectly adjusted. It is malleable and imperfect because it is always slipping from one world into another. The perfectly adjusted perish with the environments that created them. It is not really surprising, when one thinks about it, that man, who evolved with comparative rapidity, should be among earth's most dangerous juvenile delinquents.

He is literally compounded of contradictions, mentally and physically. He is at one and the same time archaic and advanced. His body and his mind are as stuffed with evolutionary refuse as a New England attic. Once he comes to accept and recognize this fact, his chances for survival may improve. He has come halfway on a trembling bridge toward heaven, but the human brain in its loss of life-preserving instincts passes also along the brink of sanity. Here is a great poet, John Donne, speaking three centuries ago of the power of the human intellect:

> Inlarge this Meditation upon this great world, Man, so farr, as to consider the immensitie of the creatures this world produces; our creatures are our thoughts, creatures that are borne Gyants; that reach from East to West, from Earth to Heaven, that doe not onely bestride all the Sea, and Land, but span the Sunn and Firmament at once; My thoughts reach all, comprehend all. Inexplicable mistery; I their Creator am in a close prison, in a sicke bed, any where, and any one of my Creatures, my thoughts, is with the Sunne, and beyond the Sunne, overtakes the Sunne, and overgoes the Sunne in one pace, one steppe, everywhere.

Man, in short, has, like no other beast, tumbled into the crevasse of his own being, fallen into the deep well of his own mind. Like modern divers in the sacrificial wells of the Maya, he has drawn from his own depths such vast edifices as the pyramids, or inscribed on cave walls the animals of his primitive environment, fixed by a magic that inhabited his mind. He retreats within and he appears outward. Even the fallen temples of his dead endeavors affect, like strange symbols, the minds of later-comers. There is something immaterial that haunts the air, something other than the life force in squirrel and chipmunk. Here, even in ruin, something drawn from the depths of our being may speak a message across the waste of centuries.

A little while ago I handled a flint knife, from Stone Age Egypt, running my hand over its beautifully rippled surface. A human mind, an artist's mind, whispered to me from the stone. I held the knife a long time, just as in another way I might hold in my mind the sunlit 'Parthenon, feeling some emanation, some re-entering power deriving from minds long past but flooding my own thought with renewed powers and novelties. This is a part, a mystical part if you will, of man's emergence into time and history.

When he entered into himself, as no other animal on the globe is capable of doing, he also entered the strangest environmental corridor on the planet, one almost infinite in its possibilities, its terrors, and its hopes. It was the world of history, of symbolic thought, of culture. From the moment when the human brain, even in its dim red morning, crossed that threshold, it would never again be satisfied with the things of earth. It would heft a stone and make of it a tool grown from the mind; fire would become its instrument; sails on the invisible air would waft it far; eventually a little needle in a box would guide men to new continents and polar snows. In each case there would also be the aura of magic. The powers would not be what we of today call natural; around them would hover a penumbral mystery drawn from the abysses of the mind itself. Time and the foreknowledge of death would rise also in that spectral light. Of the fears that beset our dawning consciousness, the brown bone on the shores of a vanished lake bed will tell us nothing. It will tell us only how we changed.

From whence did we come? Over and over again the scholar is

asked this question by those who forget the wounds and changes in the bone. Do they ask upon which continent we first stood dubiously erect? Do they ask from what limb in an ancient forest we first hung and by some idle quirk dropped down into the long grass that first received us? Do they want to know at what point we first asked a question of some wandering constellation in the night sky above our heads? Or from what marsh we first dragged our wet amphibian bodies up the shore? Or from what reptilian egg we sprang? Or from what cell in some far, steaming sea?

No, the question has to be contained and caught within the primate order to which we and all manner of ring-tailed wide-eyed lemurs, blue-chinned monkeys, and enormous apes belong. With these we share certain facets of a common bodily structure that speaks of ancient relationships. In a strange, figurative way there was a time far back along the evolutionary road when all this weird array might be seen to shrink to a single tree shrew, a single ratty insectivore upon a branch. Man, at that moment, was one of many potentials. He was and was not, and likewise all his hairy and fantastic kin. They all quivered there upon that single branch in one frail body—Socrates, Confucius, and Gargantua, along with the organ-grinder's monkey.

*   *   *

Even after the brain began to grow, it was long shielded by a shell of bone as thick as a warrior's helmet. It was as if nature itself was dubious of the survival of this strange instrument, yet had taken steps to protect it. I like to think that with the invention of a brain capable of symbolic thought—and, as an unsought corollary, philosophy—something beyond nature rejoiced to look out upon itself. That massively walled brain, even in its early beginnings, had taken life three billion years to produce. But the future of no invention can be guaranteed. As in the case of other forms of life in the past, extinction may come about some millennia hence from "natural" causes. Or—as we are constantly reminded by our experts—life's most dazzling invention may, through the employment of its own wizardry, soon be able to erase itself completely from the earth, in a matter not of millennia, but of minutes.

For the human brain, magnificent though it be, is as yet imperfect and bears within itself an old and lower brain—a fossil remnant, one might say—geared to the existence of a creature struggling to become human, and dragged with him, unfortunately, out of the Ice Age. This ancient brain, capable of violent and dominant re-emergence under various conditions of stress, contains, figuratively speaking, claws—claws which by now can be fantastically extended.

* * *

. . . Today, while no reasonable man doubts the reality of human evolution, its precise pathways are hazy, and far gaps in time and space make the exact succession of forms difficult if not impossible to determine.

* * *

. . . Man, the thinker, has occurred but once in the three billion years that may be the length of life's endurance on this planet.

He is an inconceivably rare and strange beast who lives both within himself and in his outside environment. With his coming came history, the art of the mind imposing itself upon nature. There has been no previous evolutionary novelty comparable to this save the act of creation itself. Man, imperfect transitory man, carries within him some uncanny spark from the first lightning that split the void. He alone can dilate evil by drawing upon the innocent powers contained in nature; he alone can walk straight-footed to his own death and hold the world well lost for sake of such intangible things as truth and love.

* * *

A year ago most of us who work in this haunted graveyard of the past would have said that a brain which we could truly denominate as human was perhaps no older than the lower Ice Age, and that below the million years or so of Ice Age time, man, even lowbrowed, thick-skulled man, had vanished from our ken. If, that far back, he still walked, he was not a tool-user; if he still talked, his thoughts had found no lasting expression upon the objects of his outer world. It appeared to us not that he had vanished in the seven-million-year epoch of the Pliocene, but rather that he was a thinly distributed ground ape, a late descendant upon the upland grasses, still teetering upon a dubiously adapted foot from one sparse clump of trees to another.

In July, 1961, our ideas were destined to change drastically. They were to change not so much because of a newly described form of early man from Africa—we had grown used to that—but rather because of what a new method of dating was to tell us about humanity in general.

Over the previous thirty years a startling series of discoveries in South and East Africa had revealed that the simplified versions of single-line human evolution were very unlikely to be true. It was soon realized that African humanity has a very ancient history—more ancient than, at present, we can demonstrate for any other part of Asia or Europe.

* * *

[Recent discoveries have tended to confirm Darwin's suspicion that Africa was the home of oldest man. It must be "remembered, though, that the inhospitable desert break between Africa and Asia has not always existed." There may have been much freedom of movement between the two continents. We do not know Asia as well archaeologically as Africa, hence it may be premature to presume that Africa is the home of the first men.]

All through the past few decades the labors of such pioneer scientists as Robert Broom, Raymond Dart, L. S. B. Leakey, and J. T. Robinson have succeeded in turning up amid the breccia of ancient cave deposits a hitherto totally unsuspected and apparently cultureless group of ape-men, or perhaps one should say man-apes. Instead of gorilloid, long-fanged creatures lately descended from the trees, such as the early Darwinists would have envisaged, these creatures, of whom numerous remains and several species have been recovered, brought dramatically home to us a largely unsuspected aspect of the human story, anticipated on theoretical grounds only by Darwin's great contemporary Alfred Wallace.

The idea of the gorilloid nature of early man as advanced by many nineteenth-century scientists was not borne out by the new-found fossils. Instead, the bones proved to be those of rather slightly built, erect-walking "apes" with massive molar teeth unaccompanied by projecting canines. In short these animals turned out to be a rather variable lot of short-faced, small-brained creatures already adapted for walking on their hind feet. Long arguments developed as to whether these creatures of some 500 cubic centimeters of cranial capacity—roughly akin to the brain size of a modern chimpanzee or gorilla—could have made crude tools, or at least utilized the long bones of slain animals as clubs or stabbing weapons. This was possible—but difficult to prove.

One thing has at least become evident. The man-apes represented not recently arboreal apes but, instead, an unsuspected variety of erect-walking anthropoids whose foot adaptation to a ground-dwelling existence was already greatly perfected. In Tertiary times large primates had not been confined to the trees. Instead, they had successfully brought their old-fashioned arboreal bodies down onto the grass and survived there—a feat of no mean magnitude. By some evolutionary neurological quirk they had acquired an upright posture which had freed the forelimbs from the demands of locomotion. Man bears in his body clear signs of an early apprenticeship in the trees. We now began to suspect, however, that man had served his arboreal apprenticeship much farther back in time than many scholars had anticipated. It also became evident that the number of forms and datings of what soon came to be called the Australopithecine man-apes could only suggest that not all of them were direct human ancestors. These African creatures hinted rather a variety of early man-apes, not all of whom had necessarily taken the final step of becoming human.

A group of apes had entered upon a new way of life in open parkland and grassland. Arboreal apes are not carnivorous; they are primarily vegetarians. But these man-apes, or perhaps I should say some of these man-apes, had become killers of game. Their massive jaws, however, are not evidence of this fact. Massive molar teeth may mean only the consumption of certain types of uncooked vegetation. It is the broken bones of animals in the caves they frequented which suggests that some species, at least, had become killers, using their unloosed forelimbs as weapon wielders. As for the brain, perhaps though still small, the upright posture had given this organ some qualitative advantage over the brains of our living relatives, the great apes.

Still, we had to look upon these creatures as essentially an odd, humanlike ape. Like any other animal, they had intruded into and adapted themselves to a grassland existence; it appears unlikely that they could speak. It appears unlikely, also, that all these creatures survived to become men; some may have been living fossils in their own time. The last of them may have been exterminated by the spread of man himself. But they indicate that the bipedal apes were well adapted to survive upon the ground without entering extensively upon a second road of conquest.

It remained for the direct human ancestors, from whatever bipedal group they may have sprung, to precipitate the final stage in man's development: the rise of the great brain, still marked by its ferocious past. For man entered, with the development of speech and its ever-growing product, culture, into the strangest and most rapidly changing environment on the planet, an environment limited only by his own creativeness. He entered into himself; he created society and its institutions. The exterior, natural world would be modified and pushed farther and farther back by the magic circle in which he had immured himself. Some societies would dream on for millennia in a world still close to nature; other roads would lead to the Greek thinkers and the Roman aqueducts. The history of the world-changers had begun.

*　*　*

In 1959, Dr. L. S. B. Leakey found at Olduvai the massive-jawed, small-brained creature who has come to be known as *Zinjanthropus*. Though detailed anatomical data are not available, the creature would appear to be not too distant in its anatomy from some of the known, and possibly much later, man-apes. It is, however, remarkable for two reasons. First, it was found in association with clearly shaped stone tools, long known but never found in direct contact with human remains. Thus this creature was not merely a user of chance things which he picked up; he was a thinker who shaped. Second, late last July [1961] Doctors J. F. Evenden and Garniss Curtis of the University of California announced that *Zinjanthropus* was nearly *two* million years old. They had dated the creature by a new "clock" involving the use of potassium-argon radioactive decay. If this dating method is correct, the history of tool-using man will thus have been carried back almost a million years before the Ice Age—and Dr. Leakey has reported an even earlier find, as yet undescribed, from the same vicinity.

Previously I have mentioned that man's mental development, so far as its later, bigger-brained phase is concerned, has seemed rapid. Dr. Leakey's find can be interpreted in two ways: as suggesting that the incipient steps leading to the emergence of the large brain began earlier than we have anticipated, or that man drifted in a static fashion on this simple level for a long period before some new mutation or latent dynamism generated a new leap forward in brain size. Little in the way of advanced cultural remains is known before the later Pleistocene, so that the appearance of this tool-using creature of such archaic countenance is an amazingly disturbing element to our thinking.

Have all our lower Ice Age discoveries been underestimated as to time? And what of the other, the seemingly later yet, more primitive Australopithecines? Are they, then, true cousins rather than ancestors —survivals of an even more remote past? We do not know. We know only that darkest Africa is not dark by reason of its present history alone. Contained in that vast continent may be the secret of our origin and the secret of the rise of that dread organ which has unlocked the wild powers of the universe and yet taught us all we know of compassion and of love.

Those ancient bestial stirrings which still claw at sanity are part, also, of that dark continent we long chose to forget. But we do not forget, because man in contemplation reveals something that is characteristic of no other form of life known to us: he suffers because of what he is, and wishes to become something else. The moment we cease to hunger to be otherwise, our soul is dead. Long ago we began that hunger; long ago we painted on the walls of caverns and buried the revered dead. More and more, because our brain lays hold upon and seeks to shape the future, we are conscious of what we are, and what we might be. "No man," wrote John Donne, "doth exalt Nature to the height it would beare." He saw the discrepancy between dream and reality.

Great minds have always seen it. That is why man has survived his journey this long. When we fail to wish any longer to be otherwise than what we are, we will have ceased to evolve. Evolution has to be lived forward. I say this as one who has stood above the bones of much that has vanished, and at midnight have examined my own face.

The Phenomenon of Man

MARTIN BRENNAN

Pierre Teilhard de Chardin was born in Auvergne in France in 1881, educated at the Jesuit college of Mongré near Lyons and entered the Society of Jesus at eighteen. He was ordained priest in 1911. Already as a schoolboy he had developed an interest in mineralogy and geology and during his years of training for the priesthood he became competent in the latter and in palaeontology, the study of pre-existing forms of life as preserved by fossilization. He had the doubtful privilege in 1912 of becoming involved in the Piltdown finds, being responsible the following year for the unearthing of the canine tooth of the supposed "Dawn Man." Although deceived at the time like all the other experts, in later years his assessment of the event, as quoted by Weiner in *The Piltdown Forgery*, was eminently sound.

Piltdown probably turned his [Teilhard's] attention to human evolution; at all events we find him in the following years studying under the great Marcellin Boule at the Institute of Human Palaeontology in Paris, with an intermission as brancardier with the French forces in World War I. He took his doctorate in 1922. He held the chair of geology at the Institut Catholique of Paris till 1928; but already in 1923 he was sent on a French Government mission to China. This is the first of many geological and palaeontological expeditions, some of them famous, in which he took part. He was to remain in China for over twenty years, with brief excursions home, to the United States, and to various countries in Asia. The highlight of his career was probably his participation in the discovery and appraisal of fossil remains of the very primitive type known as Peking Man. He made many other notable contributions to science in the

Martin Brennan, "The Phenomenon of Man," *Studies*, Vol. LXIX (Summer, 1960), 117-130.

allied fields of palaeontology, anthropology, and geology. Returning to France in 1946 he was the recipient of signal honors including the Legion d'Honneur. In 1948 he accepted an invitation to the United States which led to his settling there in 1951 at the Wenner-Gren Foundation, New York. Here for the four last years of his life he exercised a profound and widespread formative influence on palaeontological and anthropological research. He died on Easter Sunday, April 10, 1955.

Such in brief was the unusual external pattern of his life. But much more striking was the man himself. With the soul of a poet, with a largeness of mind that spurned the mean and the petty, and with an unconquerable urge to unify he came to view all things in a *global* perspective, a dynamic and evolutionary one. In *The Phenomenon of Man* [1] he gathered together the strands of the sciences—strands that others were satisfied to trace singly and in isolation—and wove them into a commanding evolutionary synthesis of the universe in terms of man: man the latest product of evolution, better still the axis and the leading-shoot of evolution as it moves towards God.

This vision he had completed and committed to writing during the years 1938 to 1940 while still in China. Due to the misgivings of his religious superiors his work was not published in his lifetime. After his death it was published at the instance of some of his friends. Its success in the original and in its many translations has been striking; but there has also been a considerable chorus of dissent. That we may the better, on the one hand, understand this criticism and his superiors' misgivings and, on the other, gain some insight into the book's undoubted appeal, we must first try to expose its thought and then subject it to a sympathetic yet objective critique.

Before dealing with that thought *in extenso*, a very brief preview will help to focus the picture. Père Teilhard visualizes the whole evolutionary process up to our times as comprising the organization of primitive matter through stages preparatory to the rise of life. Life culminates in thinking beings. He extends the process into the future to include a stage of superorganization of the whole human species. These four stages he calls prelife (because somehow it contains the seed of life), life, thought, and hyperlife. Even in prelife, he claims, matter possesses an inner aspect, a *within*, the rudimentary beginning of the consciousness of higher forms. He contrasts this inner aspect with the *without* of things, their tangible, measurable aspect which hitherto has formed the sole stuff of science. Père de Chardin objects to this and proposes his own synthesis, a synthesis in terms of the *within*. Starting with the *within* of crude matter he traces its rise through life (whose *within* is consciousness) to thought, or self-consciousness. Borrowing a figure from mathematics he calls this rise a curve: *the curve of the phenomenon of man*, which even in its earliest, preliving stages he calls anthropogenesis. The *within* in man rises to the plane of personality. Teilhard projects the curve into the future to show human persons in their ever-growing complex interdependencies converging in love under the divine influence to form a sort of superpersonality (hyperlife) in a self-fulfilling unanimity of mind and wills. The term of this *convergence* he calls Omega point in an obvious echo of the Alpha and Omega, the First and the Last, of the *Apocalypse*. This brief précis already indicates that in our discussion the *within* of things and Omega point will require special consideration.

Some difficulties that the reader will encounter must be mentioned straightway. In elaborating his thoughts the author coins new words. Geophysics and geology already spoke of the barysphere, the lithosphere, the hydrosphere, and atmosphere. Biology already conceived the *layer* of living things as a further envelope of the earth, the biosphere. We are now given a new word, the *noosphere* to designate the *layer* of thinking beings, man. The raising of animal life and values to the human plane as well as their further spiritualization under Omega is called *hominization*. Again, he extends and even shifts the meaning of accepted terms. Thus sometimes he uses *phylum* in its technical sense of a primary division of biological classification (for example, the phylum of reptiles, or of mammals) but he also uses it for lesser groups as the primates or even for man himself. Another striking example is *orthogenesis*. Many biologists fight shy of this word. When used it generally means a limited evolutionary movement *in a straight line* as in the progress from the small foot-high ancestors of the modern horse towards ever greater size and speed. In Teilhard's use it means the obviously *aimed, directed* character of the *whole* evolutionary movement.

Later we shall have occasion to draw attention to the highly analogous nature of his language. It is not always clear how far precisely the author wishes his analogy to extend. But he refers strictly and accurately to man's *within* as self-consciousness or reflection and such a self-conscious, reflective being and *such only* is intended when he uses the term *center* (though he unfortunately uses *centerity* in a wider sense). Lastly, he changes early on the analogy of the curve to that of an *ascending spiral*. This is very apt as each stage of anthropogenesis repeats or at least re-echoes the theme of the previous stage, at a higher level. Thus "involution upon itself" is a keynote recurring in ever higher octaves throughout the spiral's ascent. This denotes that folding in upon itself, that throwing back upon itself, due to the confinement of large numbers in a limited volume or space. It connotes the stresses and strains due to this limitation of free movement or divergence. Thus atoms confined in a planet (planetization) are thrown in upon themselves; similarly in man there is a check to divergence due to his rational nature, his power to bend back consciously upon himself in reflection; in addition, there will be increased tension due to the pressure of rapidly growing numbers on the surface of a dwindling globe. (This condition he will also call a planetization of man.) In addition it connotes the consequent stresses and strains as a result of which the spiral rises to a new level. Each new *involution*—of matter, of conscious life, of thought—leads by way of a distinct threshold, a change of state, a metamorphosis to a higher state, a further upward twist of the spiral. This in turn exhausts the potentiality of that state and a further metamorphosis or change of state is necessary if the movement is to continue: and so on.

We can now attempt to synopsize his thought; but already it is clear that this will be a difficult task.

Science, confronted with the fact of consciousness, has hitherto been content to explain it away as a queer exception in nature. But, Père Teilhard protests, the fact that we experience a conscious center, a *within* in the depth of our being means that this can only be an *outcrop* of a reality that *lines* all things. Below us we can detect it in progressive attenuation in the lower grades of life till it disappears from our view in brute matter. But it necessarily exists here also; it must be coextensive with the *without* of things. Science in constructing its model of the universe has so far neglected this *within* to concentrate on the admittedly more manageable *without*. But Père de Chardin claims that a true science will, and *must*, extend its scope to include the *within*; and he sets out to substantiate this claim by constructing a synthesis of all things in terms of the *within*.

Left to diffuse indefinitely in space, primordial matter with its contained *definite quantity of consciousness* would have achieved nothing, or at least something very different from the actual result. But being shut up within the closed surface of "a star," matter is *thrown in* upon itself. Due to this *involution*, this "planetization," and helped by the resultant tensions, it tends to aggregate, forming atoms and molecules. These in turn combine to form mega-molecules at a sidereal pace: a rate so slow as to demand an astronomical time-scale. *Pari passu* with this continuing growth in structural complexity (complexification) goes a progressive perfecting of the contained consciousness, the *within*: "a consciousness is that much more perfected according as it lines a richer and better organized material edifice." This provides him with the "Law of Complexity-Consciousness," according to which the level of consciousness of a thing or a being can be gleaned from its degree of complexity.

While still considering prelife, Père Teilhard poses the problem of spiritual energy, of which, as in the case of consciousness, he claims to have direct experience. He expressly rules out its *convertibility* with material energy though admitting their *inter*dependence: "we must eat to think." This interdependence "can in all probability be expressed only by a complex symbolism in which terms of a different order are employed." So his "solution"—"to avoid a fundamental dualism at once impossible and antiscientific"—is to presume that *all* energy is essentially physical. This essentially unitarian energy he divides into two distinct components, a *tangential* energy, the measurable energy of the *without*, of orthodox physics, which links the element with all others of the same complexity; and a *radial* energy, the energy of the *within*, which draws it towards ever greater complexity. It is mainly this latter which will occupy us henceforth.

Prelife, the ascending ("involuting") series of atoms, molecules, and mega-molecules, arrives at a degree of complexification beyond which no progress in the same line is practicable or fruitful so that only a metamorphosis, the appearance of a new thing, *life*, will continue the movement. The "cellular revolution" achieves this metamorphosis and the biosphere is born.

The first cells, though infinitesimal, were already incredibly complex. They achieved prodigious success: life swarmed not merely in the vastness of its numbers but in the richness of its forms. Though obviously directed by an over-all *aiming*, life *gropes* by means of its multitudinous forms—"groping is *directed* chance. It means . . . trying everything so as to find everything." It discovers the secret of multiplication, cell division; by *conjugation*, the fusion of two cells to form a new individual, it achieves the essence of sexual reproduction which has so greatly enriched life subsequently. Dividing cells also will tend to aggregate. But by all these means alone life will incline merely to spread out at the same level. The diversification of life at any such level he attributes to Natural Selection ("the survival · of the fittest") thereby relegating the master idea of Darwinism to an inferior role in evolution. But the orthogenetic upward thrust by which new levels are reached is due to "controlled additivity": the rejuvenations made possible by succeeding reproductions achieve something new and these *add* one to the other "in a predetermined direction."

Controlled additivity is the "vertical component" in evolution. Under its working the tree of life grows before us. It consists of an ascending series of fanning branches—"verticils of consolidated forms"—each fan rising above the other without suppressing it. As each phylum fans out "groping," "trying all," it presents the appearance of a "forest of exploring antennae." One antenna finds a "fissure," a formula not merely viable but giving the key to a further ascent and the antenna breaks through. A new phylum appears and the élan of a new discovery, a rebirth, it spreads out ramifying in all directions, forming another fanning verticil above that on which it was born. So life mounts through invertebrates, fish-like forms, fish, amphibia, reptiles, and at last mammals; and from the heart of this latest phylum the primates arise on the final stages of hominization.

The tree of life thus sketched convinces him in its unity (and beauty) that life is a unique thing on earth: it arose once and once only and shall never be achieved again except perhaps artificially in the laboratory. This great intuition is reinforced for him by what he calls the striking fact that many accidental things, many asymmetries in the basic molecules of living things which could have freely varied (and would inevitably have varied if life had arisen independently a number of times) are yet universally the same. But this unity must be viewed from a distance. Each new group as it arose was necessarily limited in numbers, and it was only when reasonably mature and having achieved numerical profusion that it had a pretty good chance of preservation by fossilization. So each new group seems to be born *fully formed* and isolated. This is the Law of the Suppression of Evolutionary Peduncles: it tends to isolate groups, and this isolation is later reinforced by the elimination of straggling intermediate connecting forms.

Man is no exception. At the end of the Tertiary Age (approximately a million years ago) at the heart of the group of primates as it fans out there are a large number of anthropoid forms. Many of these are far more man-like than any of the survivors, mean in development and relatively so in numbers, the gorillas, chimpanzees, orangutang, and so forth, that we know today. Since man's origin the elimination of most of these has increased his isolation. These forms, we are told, were so highly developed in instinctual behavior (which can often so uncannily mimic intelligence) that only a metamorphosis could lead to further real advance. This must be achieved between two individuals because it is "a critical transformation, a mutation from zero to everything." In one we still have only an extremely high degree of animal consciousness; in the next by a mighty leap consciousness has achieved *self-consciousness, reflection,* and the noosphere is born. So man came silently into the world and is spread over the great land mass of Africa and Asia when first we meet him. Science therefore can say nothing for or against strict monogenism— the theory of the origin of the whole human race from a single pair—but it does undoubtedly favor monophyletism or origin from a common genetic stock.

Looking back from our position on the tree of life the author points to that aspect which like Ariadne's thread runs through the whole giving it greater coherence and meaning: it is development of the *within,* which in animals is shown by *cerebralization.* Diffuse consciousness of the lower forms gives way to the revolutionary development of a single center of control, the brain, which at each subsequent level of the tree assumes a greater degree of complexity and coordination through the progressive expansion of the cerebrum. This is particularly so among the mammals and in these in turn the primates, and particularly the anthropoids, develop it prodigiously, so that the step to man with its tremendous psychic gap is associated with the minimum of *anatomical* change. Other groups went aside from the main trend and specialized on a side line, as, for example, the horses developing their limbs for speed and the bats developing theirs for flight. But the primates specialized along the principal axis of development as shown by Ariadne's thread—they enlarged their brains and, in man, they came to possess the earth. This thread "provides a direction, and by its consequences *it proves that evolution has a direction.*" It places man, no longer at the center of a static universe but on the summit of the tree of life, "the axis and the leading shoot of evolution."

Like any other new "phylum" man tends to ramify, but the cohesion born of thought holds together the nascent branches, so that like the veins of a leaf rather than a verticil of branches they are contained by the webbing of thought, their psychic sheath. Thus man is continually being enriched from within by the very force that would have split other phyla in a comparable period into innumerable species. All through the palaeolithic period the new "phylum" was free to spread; could man have done so indefinitely the outcome would have been different. But by the beginning of the Neolithic Age he has fully occupied the earth and can freely diffuse no longer. Instead of following his animals and culling the fruits of the earth, he must propagate and conserve them on the spot. And so begins an intense phase of "involution" with its attendant psychic, social, and political stresses which have been rising to our modern crescendo. Man is socializing himself (and it is quite characteristic of Père de Chardin's thought that man's social and socializing activity is within the scope of biology). Social, political, and cultural unions have been continually arising, transcending and tending to obliterate the boundaries of merely biological race. Even when individuals, and especially nations, succumbed to egotism and sought for themselves a fuller living at the expense of and apart from the common surge of mankind, the ineluctable unity of the race has won, the vanquished have in turn molded the conqueror and the simple eliminations of the prehuman struggle for existence have been very rare. Socialization, the author claims, is a property of a mature phylum, though he is forced to admit that the most obvious examples below man are freakish in appearance and, in the last analysis, are not phyletic but confined to the progeny of one mother, as in the beehive and the ant-hill. In man it is producing such a degree of physical communion and economic interdependence among peoples that they can no longer develop save by interpenetration of one another.

So socialization and the advance of science and technology is unleashing a tremendous upsurge of unused powers; technical advances enable each one to be virtually present almost simultaneously throughout the known world; standards and their consequent material demands have been rising steeply especially in the West through which (including the Mediterranean area) the axis of progress has swept for the last 6,000 years. The consequent "planetization" of consciousness and its unity or rather unanimity, the growing all-embracing exigencies and complex interdependence of the new humanity, resembles nothing more than a new giant organism preparing for birth. The involution begun in the Neolithic Age is about to culminate, through a new change of state, in the hyperpersonal.

But man is in crisis: modern malaise and his new realization of the vastness of space-time and his own apparent isolation in it appalls him. If he is not to falter he must be assured of success, of the certainty of fulfillment; as a rational being he cannot choose a road that he knows to be blocked. Endowed with thought, whose *nature* is to discern infinite horizons ahead, he can only move in the hope of achieving a supreme consummation. He must seek an inexhaustible future. Infallibly—though not absolutely necessarily—he must reach his goal or the whole mighty evolutionary process fails in him and is unintelligible. This goal cannot be on earth nor even in space-time or it will inevitably end with them. Nor can it be an impersonal goal: each conscious center must seek and be assured of conscious survival.

So man has rational grounds for an act of (natural) faith in his survival, which allows him to bend to his task and take his place in the convergent mass of "centers." The collectivity towards which we saw him "involuting" cannot be an impersonal All, but a union of consciousnesses, each of which in communicating itself (to Omega and the others focused on Omega) does not lose itself but is perfected and uplifted in the higher unanimity of the superpersonal. But conscious centers tend to resist "compression"; they can only be *drawn* together under the power of a great attractive force, and this force is love. We must accept, he says—and science must extend its scope to include—the reality of some *source* and *object* of love "at the summit of the world above our head," under whose influence the "grains of thought" focus themselves. But if centers at present existing are to achieve their destiny, this supremely lovable and loving focus, which is necessarily personal, must be already supremely present. And this focus, this center of centers, is Omega point. So fully does Père Teilhard find this picture in consonance with the God of Christian Revelation and the whole Christian phenomenon that he confesses he should never have dared to conceive it if he had not already in his consciousness as a believer found its *living reality*.

Almost every page of this work could call for comment: a résumé, even as apparently full as we have given, necessarily leaves a great deal unsaid. We have already mentioned the vague mold of his thought. This is set in a matrix which is shot through and through with extreme analogy. Unless we bear this in view we shall constantly push the thought further than was intended; but even when due allowance is made for it we are frequently jolted by the mode of expression. Thus the *within* is glossed by "centerity," freedom, love, and expressly equiparated to consciousness, which in the very movement of the curve is shown to be present from crude matter up to, and not excluding, Omega point. Note also his reference to the "elemental freedoms" of atoms and molecules, the "primordial dust of consciousness." Further, *love* in man is but the hominized version of the attraction that enabled atoms to form molecules. And "are not the artificial, the moral, and the juridical simply the hominized versions of the natural, the physical, and the organic?" Yes, of course, in the sense that love and moral and juridical values are based on man's nature just as, analogously, the chemical, physical, and organic properties are based on the nature of the element or natural compound. However, a much more basic question must be solved before we can rationally discuss the thought in greater detail.

Père Teilhard claims that his work is science which he equiparates practically with phenomenology or the systematic presentation of phenomena which succeed one another, without claiming any relationships of cause and effect between them. No matter how metaphysical it may appear he claims that on closer inspection it will be seen to be only *hyperphysics* (physics in his extended sense is natural science as distinct from metaphysics). We could perhaps gloss this word as a *theoretical biology* and as such it would be legitimate science, though far from being merely phenomenological. But more than once we are presented with arguments that are of the very essence and core of metaphysics, as when he says "the more man becomes man the less will he be prepared to move except toward that which is interminably and indestructibly new. Some absolute is implied in the very play of his operative activity." Again when he argues to a personal conscious "Center of centers" at Omega point he is not being scientific in any legitimate modern use of the word, he is philosophizing. True, the modern philosopher's *point de départ* will be observation corrected by science, scientific observation. But when he raises his superstructure on this he enters the realm of metaphysics. Teilhard has been so long dealing in strictly scientific terms, accepting them on the basic authorization that only metaphysics can give, that one gets the impression that he has unconsciously narrowed the gap between the two orders to the point where insensibly the metaphysical validity is attached to the scientific concept which now seems to stand in its own right. Teilhard crosses and recrosses the frontier with the ease of one who is unaware of its existence. But he is speaking to scientists most of whom likewise philosophize while anathematizing metaphysics; he is not posing: he genuinely begins speaking their language, because it is his own; but he manifestly hopes to win them, through it, to the whole vision which is his. But this initial inconsistency should not deter us from seeking and appraising what is of worth in that vision, whether it is garbed in the language of science, of philosophy, or of religion.

And so to the *within* of things. There is a sense in which this concept is perfectly valid; but it is a metaphysical sense. Some at least of the analogies of Père de Chardin may have been largely figures of speech or analogies of attribution, as when we say that a climate, food, exercise, or even a complexion is healthy. Here health is properly only in the person in whom the other analogues are either the cause or the sign of health, the primary analogue. But there is an analogy which is of fundamental importance in metaphysics. It arises from the fact that in reality, while things are not perfectly the same, nevertheless they are not entirely different. This imperfect similarity can be expressed as a proportion, or proportionality. Thus we can say that there is something in the atom, its *within*, which is to our consciousness as the being of the atom is to our being. (This sort of analogy may seem strange or even trivial at first sight. But without it we could make no positive statements about the nature of God.) So far so good: but one is dismayed when one sees him quoting with relish (though only in a footnote) J. B. S. Haldane's panpsychical materialist claim that if the scientific viewpoint is correct we shall find life and mind at least in rudimentary forms all through the universe. Teilhard thinks metaphysicians should rejoice at this. But metaphysicians are painfully aware that panpsychical theories of this materialistic type are but a bankrupt effort to explain the striking fact of thought without admitting the bogey of a spiritual soul, or else being reduced to the patent absurdities of mechanism or behaviorism, no matter how titivated in a modern scientific dress. The former *explains* thought as basically a mere pattern, however sublimated, of the mechanical motions of matter; the latter reduces it to the muscular modifications that accompany the physical movements of speech, as spoken, heard, or read. As Teilhard pleads so eloquently for the spiritual soul, we shall take his *within* in the sense of a metaphysical analogy and ignore as a momentary aberration his appeal to Haldane.

This is an appropriate place to note the apparent contradiction in his "solution" of the problem of spiritual energy whereby he assumes that all energy is physical and then assigns it two components, the "radial" and "tangential." It would seem that this could hold for animals, taking "spiritual" analogously as the Schoolmen would. But in man—and Père Teilhard's position is both a plea and an attempt to bring man into the scientific scheme—it amounts to a *denial* of the problem. In man, it must be emphasized, we have *experience* of an energy, the energy of thought and volition which is utterly and intrinsically irreducible to physical energy, however extrinsically it may depend on it as on a condition. On the author's own showing, this radial in man will escape from the tangential in death, as "souls break away, carrying upward their incommunicable load of consciousness," while at the animal's death its radial is reabsorbed in the tangential becoming thereby a prey to entropy. Again, in view of his clear stand on the spirituality of thought and of the soul (reinforced by the above quotation) we must take his predication of radial in their regard as simply analogous.

But there is so much one wants to praise that it is distasteful to have to criticize or to appear, condescendingly, to correct. His description of the rise of thought is pure poetry, and Teilhard shows that he is clear about the abyssal nature of the leap involved—yet even here the unfortunate use of the terms "threshold" and "change of state" might blur this awareness, implying, as they do if taken strictly, a mere change of something pre-existing as when a larva pupates or water becomes ice or steam. And the whole discussion of the tree of life, which, with the intuition born of life-long contemplation, he causes to grow and form before our enchanted view in all its beauty and unity and majesty, is a sheer joy to read. This section also underlines by the very vigor and vitality of its movement the claims of finality to a prominent place in any solid theory of biology. It is a portent and a sign of things to come that this finalism has been listened to with respect, if not yet with general acceptance. But like the whole evolutionary process which he evokes with such power, the axis of Teilhard's thought, in this respect at least, points toward the future.

What of the thoroughgoingness of his evolutionism? With the enthusiasm of a reformer he exaggerates its extrabiological validity. That it has invaded all realms of life and often with valuable results is undeniable; that it has *conquered* all is rhetoric. In particular when he makes this claim, unqualified, for the history of religions, Schmidt and the Vienna School will justly rebel. But within the confines of biology it is quite legitimate (at most excepting Omega point, which in any case is not biology). *Granted* that Divine Wisdom decided on an evolutionary order of creation—with all the evidence accumulating it would be difficult to deny it; and who does not see, if he wants to see, how much more clearly it impresses the majesty of creation on our minds?—in this evolutionary hypothesis the scientist as such can but chronicle the succession of related forms, gaining thereby on his own plane a great knowledge, a full intuition. But as a scientist the questions the philosophers pose are outside his scope. The latter may posit special interventions, in the origin of life and especially in that of the human soul (and *each* human soul). But for the scientist there can be but a series which is manifestly nonliving at one end, dazzlingly alive towards the other: he may not even be able to say which term of the series begins to live. In fact some Scholastics, claiming that the modern dichotomy of *matter* v. *life* is an illegitimately induced shift from the "classical" dichotomy of the Schools, *matter* v. *spirit*, would deny the need of any special intervention in the origin of life. Be that as it may, these special interventions wherever necessary cannot be anything extrinsic added on to the creative decree. This decree, because eternal, is ever present, simple, and indivisible in itself, and the phenomenal series and any "interventions" are but the working out in time and space of a timeless, extraspatial, and ever-present fiat.

Omega point crowns and closes this evolutionary process, this "movement of synthesis." This is by far the most difficult concept of the author, partly because in its formulation he seems to shift his ground. At first we are told that Omega point is the convergence of centers on a focus, a Center of centers. Then we are fairly warned in a footnote that the term will be thenceforth restricted to this focus, this Center of centers. In this case it is obviously God, though presumably as known by the light of human reason. Later he identifies this with the God known in Revelation. Thus far we can define Omega point as God attracting and drawing all souls, all conscious centers, to Himself; and the state of aggregation produced by this attractive power can in a broad sense be called Omega point. But this aggregation has two facets—the socio-politico-religious unity in process of development here below, and its supernatural aspect which is but the beginning (embryonic, yet of the same essence) of the eternal aggregation in the City of God of all those souls who freely respond to the attraction of Omega. This obviously suggests the Mystical Body of Christ, and interpreters have been quick to suggest it.

But the élan with which Père Teilhard argues to Omega point carries him along, and us with him, in such a way that we do not at first see the immensity of the jump involved. This portion could be interpreted as an effort to put the argument for God's existence based on final causes in a form that will not repel the scientist. It may be in the same spirit that he refrains from speaking of God's creative activity. He speaks only of a Prime Mover ahead, therefore one moving finally not efficiently. As he states it, the argument may be conceded some cogency, but it does not conclude with the rigor of its strictly metaphysical form. But to conclude by reason to a Divine Cause, a Person, and then quietly assume, a he does, the main data of Christian Revelation, placing Christ at the heart of humanity in its ascent to God, is to run the dire peril of making the supernatural the *connatural* term of the evolutionary series. Grace, the supernatural life of man redeemed, as it is in some profound way a sharing in the life of God Himself cannot be, cannot even appear to be, the culmination of any natural process: it cannot be in any strict sense required or demanded by any created nature, even angelic. True Christ *did* in fact by His Incarnation undertake the headship of this supernatural entity by the most stupendous condescension of all time. To refer to this wondrous event as a "prodigious biological operation" while true as to its term is more than unhappy: it neglects the utter transcendence of the operation and tends to strengthen the unfortunate impression that he regards the supernatural as the last and greatest of many terms in a single series. Teilhard *never* expressly says so; in fact he obviously awoke to the danger after his book was complete and expressly said the opposite in a footnote. In effect this note says that at the summit of the world, in line with Omega point but still more elevated than it, is "something" which in the text he almost instantly glosses as "another and Supreme Someone," surely the God of Revelation. So we must finally correct our idea of Omega point taking it as that perfecting, that "planetizing" of the human species to which God by a supremely free choice imparts the supernatural, the participation of His own Divine Life. By means of this, mankind forms ever more and more in and through Christ a supernatural organism, the Mystical Body of Christ.

Thus corrected, as Teilhard did, though perhaps not vigorously enough, we have the inspiring vision of God's free creative activity preparing from all eternity the seedbed to receive the seed of the divine life through no exigence or merit of its own but by a "supreme condescension." But what of the human aspect of this supernatural reality, the earthly state of conscious and voluntary socialization with its great increase in the fullness of living, of knowledge, of technical power, and so, in a sense, of being? This is a reasonable hypothesis in view of present trends. And the "hominization" it involves will readily be granted because in spite of wars and injustices, even in the recent past, it is hardly too optimistic to hold that there is a continual increase in the acceptance of truly human values. The lot of the average man today, at least in the West, is far higher, his worth and dignity safeguarded better than at any known period of the past. This is not surprising if we remember the divine leaven continually at work beneath the surface; and one has little sympathy for the criticism that man's cultural and moral rise, his "hominization," has not been uniform: the ups and downs of this curve would be inconspicuous on the "planetary" or astronomical time-scale postulated. But that that complexification should issue in a new *human* superperson is something that most of us will accept, if at all, only in a very analogous sense of great unanimity in extreme complexity of numbers and interdependence.

Teilhard's work has been criticized for its skimpy treatment of the question of evil. When he touches the question of *moral* evil—and then only fleetingly—he postulates its true kernel, the free refusal by particular "centers" of the Center of centers, culminating in the withdrawal of all such centers to a counter-focus, an antagonistic pole, at the end of the world. This certainly seems to err by *defect*. Earlier in the work he hints at the possibility of suspecting some primordial aberration in view of the more than expected amount of evil in the world. But this is merely an *obiter dictum* and could hardly mean more than that a naturalist with his knowledge of nature is not surprised when revelation teaches original sin.

We need only mention the word pantheism to exclude it—the author excludes it vigorously and logically and yet, especially before the publication of his works, the word was linked with his name. It is easy to see how some of his phrases, often supercharged with analogy, when remembered or read out of their context could easily give color to the charge. Note his reference to mankind as "a mass of hominized substance." He also speaks of man as knowing "that he is at one with and responsible to an evolutionary all" and "that a universal will to live converges and is hominized in him."

The extraordinary success of this work is significant. It may partly be due to the adventitious interest of the circumstances of its delayed publication. Even more is it undoubtedly due to that highly analogous mold already commented upon which allows widely differing schools of thought to view it each in its own light. But allowing for all this, there is a very solid residuum which can only be due to the answer it offers or tries to give to the perplexity of the times. Rank materialism was eclipsed with the debacle of positivist progress in two world wars and the post-positivist world still needs and is beginning to want a set of values to ease its *Angst*, its malaise of soul, which Teilhard recognized. The expected rebound would seem to be towards more human values, particularly, in this context, towards a richer and more humanist science. To us Teilhard's work needs correction or at least clarification and for this he himself humbly appealed. But to the perplexed world he offers a well-grounded optimism, a sane belief in continuing progress all the more effective because directly in line with the natural reaction of the human spirit against determinism and defeatism and towards a clearer realization of the richness and fullness of its own destiny. This reaction still inarticulate seems to be steadily gaining ground: and at this opportune moment in human development the world can accept the priest in the person of an eminent man of science.

Reference

1. *The Phenomenon of Man*, Introduction by Sir Julian Huxley, Bernard Wall, trans. (London: Collins, 1959).

PART THREE

The Origin and Purpose

of the Universe

Something so old and given as the universe itself seems on the brink of revealing new aspects of itself to man, or, rather, is daily revealing more of itself as it is explored by spacemen, space-probing rockets, and the radio telescope. Any conviction that God made it all does not exonerate the believer in spirit or revelation from facing up to the possible implications of scientific theories about its origin. Two theories that hold the center of the stage today are explained by British astronomer A. C. B. Lovell, who also suggests some of the questions these theories give rise to in man's mind. Is it possible, for instance, at this time to say that this or that theory is wrong, or that it is compatible with reason or revelation? How is time related to creation? What *is* time? Are all theories about the probable origin of the universe of equal insignificance in the face of the reality of creation by God?

But no matter which theory one may opt for, we are still left with the vastness of the universe. For example, Harlow Shapley says that the minimum number of stars in the universe is 100,000,000,000,000,-000,000. Can man still claim a unique place in it? Should not he rather, humbly, accept the fact of his utter expendability? A profound thinker, Paul Tillich, Protestant theologian now at the University of Chicago, tackles the problems for man in this almost infinite enlargement of his view of space. He discusses man's significance in this universe. With refreshing openness he suggests how this creature, living on a planet toward the outer rim of one of thousands of galaxies, can be given any meaning. He asks further: How do the discoveries in space, its continued opening up, harmonize with Christ's cosmic position as given in the letters of St. Paul? Or does the space-age point of view doom Christianity to be regarded as provincial? Further, if man destroys himself, will this be final proof of the initial absurdity of the whole of creation, or could we still salvage some meaning in man's existence? As usual Tillich's more secondary observations are also replete with suggestions to be followed up with further thought or discussion.

CHAPTER 6 The Origin

of the Universe

A. C. B. LOVELL

. . . I want to talk to you about the problem of
the origin of the universe. I suppose it would hardly be an exaggeration to say that this is the greatest challenge to the intellect which faces man, and I cannot pretend that I have any new solution to offer you. However, . . . , today the air is alive with a new hope and expectancy, because our new instruments may be reaching out so far into space that we may soon be able to speak with more confidence. I am going to set out the problem as I see it, and I hope you will get an idea of these vast cosmological issues and of the implications of the alternative solutions which lie ahead. At the end I shall tell you what I think about it all as an ordinary human being.

. . . Observational astronomy tells us about the universe as it exists out to distances of about two thousand million light years. At that distance we are seeing the universe as it existed two thousand million years ago. Within this vast area of space and time we can study the innumerable stars and galaxies, and from these observations we can attempt to infer the probable nature and extent of the cosmos beyond the range of observations.

I think there are three stages in which we might consider this problem. The first is to inquire whether the observations are likely to be extended in the future to even greater distances and thereby penetrate even farther into past history than the present two thousand million years. The second stage is an appeal to cosmological theory, an inquiry as to the extent to which the present observations agree with any particular cosmology and the nature of the past and future as predicted by these theories. Finally, we shall reach a stage where theories based on our present conceptions of physical laws have nothing further to say. At this point we pass from physics to metaphysics, from astronomy to theology, where the corporate views of science merge into the beliefs of the individual.

The vast region of space and time enclosed by the present observations includes several hundred million galaxies of stars. As far as we can see, the over-all large-scale structure of the universe within these limits has a high degree of uniformity. When we look at these distant regions we find that the light is reddened, indicating that the galaxies are receding from us. As far as we can see, the red shift of the most distant nebulae is still increasing linearly with distance. There is no indication that we are seeing anything but a small part of the total universe. However, in the second stage of our inquiry we shall see that an observational test between rival cosmological theories demands a still further penetration, and an extension of the present observational limit is a matter of some urgency in cosmology. Unfortunately there are fundamental difficulties introduced by the recession of the galaxies which no device of man will ever surmount. At the present observable limit of the large optical telescopes the galaxies are receding with a speed of about one-fifth of the velocity of light. From this aspect alone we face a limit to future progress. Even if no other effects intervened we could never obtain information about those farther regions of space where the velocities of recession of the galaxies reach the speed of light. The light from the more distant galaxies will never reach us. In Eddington's phrase, "Light is like a runner on an expanding track with the winning post receding faster than he can run."

There are, moreover, further difficulties which will hinder the approach to this fundamental limit. If the remote galaxies were stationary, then all the light emitted, say, in one second would reach our telescopes. But the galaxies are moving away with speeds which are an appreciable fraction of the velocity of light, and as the speed increases less and less of the light actually emitted by the galaxies in one second reaches our instruments. This degradation of the intensity of the light coupled with the accompanying shift in wave length to the red end of the spectrum worsens still further the technical difficulties of these observations.

The radio telescopes may well be in a stronger position with respect to these hindrances. To begin with, the collisions of galaxies, which I described in an earlier lecture, generate very powerful radio emissions, and the shifts in wave length which accompany the recession do not present the same observational difficulties as in the optical case. In fact, the present belief is that many of the objects already studied by their radio emissions lie at distances which exceed considerably the present two thousand million light years' limit of the optical telescopes. Therefore, we can, I think, answer the first stage of our inquiry with some degree of certainty in the following way. The present observable horizon of the universe will be pushed back by a limited amount in the near future, perhaps to a few thousand million light years. Then we must be content. No further strivings or inventions of man will enable us to probe the conditions which existed in epochs of history beyond these few thousand million years. They are gone forever beyond the fundamental limits of observability.

At this point we reach the second stage of our inquiry, where we appeal to cosmological theory. The question is this: Can we formulate a theory in terms of known physical laws whose predictions agree so well with the present observable universe that we can predict the past and future?

Indeed, when we turn to the cosmological theories which are today seriously considered by astronomers we find a most absorbing state of affairs. Not one, but several theories can explain from acceptable postulates the present observable state of the universe. These predictions bring us face to face with the ultimate problem of the origin of the universe in ways which are startlingly different. But the new techniques in astronomy may be on the verge of producing observational data which may be decisively in favor of one or other of these cosmologies. At least one of these alternatives would, I think, present theology with a very serious dilemma. In fact, if the full implications of the theory eventually receive the support of astronomical observations it is difficult to see how certain fundamental doctrines could be maintained in their present harmonious relation with our physical knowledge of the universe.

First of all, though, I want to discuss the cosmological theories which are generally classed as the evolutionary models of the universe. I think it would be correct to say that these theories, which are a consequence of Einstein's general theory of relativity, are regarded with the most favor by the majority of contemporary astronomers. In passing, perhaps I should add that in the light of our present knowledge it does not seem worthwhile discussing for our present purpose any of the cosmological theories which preceded the introduction of the theory of general relativity in 1915. The application of Newton's theory of gravitation, in which the attraction between bodies varies inversely as the square of their distance apart, to the large-scale structure of the universe would require that the universe had a center in which the spatial density of stars and galaxies was a maximum. As we proceed outward from this center the spatial density should diminish, until finally at great distances it should be succeeded by an infinite region of emptiness. The observed uniformity in the large-scale structure of the universe is clearly at variance with these ideas. Neither does any theory based on Newton's law of universal attraction and conservation of mass offer hope of explaining the observed expansion and recession of the nebulae. On the other hand, in Einstein's theory of general relativity gravitation is not explained in terms of a force but of the deformation of space near massive bodies. In our ordinary life we treat space as though it were flat, or Euclidean, in the sense that the geometrical properties obey the axioms of Euclid as we were taught in school. For example, the three angles of a triangle add up to two right angles. According to Einstein's theory, however, these simple conceptions must be abandoned, and though in ordinary circumstances the differences are insignificant, nevertheless when we consider the properties of space near a massive star, for example, the conceptions of a flat space no longer apply.

If we could construct a sufficiently large triangle under these conditions, we should find that the three angles no longer added up to two right angles. In fact, the situation would be similar to the triangle formed by three curved lines drawn on the surface of a sphere. The basic conceptions of Einstein's theory were quickly verified by the discovery that it could account for the previously inexplicable perturbations in the motion of the planet Mercury as it approached the sun, and by the discovery that the light rays from a distant star when viewed so that it was nearly in line with the sun were deflected by the sun's gravitational field.

Einstein attempted to apply his new ideas of the gravitational curvature of space-time to the universe as a whole. In this case the curvature of space would be influenced not only by one star, but by countless stars and galaxies. However, in the large-scale view, as we have seen, the distribution has a high degree of uniformity, and the problem of the over-all curvature of space can be related to the average density of the matter in the universe. In working out the equations, Einstein was unable to find any solution which described a static universe. We must remember that this was a decade before the discovery of the recession of the nebulae, and any cosmological theory which did not provide for a static cosmos could have been little more than a curiosity.

Faced with this dilemma, Einstein realized in 1917 that the difficulties could be surmounted by the introduction of a new term in his equations. This is the famous λ term, or the cosmical constant, over which there was to be so much future dispute. This new term appears in the equations as an arbitrary universal constant. Its interpretation in terms of a physical model of the universe is that it introduces an effect analogous to repulsion. This cosmic repulsion increases with the distance between bodies, and is to be regarded as superimposed on the usual forces of Newtonian attraction. Thus at great distances the repulsion outweighs the attraction, and in the equilibrium condition the Newtonian attraction and cosmical repulsion are in exact balance.

We cannot follow in detail the subsequent developments, which are of the utmost complexity. Some years after the introduction of these ideas the whole situation was altered in dramatic fashion by the discovery that the universe was nonstatic but was expanding. At about the same time the Russian mathematician, Friedman, found other solutions of Einstein's equations which predicted either an expanding or contracting universe. In fact, now it has for long been realized that the equations of general relativity cannot define a unique universe because there are three unknowns in the equations, whereas observationally we have only two sets of data. The possible types of nonstatic universes fall into three main families determined by the various possible combinations of the sign of the cosmical constant and the space curvature. These are a universe which starts from a point origin at a finite time in the past and expands continuously to become infinitely large after an infinite time, a universe whose radius has a certain finite value at the initial moment of time, and thence expands to become infinite after an infinite time, and lastly a universe which expands from zero radius to a certain maximum and then collapses to zero again, this process of oscillation being capable of indefinite repetition. Within each of these three main categories a large number of possible models can be constructed differing in various points of detail. For the past thirty years cosmologists have sought for arguments based on the observed characteristics of the universe which would identify the actual universe with one of the theoretical models.

All that I propose to do here is to give some examples of these evolutionary models, one of which is today believed by many cosmologists to describe the past history with some degree of certainty. The first example is a solution discovered by the Abbé Lemaître in 1927 and developed by Eddington. I have already said that by introducing the cosmical constant Einstein was able to specify a static condition of the universe in which the Newtonian attraction and cosmical repulsion are in exact balance. However, this equilibrium is unstable. If something upsets the balance so that the attraction is weakened, then cosmical repulsion has the upper hand and an expansion begins. As the material of the universe separates, the distance between the bodies becomes greater, the attraction still further weakens, the cosmical repulsion ever increases, and the expansion becomes faster. On the other hand, if the equilibrium were upset in the other way so that the forces of attraction became superior, then the reverse would occur and the system would contract continuously. Eddington's view was that in the initial stage the universe consisted of a uniform distribution of protons and electrons, by our standards very diffuse. This proton-electron gas comprised the entire primeval universe, which would have had a radius of about a thousand million light years. At some stage an event or series of events must have occurred in this diffuse gas which determined that the universe was launched on a career of expansion and not contraction. There were many views as to how this might have happened. Eddington held that the accumulation of irregularities in the gas started the evolutionary tendency. Soon, condensations formed in the gas and those ultimately became the galaxies of stars. On these views the present radius of the universe must be about five times that of the initial static primeval universe.

In the light of modern knowledge this theory receives little support. The time scale of its evolution is too short, and one cannot find a compelling reason why the primeval gas should have been disturbed in such a way as to determine that the universe was launched on a career of expansion rather than contraction. The initial condition is a special case, ephemeral and fortuitous. As far as the laws of physics are concerned, one can only say that by chance the initial disturbances were such as to determine the history of the universe. One cannot feel very happy that such a chance occurrence some thousands of millions of years ago should have determined the fundamental features of the universe. Moreover, although originally the theory as expounded by Jeans and Eddington undoubtedly had attractive features for some theologians, I feel now that this might well have been enhanced by feelings of relief that the vastness, uniformity, and organization of the universe which had just been revealed still remained outside the conceivable laws of physics in its initial state. Indeed, when considering these initial conditions Jeans spoke in terms of "the finger of God agitating the ether," implying a divine intervention at a predictable time in past history after which the laws of physics became applicable. This degree of familiarity with divine processes is, I think, undesirable theologically, and for science it evades the problem by obscuring the ultimate cosmological issue.

Moreover, there is another problem which must be faced. The event which we have considered in the unstable static assemblage of primeval gas predetermined the subsequent history of the universe. One must still inquire how long the gas existed in this condition of unstable equilibrium and how the primeval gas originated. Science has nothing to say on this issue. Indeed, it seems that the theory requires the exercise of yet another divine act at some indeterminate time before the occurrence which set off the gas on its career of condensation and expansion.

Of course, this particular model is now of little more than historical interest as being one of the first of the evolutionary theories based on general relativity to receive serious attention. It provides, however, a remarkable example of the influence in cosmology of the predilection of the individual. When faced with the various possible cosmological models which we have outlined, Eddington said this: "Since I cannot avoid introducing this question of a beginning, it has seemed to me that the most satisfactory theory would be one which made the beginning not too unaesthetically abrupt. This condition can only be satisfied by an Einstein universe with all the major forces balanced." He continues, "Perhaps it will be objected that, if one looks far enough back, this theory does not really dispense with an abrupt beginning, the whole universe must come into being at one instant in order that it may start in balance. I do not regard it in that way. To my mind undifferentiated sameness and nothingness cannot be distinguished philosophically." In this way Eddington attempted to rationalize the basis on which to build the universe.

I have already mentioned the Abbé Lemaître. His original work in 1927, published in a little-known journal, was discovered by Eddington. Although Eddington remained faithful to this idea that the universe evolved from the static but unstable Einstein universe, the conception was soon abandoned by Lemaître himself. For the past twenty-five years Lemaître's name has been associated with another model whose origin recedes even farther back in time than the static Einstein state. Of all cosmologies, it is, perhaps, by far the most thoroughly studied. We shall see later that during the last few years a tremendous clash has occurred with other opinions, but at the present time there are no known features of the observable universe which are incompatible with Lemaître's evolutionary cosmology. Lemaître's model is typical of one of the groups of theories inherent in general relativity, according to which the universe originated at a finite time in the past and expands to an infinite size at an infinite future time.

Perhaps we can most easily visualize this conception by taking the universe as we see it now and inquiring quite simply what might have been the situation long ago. The observations of the distant galaxies show that their light and radio emission is shifted in wavelength so that as received on the earth the light is redder and the radio waves longer in wavelength than those which are actually emitted. The interpretation of this shift is that we are separating from the galaxies at a very high speed, and that the speed of recession increases as we move out into space. At the limits of present-day observation the speed of recession is about thirty-seven thousand miles per second, which is a fifth of the velocity of light. The observation which gives us this figure is of a cluster of galaxies in Hydra photographed in the 200-inch telescope. The so-called cosmological principle which is inherent in Lemaître's theory implies that if human beings equipped with similar instruments existed on a planet in this Hydra cluster of galaxies, then they would see the cluster of galaxies to which we belong at the limit of their powers of observation, and the velocity of recession would also be thirty-seven thousand miles per second. It is important to rid ourselves of any idea that because all around us we find galaxies in recession, then we are the center of the recessional movement. This is not the case. It is an impression which we obtain because we can see only a small part of the total universe.

To return to this cluster of galaxies in Hydra. We are now seeing it as it was two thousand million years ago moving away at a rate of thirty-seven thousand miles a second. What is the likely past history of this and all other similar galaxies? Up to a point this question is not too difficult to answer. For example, a minute ago we were two million miles closer to this cluster than we are now. A year ago we were over a billion miles closer. If we recede back into history in this manner we realize that the galaxies such as Hydra which are now almost beyond our view must have been very much closer to us in the remote past. In fact, if we proceed in this way, then we reach a time of about eight or nine thousand million years ago when all the galaxies must have been very close together indeed. Of course, the galaxies themselves have evolved during this time, but the primeval material from which they were formed must have existed in a space which is very small compared with the universe today.

With important reservations which I shall deal with now, this in essence is the fundamental concept of Lemaître's theory, namely, that the universe originated from a dense and small conglomerate which Lemaître calls the primeval atom. I shall return in a moment to the conditions which might have existed at the beginning, and to the possible events which might have initiated the disruption and expansion of the primeval atom. It is in fact necessary to emphasize that the theory does not demand the formation of the galaxies in the first phase of the expansion. The primeval atom contained the entire material of the universe, and its density must have been inconceivably high—at least a hundred million tons per cubic centimeter. The initial momentum of the expansion dispersed this material, and after thousands of millions of years the conditions applicable to the so-called Einstein universe would have been reached. Then the size of the universe was about a thousand million light years and the density would have been comparable to that with which we are familiar on earth. According to Lemaître, at this stage the initial impetus of the expansion was nearly exhausted and the universe began to settle down into the nearly static condition which we have previously considered, where the forces of gravitational attraction and cosmical repulsion were in balance. The mathematical treatment indicates that the universe must have stayed for a long time in this condition. It is during this phase that the great clusters of galaxies began to form primeval material. Then the conditions of near equilibrium were again upset, the forces of cosmical repulsion began to win over those of gravitational attraction, and the universe was launched on the career of expansion which after nine thousand million years brought it to the state which we witness today.

The time scale determined by tracing back the past history of the galaxies brings us not to the beginning of time and space, but merely to a condition which existed a few thousand million years ago when the universe was probably about one-tenth of its present size and consisted of the original gaseous clouds from which the clusters of galaxies began to form. The processes of the formation and evolution of the galaxies from this early stage are the subject of very detailed mathematical treatment. There is, at present, every reason to believe that a satisfactory explanation of the evolution of the universe from that condition can be given in terms of the known laws of physics. But when we pass on to consider the even earlier stages, difficulties and uncertainties appear. How much farther do we have to go back in time to the condition of the primeval atom? The theory does not determine this with any precision, because the delay which the universe suffered during the equilibrium phase when the gaseous clouds were forming into galaxies cannot be specified. One can, however, say this—that the explosion or disintegration of the primeval atom must have occurred between twenty thousand million and sixty thousand million years ago. In other words the period of about nine thousand million years ago, when the galaxies began to form and the present period of expansion began, represents a comparatively recent phase in the history of the universe.

... next ... I shall talk about the alternative view which science can offer on the origin of the universe, but before doing this I want to dwell a moment on the implications of this evolutionary theory. The time scale, although vast, is conceivable in human terms. From the initial moment of time when the primeval atom disintegrated, astronomy and mathematics can attempt to describe the subsequent history of the universe to the state which we observe today. Moreover, there is every chance that in the foreseeable future man will produce experimental tests which will either substantiate or destroy this picture. But when we inquire what the primeval atom was like, how it disintegrated, and by what means and at what time it was created, we begin to cross the boundaries of physics into the realms of philosophy and theology. The important thing at that stage is what you and I think about this situation, this beginning of all time and space.

As a scientist I cannot discuss this problem of the creation of the primeval atom because it precedes the moment when I can ever hope to infer from observations the conditions which existed. If, indeed, the universe began in this way, then the concepts of space and time with which we deal originated at some moment between twenty thousand million and sixty thousand million years ago. Time, in the sense of being measured by any clock, did not exist before that moment, and space, in the sense of being measured by any yardstick, was contained entirely within the primeval atom. The vast regions of space which we survey today are just a small part of those which were originally the space of that small conglomerate.

We can, of course, speculate on the issues of the creation of the primeval atom and its initial condition, but it is the philosopher who must first build a scheme which is self-consistent and which leads us smoothly into beginning of space-time where the mathematician can take over. Or one can simply refuse to discuss the question. If we wish to be materialistic, then we adopt the same attitude of mind as the materialist adopts in more common situations. The materialist will begin in the present case at the initiation of space-time when the primeval atom disintegrated. That quite simply evades the problem, and in . . . [the following section] I shall describe some alternative theories and the kind of framework which might eventually form a metaphysical scheme before the beginning of time and space.

II

. . . I described [above] one of the evolutionary theories of the origin of the universe. According to this theory, all the material of the universe and all of time and space were originally concentrated in a super-dense primeval atom which disintegrated about twenty or sixty thousand million years ago. . . . I shall [now] describe the theory of continuous creation, which has quite different implications, but before I do that I want to consider this problem of the beginning which is inherent in the evolutionary theories. With an effort of imagination the human mind can trace its way back through the thousands of millions of years of time and space, and we can attempt to describe in common concepts the condition of the primeval atom. The primeval atom was unstable and must have disintegrated as soon as it came into existence. There we reach the great barrier of thought because we begin to struggle with the concepts of time and space before they existed in terms of our everyday experience. I feel as though I've suddenly driven into a great fog barrier where the familiar world has disappeared.

I think one can say that philosophically the essential problem in the conception of the beginning of the universe is the transfer from the state of indeterminacy to the condition of determinacy, after the beginning of space and time when the macroscopic laws of physics apply. When viewed in this way we see that the problem bears a remarkable similarity to one with which we are familiar. This is the indeterminacy which the quantum theory of physics introduces into the behavior of individual atoms, compared with the determinacy which exists in events where large numbers of atoms are involved. The process of thought by which we reduce the multiplicity of the entire universe to its singular condition of the primeval atom is equivalent in principle to the reduction of the chair in which you are sitting to one of its individual atoms. Not in the evolutionary sense of course, but in the sense that quantum theory and the principle of uncertainty explains why the behavior of the individual atom is indeterminate and why it is impossible for you to find out the condition of the atom with any precision, because you will disturb it in the very process of investigation. In fact, the application of the fundamental concepts of quantum theory to the cosmological problem enables us to begin the struggle with the barrier which arises whenever we think about the beginning of space and time.

The primeval atom was a singular state of the universe, as incapable of precise specification by physical methods as the familiar individual particle in the uncertainty principle of modern physics. When the primeval atom disintegrated the state of multiplicity set in and the universe became determinate in a macroscopic sense. Philosophically, space and time had a natural beginning when the condition of multiplicity occurred, but the beginning itself is quite inaccessible. In fact, in the beginning the entire universe of the primeval atom was effectively a single quantum unit in the sense that only one of the future innumerable potential states existed. I am aware that this discussion is merely a line of metaphysical thought. Its importance lies in the parallel with the fundamental difficulties and basic indeterminacies in modern quantum theory. If future advances should occur in these directions, then it may become possible to speak with more certainty about the condition of the original cosmological quantum. In the light of our present knowledge of atomic physics it is possible only to surmise the kind of condition which might have existed. I suggested earlier that the density of matter in this primeval atom was inconceivably high. This is arrived at by a simple arithmetical deduction from the probable total mass of the universe as we see it now, and by assuming that the radius of the primeval atom was not greater than, say, a few million miles. However, it is possible that the primeval atom was not like this, but that it consisted of intense radiation and corpuscular rays which formed the primeval gas during the first phases of the expansion. In fact, it is a fundamental concept of Lemaître's theory that the cosmic radiation which we observe today is a relic of this early state. A characteristic of this picture of evolution is the long time scale involved in the transformation of the intense energy of the original primeval atom, first into the gaseous clouds of hydrogen and then by processes, which awaited the high temperatures and pressures which arose when stars began to form, into the other elements with which we are familiar today. If pressed to describe this primeval atom in conventional terms one would, I think, refer to a gigantic neutron. By radioactive decay this neutron suffered a tremendous explosion. Protons, electrons, alpha particles, and other fundamental particles emerged from it at great velocity and continued to fill all space nearly uniformly as this basic material expanded for many thousands of millions of years until the clusters of galaxies began to form.

An alternative picture of the condition of the primeval atom has been given by Gamow, who believes that it consisted entirely of high-temperature thermal radiation. Five minutes after the expansion began the temperature of the universe was a thousand million degrees; after a day it had fallen to forty million degrees—say, nearly to the temperature of the center of the sun; after ten million years it had fallen to an average temperature, which we call room temperature. On this theory of Gamow all the chemical elements which we deal with today must have been formed within the first thirty minutes of the life of the universe.

Gamow differs from Lemaître in other important respects. In Lemaître's theory the force of the initial disintegration was exhausted after a few thousand million years, and the expansion which we witness today came into play only as a result of the forces of cosmical repulsion which developed when the galaxies began to form. In Gamow's theory the force of the initial explosion was so great that the expansion of the universe was attained without invoking the force of cosmical repulsion. In other words, the beginning in the Gamow theory is close to the nine thousand million years which we deduce by tracing back the history of the galaxies, and there is no protracted period in the state of diffuse gas with all the major forces balanced as in Lemaître's theory.

The most distinguished living exponent of the evolutionary theory of the origin of the universe is himself in Holy Orders. For him and for all who associate their universe with God, the creation of the primeval atom was a divine act outside the limits of scientific knowledge and indeed of scientific investigation. The probable condition of intense radiation in the primeval atom is entirely consistent with the divine command "Let there be light." It would, of course, be wrong of me to suggest that this view of the origin of the universe demands necessarily the possibility of creation of matter by a divine act. On the contrary, those who reject God adopt a strictly material- istic attitude to the creation of the primeval atom. They would argue that the creation of the primeval material had no explanation within the framework of contemporary scientific knowledge, but would escape from the dilemma by reserving the possibility that science would, if given the opportunity of studying these initial conditions, find a satisfactory solution. Or they would evade the problem of a beginning altogether by following a further line of thought due to Gamow that the primeval atom was not the beginning, but merely a state of maximum contraction of a universe which had previously existed for an eternity of time. I think, however, that for theology, there is one important observation to make. If the universe was created and evolved in the manner just described, then the concep- tion that the creation of the primeval material was a divine act can never be attacked by scientific investigation. A set of conditions which existed over twenty thousand million years ago, and which can never return again, is forever beyond investigation.

The theory which we have discussed envisages a once for all crea- tion in the remote past followed by a steady evolution to the present conditions. The alternative to this theory is that the creation of matter is taking place continuously and that although stars and galax- ies evolve from this basic material, the universe, when considered as a large-scale structure, is in a steady state. We can illustrate this view by considering the future history of the galaxies which are now near the limit of observation. We are receding at great speed from these galaxies. In a billion years' time the galaxies will have passed forever from our field of view and other galaxies which are now closer to us will have moved out to our observable horizon. So much is common ground on both the evolutionary and steady-state theories. The sharp distinction arises when we compare the picture of the universe within the observable horizon now and in a billion years' time. On the evolutionary theory more and more galaxies move out of our field of view, and the number of galaxies which we can see with our instru- ments will forever decrease. In other words, the average spatial den- sity of the universe is decreasing. On the steady-state theory this is not the case. Although individual galaxies recede beyond the ob- servable horizon, others are always being created to take their place.

In a billion years' time the universe will look to us very much as it does now. The individual galaxies will have changed, but their average spatial density remains the same, because matter is always in creation throughout all of space. The cosmological principle of the evolutionary theory in which the universe would appear to be the same to any observer, wherever he was situated in space, has become the perfect cosmological principle according to which the universe is the same throughout all space and time.

The implications of this point of view are, of course, profound. For example, there cannot have been a beginning in any scale of time at all. If we trace back in time the history of the galaxies, they dissolve into gas and then into uncreated matter as they move in toward us, whereas others come into view from beyond the observable horizon. At a time of twenty thousand million years ago the evolutionary models picture the universe as a concentrated conglomerate of gas, whereas the steady-state universe would have appeared as it does today. Indeed, however far we go back in time, there is no stage at which we can say that the universe, as a whole, had a beginning. In the only language at our command we can say that the history of the universe on the steady-state theory extends to an infinite time in the past.

Whereas there is hope that we can put our inferences about the past to an experimental test, we can discuss the future only in terms of the predictions of cosmological theory. Here again there are great differences between the evolutionary and steady-state models. The predictions of the steady-state theory are quite clear. The universe has an infinite extent in space and an infinite future in time. There is, of course, a limit to the observable universe from any one place in it, determined by the speed of expansion. But if an intelligent being exists at our observable limit, he would find himself surrounded by a similar universe of galaxies and so on without end. Neither does the theory of continuous creation place any limitation on the future extent in time. In the same way that a billion years ago the universe would look the same as it does now, so in a billion years of future existence the over-all large-scale picture will be unchanged.

The future on the evolutionary models is quite different. The total content of matter was fixed once and for all at the time of creation.

The expansion is thinning out the galaxies, and in a billion years our view of space would indeed be vastly different from what it is today. In some variations of the evolutionary theory the process of expansion is expected to reverse when the spatial density has fallen to a certain value, and then the contraction of space would bring the ageing galaxies into view again. But even in such variations of the evolutionary models the ultimate death of the universe seems inescapable, because the energy with which the universe was imbued at its creation is relentlessly becoming less available.

The finite limitations of space, time, and content in some of the evolutionary models lead one to ask whether our universe is, in fact, the entire cosmos. It is a question which at present cannot be discussed with profit. There is no feature of the theory which would preclude the existence of other universes created at different times, but unless we are hopelessly wrong in our interpretation of our observation of the universe we see, there is no conceivable way in which we can ever penetrate the regions of time and space where they might exist.

The conflict between the steady-state and evolutionary theories is of the very greatest significance to cosmology and to human thought. The evolutionary theory places the creation of matter at a definite moment in the remote past, beyond human investigation. Although the steady-state theory has no solution to the problem of the creation of matter, it is important to appreciate that if this theory is correct, then the primeval gas is being created now, at this moment, and hence is open to human investigation. On the whole, I think it must be incontestable that the steady-state theory is more materialistic than the evolutionary theory. It could be said that the creation process is a divine act which is proceeding continuously, and which is beyond the conception of the human mind. On the other hand, it cannot be denied that this may be a somewhat perilous attitude for the simple reason that the tools of science can probe the regions of space where this creation is occurring. In fact, in the equations of the cosmologists a creation term already exists. Philosophically, it is, I think, important to emphasize the approachability of the creation of hydrogen which is inherent in these modern theories of continuous creation. Otherwise the metaphysical impact would not be severe. In this sense the concept was stated long ago by Kant in these words ". . . the remaining part of the succession of eternity is always infinite," he said, "and that which has flowed is finite, the sphere of developed nature is always but an infinitely small part of that totality which has the seed of future worlds in itself, and which strives to evolve itself out of the crude state of chaos through longer or shorter periods. The creation," he went on, "is never finished or complete. It has, indeed, once begun, but it will never cease." But, of course, Kant's doctrine was egocentric, in the sense that God had completed the creation in the part of the cosmos which we can see. In the contemporary theories of continuous creation the processes of formation should still be occurring all around us, and are therefore open to human investigation.

I think it is true to say that during the last few years the cosmological issue has crystallized into a conflict between these evolutionary and steady-state theories of the origin of the universe. The variations in detail within these two broad principles are numerous. Many of these differences are highly abstract, but insofar as the stream of human thought is concerned, these internal variations are of small consequence compared with the major issue as to whether creation is occurring now and throughout all time in the past and in the future, or whether the fundamental material of the universe was created in its entirety some billions of years ago.

It seems possible that we may be on the verge of settling by experimenal observation which of these two principles is correct. In fact, the group of young cosmologists who have promulgated the theories of continuous creation have always emphasized that, as distinct from the theoretical arguments which have surrounded the variations of evolutionary cosmology in the last thirty years, the new theories should be capable of direct experimental test. For example, if with our telescopes we could penetrate so far into space that we could see a cluster of galaxies from which the light had taken nine thousand million years to reach us, then it would be possible to reach a clear decision. For at that time in the past on the evolutionary theory the clusters of galaxies were only just beginning to form from the primeval gas. Well, of course, such a straightforward observation is impossible because of the limited range of our telescopes. I said earlier that the most distant object yet identified in the telescopes is the cluster of galaxies in Hydra at about two thousand million light years. Although the light from this cluster has been traveling through space for two thousand million years, it is too close to us in time and space to be of use in distinguishing between the two theories.

It is, however, on the verge of the regions of space and time where the universe would be expected to be significantly different if creation was still in progress compared with the conditions in an evolutionary universe. If time and space had a beginning, then when the universe was only a few thousand million years old it would be much more compact than it is today. The galaxies would be in existence, but they would be packed closer together compared with their spatial density today. The spatial density today—by which I mean the number of galaxies within, say, fifty or a hundred million light years of the Milky Way—can be determined by the large telescopes. If we could count the number in a similar volume of space at a distance of several thousand million light years we should in effect be making a count of the galaxies as they existed several thousand million years ago. If creation is still taking place, then on the steady-state theories this number should be the same as today. If the evolutionary model is correct, then the spatial density at this distance in time and space will be much greater.

The possibility of carrying out this decisive observational test excites the imagination. Unfortunately it seems likely that the hindrances introduced by the atmosphere of the earth will prevent the great optical telescopes from penetrating to the required regions of space. It may well be that only when optical telescopes can be carried in earth satellites or erected on the moon will it be possible to look back into the past to this extent. Before the advent of such futuristic enterprises it seems likely that the great radio telescopes will give us the answer we require. You may remember that in a previous talk I referred to the collisions of galaxies which, for reasons not yet understood, generate radio waves which can easily be picked up in the radio telescopes, although the light from these galaxies is so faint that they are near the limit of the normally observable universe. We can already study galaxies in collision at such distances that they must be far beyond the range of the optical telescopes. We believe that these investigations are already taking us so far out in space and so far back in time that the radio waves have been on their journey for a few thousand million years. The circumstantial evidence for this belief in the origin of many of the unidentified radio sources is very strong, and if this is confirmed we have the tools with which human beings can bring the cosmological issues to a decisive test.

The concept of continuous creation also presents us with another opportunity to make an even more direct and decisive test. If the theory is correct, then the hydrogen gas which forms the primeval material of the galaxies must be in creation at a considerable rate. The theory demands the appearance of hydrogen at the rate of several billion trillion tons per second in the observable universe. Although this figure is vast, in fact, by ordinary human concepts of terrestrial space the rate is exceedingly slow. It represents the creation of only a few atoms of hydrogen per cubic mile of space per year. The presence of this hydrogen in intergalactic space may well be detectable in the near future by the radio telescopes.

As individuals we must therefore face the possibility that within the next few years astronomers may be able to speak with unanimity about the ultimate cosmological problem. Only the materialist can turn aside unmoved by this prospect. For others, a settlement of this cosmological issue might mean an affirmation or rejection of deeply embedded philosophical and theological beliefs.

So far I have tried to present the contemporary background without prejudice, but no doubt before I finish you will expect me to say a word about my own personal views. At the moment our outlook in astronomy is optimistic. A new epoch has been opened by the development of radio telescopes, and we are perhaps within a generation of an even more astonishing one because of the inherent possibilities of astronomical observations from earth satellites or the moon. We can only guess as to the nature of the remote regions which might be photographed by telescopes removed from their earth-bound environment. In the case of radio telescopes this development is still very young. Three hundred years elapsed between Galileo's small telescope and the inauguration of the 200-inch telescope on Mount Palomar. In the development of radio telescopes we have not covered a tenth of that time-span. I think therefore that our present optimism may well be of the kind which comes from the initial deployment of great new instruments and techniques. I have no doubt that within a few years these instruments will enable us to resolve the conflict which I have described between the evolutionary and steady-state models. In this process new difficulties will certainly appear, and these might make my present description of the universe as out of date as the static egocentric description which was in vogue in the first twenty years of this century. When we are dealing with time-spans of thousands of millions of years it would be sheer impudence to suggest that the views of the cosmos which have evolved from the techniques developed in our age possess any degree of finality. My present attitude to the scientific aspects of the problem is therefore neutral in the sense that I do not believe that there yet exist any observational data which are decisively in favor of any particular contemporary cosmology. The optimism with which I believe that we are on the verge of producing the necessary observational data is tempered with a deep apprehension, born of bitter experience, that the decisive experiment nearly always extends one's horizon into regions of new doubts and difficulties.

On the question of the creation of the primeval material of the universe it seems to me unlikely that there can ever be a scientific description, whether in terms of the evolutionary or steady-state theories. If the idea of continuous creation is substantiated, then science will have penetrated very far indeed into the ultimate processes of the universe. It might then appear that a completely materialistic framework would have been established, but it does not seem to me that this is the case. If one imagines a scientific device which is so perfect that it could record the appearance of a single hydrogen atom as demanded by the continuous-creation theory, then the scientific description of the process would still be imperfect. The same basic and quite fundamental difficulty would appear, as I have described in the case of the primeval atom, in the further effort to obtain information about the nature of the energy input which gave rise to the created atom.

If I were pressed on this problem of creation I would say, therefore, that any cosmology must eventually move over into metaphysics for reasons which are inherent in modern scientific theory. The epoch of this transfer may be now and at all future time, or it may have been twenty thousand million years ago. In respect of creation the most that we can hope from our future scientific observations is a precise determination of this epoch. I must emphasize that this is a personal view. The attitudes of my professional colleagues to this problem would be varied. Some would no doubt approve of this or a similar line of metaphysical thought. Others would not be willing to face even this fundamental limit to scientific knowledge, although, as I have said, an analogous limitation occurs in modern scientific theory which describes the well-known processes of atomic behavior. Some, I am afraid, will be aghast at my temerity in discussing the issues at all. As far as this group is concerned, all that I say is that I sometimes envy their ability to evade by neglect such a problem which can tear the individual's mind asunder.

On the question of the validity of combining a metaphysical and physical process as a description of creation, this, as I said earlier, is the individual's problem. In my own case, I have lived my days as a scientist, but science has never claimed the whole of my existence. Some, at least, of the influence of my upbringing and environment has survived the conflict, so that I find no difficulty in accepting this conclusion. I am certainly not competent to discuss this problem of knowledge outside that acquired by my scientific tools, and my outlook is essentially a simple one. Simple in the sense that I am no more surprised or distressed at the limitation of science when faced with this great problem of creation than I am at the limitation of the spectroscope in describing the radiance of a sunset or at the theory of counterpoint in describing the beauty of a fugue.

When I began my talks I mentioned the mixture of fear and humility with which I approached the task. Now you see the irony of the modern astronomer's life in its entirety. The devices of a world war have been forged, with the help of the fear of another, into a system of scientific experiments which take us back through time and space to deal with the problems of the origin of the universe.

CHAPTER 7

Man and Earth

PAUL TILLICH

*When I look at thy heavens, the work of thy fingers, the moon and·
the stars which thou hast established; what is man that thou art
mindful of him, and the son of man that thou dost care for him? Yet
thou hast made him little less than God, and dost crown him with
glory and honor. Thou hast given him dominion over the works of
thy hands; thou hast put all things under his feet.*

PSALMS 8:3–6

I

Some time ago representatives of the world of science demanded a new line of research. They called it a "science of
survival." They did not mean the survival of individuals or social
groups, of nations or of races—that would not be new—but the survival of civilized mankind, or of mankind as a whole, or even of
life altogether on the surface of this planet. Such a proposition is
a sign that we have reached a stage of human history that has only
one analogy in the past, the story of the "Great Flood," found in
the Old Testament and also among the myths and legends of many
nations. The only difference between our situation and that of the
Flood is that in these stories the gods or God brings about the destruction of life on earth because men have aroused divine anger.
As the book of Genesis describes it: "The Lord was sorry that he
had made man on the earth and it grieved him to his heart. So the
Lord said, I will blot out man, whom I have created, from the face
of the ground, man and beast and creeping things and birds of the
air, for I am sorry that I have made them." In the next verse, the
story answers the question of possible survival—"But Noah found

Reprinted with the permission of Charles Scribner's Sons from *The Eternal
Now*, pp. 66-78, by Paul Tillich. Copyright © 1963 Paul Tillich.

favor in the eyes of the Lord." Through him, we read, not only man but also a pair of each species of animal was to make possible the survival of life upon the earth. Today, the destruction and survival of life have been given into the hands of man. Man who has dominion over all things, according to the psalm, has the power to save or destroy them, for he is little less than God.

How does man react to this new situation? How do *we* react? How *should* we react? "The earth and we" has ceased to be merely a subject for human curiosity, artistic imagination, scientific study, or technical conquest. It has become a question of profound human concern and tormenting anxiety. We make desperate attempts to escape its seriousness. But when we look deep into the minds of our contemporaries, especially those of the younger generation, we discover a dread that permeates their whole being. This dread was absent a few decades ago and is hard to describe. It is the sense of living under a continuous threat; and although it may have many causes, the greatest of these is the imminent danger of a universal and total catastrophe. Their reaction to this feeling is marked either by a passionate longing for security in daily life, or an exaggerated show of boldness and confidence in man, based on his conquest of earthly and trans-earthly space. Most of us experience some of these contradictory reactions in ourselves. Our former naïve trust in the "motherly" earth and her protective and preserving power has disappeared. It is possible that the earth may bear us no longer. We ourselves may prevent her from doing so. No heavenly sign, like the rainbow given to Noah as a promise that there would not be a second flood, has been given to us. We have no guarantee against man-made floods, that destroy not by water but by fire and air.

Such thoughts give rise to the question—what has the Christian message to say about this, our present predicament? What has it to say about life on this planet, its beginning and end, and man's place on it? What has it to say about the significance of the earth, the scene of human history, in view of the vastnesses of the universe? What about the short span of time allotted to this planet and the life upon it, as compared to the unimaginable length of the rhythms of the universe?

Such questions have been rarely asked in Christian teaching and preaching. For the central themes of Christianity have been the dramas of the creation and fall, of salvation and fulfillment. But sometimes peripheral questions move suddenly into the center of a system of thought, not for any theoretical reason, but because such questions have become, for many, matters of life and death. This kind of movement has very often occurred in human history as well as in Christian history. And whenever it has occurred, it has changed man's view of himself in all respects, as it has changed the understanding of the Christian tradition on all levels. It may well be that we are living in such a moment, and that man's relation to the earth and the universe will, for a long time, become the point of primary concern for sensitive and thoughtful people. Should this be the case, Christianity certainly cannot withdraw into the deceptive security of its earlier questions and answers. It will be compelled forward into the more daring inroads of the human spirit, risking new and unanswered questions, like those we have just asked, but at the same time pointing in the direction of the eternal, the source and goal of man and his world.

Our predicament has been brought about chiefly by the scientific and technical development of our century. It is as foolish as it is futile to complain of this development. For there it lies before us— a realm created by man quite beyond the realm that was given him by nature when he first emerged from earlier forms of life. There it *is*, changing our lives and thoughts and feelings in all dimensions, consciously, and even more, unconsciously. Today's students are not what students of the preceding generations were. Today's hopes and anxieties are strange and often unintelligible to the older among us. And if we compare our two generations with any in earlier centuries, the distance separating us from them becomes really immense.

Since this sudden thrust forward has been brought about by science and its application, must not science itself have the last word about man, his earth and the universe? What can religion add? Indeed, hasn't religion, whenever it did try to explore these subjects, interfered with scientific development, and therefore been pushed aside? This certainly happened in the past, and is happening again today. But it is not religion in itself that interferes; it is the anxiety and fanaticism of religious people—laymen as well as theologians— marked by a flight from serious thought and an unwillingness to distinguish the figurative language of religion from the abstract concepts of scholarly research. In many sections of the Christian world, however, such distortion and misuse of religion have been overcome. Here one can speak freely of man and his earth in the name of religion, with no intention of adding anything to scientific and historical knowledge, or of prohibiting any scientific hypothesis, however bold.

What then has the Christian message to say about man's predicament in this world? The eighth Psalm, written hundreds of years before the beginning of the Christian era, raises the same question with full clarity and great beauty. It points, on the one hand, to the infinite smallness of man as compared to the universe of heavens and stars, and, on the other hand, to the astonishing greatness of man, his glory and honor, his power over all created things, and his likeness to God Himself. Such thoughts are not frequent in the Bible. But when we come across them, they sound as though they had been written today. Ever since the opening of the universe by modern science, and the reduction of the great earth to a small planet in an ocean of heavenly bodies, man has felt real vertigo in relation to infinite space. He has felt as though he had been pushed out of the center of the universe into an insignificant corner in it, and has asked anxiously—what about the high destiny claimed by man in past ages? What about the idea that the divine image is impressed in his nature? What about his history that Christianity always considered to be the point at which salvation for all beings took place? What about the Christ, who, in the New Testament, is called the Lord of the universe? What about the end of history, described in biblical language as a cosmic catastrophe, in which the sun, the moon, and the stars are perhaps soon to fall down upon the earth? What remains, in our present view of reality, of the importance of the earth and the glory of man? Further, since it seems possible that other beings exist on other heavenly bodies, in whom the divine image is also manifest, and of whom God is mindful, and also whom He has crowned with glory and honor, what is the meaning of the Christian view of human history and its center, the appearance of the Christ?

These questions are not merely theoretical. They are crucial to every man's understanding of himself as a human being placed upon this star, in an unimaginably vast universe of stars. And they are disturbing not only to people who feel grasped by the Christian message, but also to those who reject it but who share with Christianity a belief in the meaning of history and the ultimate significance of human life.

Again, the eighth Psalm speaks as though it had been conceived today—"Thou hast made him little less than God; thou hast given him dominion over the works of thy hands." It gives, as an example, man's dominion over the animals; but only since modern technology subjected all the spheres of nature to man's control has the phrase "little less than God" revealed its full meaning. The conquest of time and space has loosened the ties that kept man in bondage to his finitude. What was once imagined as a prerogative of the gods has become a reality of daily life, accessible to human technical power. No wonder that we of today feel with the psalmist that man is little less than God, and that some of us feel even equal with God, and further that others would not hesitate to state publicly that mankind, as a collective mind, has replaced God.

We therefore have to deal with an astonishing fact: the same events that pushed man from his place in the center of the world, and reduced him to insignificance, also elevated him to a God-like position both on earth and beyond!

Is there an answer to this contradiction? Listen to the psalmist: he does not say that man *has* dominion over all things or that man *is* little less than God; he says—"*Thou* hast given him dominion over the works of thy hands; *thou* hast made him little less than God." This means that neither man's smallness nor his greatness emanates from himself, but that there is something above this contrast. Man, together with all things, comes from Him Who has put all things under man's feet. Man is rooted in the same Ground in which the universe with all its galaxies is rooted. It is this Ground that gives greatness to everything, however small it may be, to atoms as well as plants and animals; and it is this that makes all things small, however great—the stars as well as man. It gives significance to the apparently insignificant. It gives significance to each individual man, and to mankind as a whole. This answer quiets our anxiety about our smallness, and it quells the pride of our greatness. It is not a biblical answer only, nor Christian only, nor only religious. Its truth is felt by all of us, as we become conscious of our predicament—namely, that we are not of ourselves, that our presence upon the earth is not of our own doing. We are brought into existence and formed by the same power that bears up the universe and the earth and everything upon it, a power compared to which we are infinitely small, but also one which, because we are conscious of it, makes us great among creatures.

II

Now let us recall the words of God in the story of the Flood: "I am sorry that I have made man." They introduce a new element into our thinking about man and the earth—an element of judgment, frustration and tragedy. There is no theme in biblical literature, nor in any other, more persistently pursued than this one. The earth has been cursed by man innumerable times, because she produced him, together with all life and its misery, which includes the tragedy of human history. This accusation of the earth sounds through our whole contemporary culture, and understandably so. We accuse her in all our artistic expressions, in novels and drama, in painting and music, in philosophical thought and descriptions of human nature. But even more important is the silent accusation implied in our cynical denunciation of those who would say "yes" to life, in our withdrawal from it into the refuges of mental disturbance and disease, in our forcing of life beyond itself or below itself by drugs and the various methods of intoxication, or in the social drugs of banality and conformity. In all these ways we accuse the destiny that placed us in this universe and upon this planet. "Thou dost crown him with glory and honor," says the psalmist. But many of us long to get rid of that glory and wish we had never possessed it. We yearn to return to the state of creatures which are unaware of themselves and their world, limited to the satisfaction of their animal needs.

In the story of the Flood it is God Who is sorry that He made man, and Who decides to blot him from the face of the earth. Today it is man who has the power to blot himself out, and often he is so sorry that he has been made man that he desires to withdraw from his humanity altogether. Many more people than we are aware of in our daily experience feel this desire; and perhaps something in us responds to them. Can it be that the earth, fully conquered by man, will cease to be a place where man wants to live? Is our passionate thrust into outer space perhaps an unconscious expression of man's flight from the earth? There are no sure answers to these questions, which, nevertheless, must be asked, because they cut through false feelings of security about the relation of man to the earth. The old insight that "man is but a pilgrim on earth" is echoed in these questions, and applicable today to mankind as a whole. Mankind itself is a pilgrim on earth, and there will be a moment when this pilgrimage comes to an end, at some indefinitely remote time, or perhaps soon, in the very near future. Christianity gives no indication of the length of man's history; the early Church expected the end at any moment, and when it did not come and the Christians were profoundly disappointed, the span was extended. In modern times, the span has been stretched to an unlimited extent. Scientists speak today of the millions of years that human history could continue. Millions of years, or thousands of years, or tomorrow—we do not know! But we ask—what is the meaning of this history, whenever it began, whenever it will end? And we ask at the moment not what it means for you and me, but, rather, what it means for the universe and its ultimate goal.

In the old story, God repented of having created man. The implication is that God took a risk when He created man, and every risk carries with it the possibility of failure. God Himself considered the creation of man a failure, and made a new effort. But nothing assures us that this new effort did not also result in failure. The first time, according to the story, nature executed the divine judgment on man. This time, man may himself be the executioner. Should this occur, the privileged position of the earth, of which the astronomers speak and in which man has always believed, would seem to prove to have been of no avail. It would seem as though its unique role had been given it in vain.

We should not crowd such thoughts away, for they deserve to be taken seriously. Indeed, it seems to me, it is impossible for thoughtful people today to crowd them away. What has the Christian message to say about them? I repeat—it tells us nothing about the duration of human history. It does not say that it will continue after tomorrow, nor how it will come to an end in scientific terms. None of this is its concern. What the Christian message does tell

us is that the meaning of history lies above history, and that, therefore, its length is irrelevant to its ultimate meaning. But it is not
irrelevant with respect to the innumerable opportunities time affords
for creation of life and spirit, and it is for these that we must fight
with all our strength. Furthermore, if history should end tomorrow,
through mankind's self-annihilation, the appearance of this planet
and of man upon it will *not* have been in vain. For a being shall
have at least appeared once, in the billions of years of the universe,
towards whose creation all the forces of life on earth worked together,
and in whom the image of the divine Ground of all life was present.
At least once, a living being shall have come into existence, in whom
life achieved its highest possibility—spirit. This is the ultimate source
of man's greatness, and those of us who openly or covertly accuse
life should open ourselves to this truth: in the short span of our life,
and the short span of human history and even of the existence of
this planet, something of eternal significance *did* happen—the depth
of all things became manifest in *one* being, and the name of that
being is *man*, and you and I are men! If we cannot accept this, and
insist that this could have been so but was not, and that mankind
is evil, and that the earth is contaminated by man's guilt, and that
the blood of the murdered in all periods cries for revenge to heaven
so that even God was forced to repent of His creation, then let us
contemplate these words: "The man Noah found favor in the eyes
of God." This one man represents something in every man that
makes him a mirror of the divine in spite of evil and distortion. And
the Christian message continues: there is one man in whom God
found His image undistorted, and who stands for all mankind—the
one who, for this reason, is called the Son and the Christ. The earth,
contaminated by man, is purified and consecrated through man—
namely, through the divine power of healing and fulfillment, of love
and blessedness, made manifest in the one man and at work in all
mankind, in all periods, and in all places. This is what justifies human history, as it also justifies the earth that, for millions of years,
prepared for the advent of man, and justifies the universe that produced the earth.

And yet, the universe is justified not only by the earth, nor is
creation justified by man alone. Other heavenly bodies, other histories, other creatures in whom the mystery of being is manifest may

replace us. Our ignorance and our prejudice should not inhibit our thought from transcending the earth and our history and even our Christianity. Science and the poetic imagination have made this leap, and Christianity should not hesitate to join them. Further, it should not hesitate to show that the Christian experience of divine power and glory implies an inexhaustible divine creativity, beyond the limits of earth or man and any part or state of the universe.

This means that we cannot seek for a beginning or an end of the universe within the past and future of measurable time. "Beginning" and "end" are not behind and before us, but above us in the eternal. From the eternal everything comes and to it everything goes, in every moment of life and history, in every moment of our planet and the universe to which it belongs. Creation is past *and* present. Fulfillment is future *and* present. It is in the present that past and future meet, because they come from, and go to, eternity.

The question of man and his earth, this question that has plunged our time into such anxiety and conflict of feeling and thought, cannot be answered without an awareness of the eternal presence. For only the eternal can deliver us from our sensation of being lost in the face of the time and space of the universe. Only the eternal can save us from the anxiety of being a meaningless bit of matter in a meaningless vortex of atoms and electrons. Only the eternal can give us the certainty that the earth, and, with it, mankind, has not existed in vain, even should history come to an end tomorrow. For the last end is where the first beginning is, in Him to Whom "a thousand years are but as yesterday."

PART FOUR   # What Is Man?

With varying degrees of completeness and plausibility the mental sciences have in the past and do now offer explanations of man's intriguing mental behavior. Behaviorism, neurophysiology, and, most recent on the scene, cybernetics, all promise a clarification of man's inner structure. Cambridge professor Fred Hoyle shows himself a most outspoken and explicit proponent of cybernetics as the explanation of man in his book *Man and Materialism*. He unabashedly draws the "materialist" conclusions from this:

> The essence of materialism lives in a refusal to separate man and his environment into the mutually exclusive categories of "spiritual" and "material." . . . A star is not necessarily more important than a man, or vice versa. Star and man are in the same boat. . . .
>
> It is urged by the opponents of materialism that while it has been found possible to understand in some detail how stars behave, no one has so far been able to understand with real precision how men behave. Instead of admitting this as proof that stars and men belong to rootedly different categories, the materialist points out that a star is a much simpler structure than a man, so it is no wonder that we know less about the inside of our own heads. The materialist cannot remain content with this, however. He will only score a complete victory over his opponents if he is able to show that the behavior of man can indeed be understood with precision, thereby destroying the case against him.
>
> The present volume is my own attempt . . . the problems are too difficult for any writer to hold more than partial success as an ambition. Now why is the problem so difficult? In mathematical terms, because human behavior is controlled by an interlocking system of nonlinear feedback loops.*

Despite the limitations that Hoyle sees in the present state of the scientific explanation of man, sufficient precision and sophistication exists in these sciences to give the apologist for spirit much to

* Fred Hoyle, *Man and Materialism* (New York: Harper & Row, Publishers, 1956), p. xix.

121

ponder. In the first essay in this section British physiologist Sir Francis Walshe puts before us the inherent limitations he sees in his science and urges that the same limitations are native to any natural science which seeks to have the final word on man. His treatment points up the complex problems still open to research, problems touching the relationship (and existence) of spirit and body in man. We are brought back to some of the difficulties we alluded to in the Introduction to Part Two. While rejecting the Cartesian dichotomy, Walshe holds strongly to the hylomorphic understanding of man. Both Hoyle and Teilhard de Chardin seem to belong to a third category which denies the distinction between body and spirit or, at least, suggests strongly that they are inextricable from each other. Are we, possibly, to take a clue from contemporary existentialism, contemporary psychology and psychiatry, and the current revival of biblical categories and see man as a concrete, existing, unified being rather than as *any* kind of composite?

In the second essay Yale psychologist Gordon Allport shows us man's inner life as seen in modern psychology. His short review of the recent history of psychology is illuminating; in addition he clarifies and relates the key terms used in discussions of man's inner life by contemporary psychologists of various schools. Allport himself claims no metaphysical position, but his fairly exhaustive analysis of the functions of the self cannot but suggest to the reader many questions about man's inner structure. Granted that contemporary scientific psychology must work *as if* there were no soul, does this say anything positive about the existence of the soul? What significance can the philosopher or Christian thinker attach to the rather general reintroduction of some notion of self into modern psychology? Or are all philosophical deductions from this fact bound to be unwarranted? Is there any residue of the traditional and more strictly philosophical notions of liberty, abstraction, and intentionality in the psychological concepts Allport describes?

CHAPTER 8   # Some Views Upon the Nature

of the Relationship

Between the Mind and Brain

SIR FRANCIS WALSHE

Some years ago, in a Hughlings Jackson lecture, I ventured to give some personal views upon the nature of the relationship of mind to brain. I said nothing original, yet something rather different from what we are accustomed to hear in those popular symposia on the brain-mind relationship, or upon brain mechanisms and consciousness, of which we have had a number of examples in recent years. The views I expressed had the sanction of philosophers from Aristotle to Aquinas, and, in a measure, of such physiological geniuses as Hughlings Jackson and Sherrington, but there is little interest in them at the present time in a scientific world still intensely preoccupied with the concepts of cybernetics and biophysics: preoccupied in the sense that some scientists find they cannot easily entertain any concepts which transcend these fragmentary ideas.

How we approach this problem depends largely upon our concept of nature and of natural science. Therefore, I define natural science as being "the study of nature as perceived: a study wherein nature is disclosed as a complex of entities whose mutual relations can be thought of and discussed without reference to sense awareness or thought about it." This is to say that we can be perfectly good natural scientists without bothering our heads about the nature of perceiving, or the theory of knowledge—epistemology, as it is called. This is a complex definition, which I have taken from a great mathematician

Sir Francis Walshe, "Some Views upon the Nature of the Relationship Between the Mind and Brain," *The Journal of Medical Education*, Vol. XXXIV (November, 1959), 1110-1117.

and philosopher, Alfred North Whitehead.[1] Its full import will appear later, but in the meantime I wish to point out that nature, that is, the world as perceived, does not comprehend all that the human mind can entertain. Science is but one universe of discourse, and he would be a bold man who maintained that there is no other possible universe of discourse about man than that of natural science. I say "a bold man"; perhaps I should have said a foolish man.

Yet, for many scientists, their scientific knowledge is almost wholly confined to what may be observed in circumstances so out of the ordinary that they do not happen in the natural course of events: to take a familiar example, the punctate electrical stimulation of the surface of the cerebral cortex, a form of procedure grossly unphysiological and therefore biologically irrelevant, as von Frey pointed out many years ago. These scientists use carefully constructed instruments and apparatus, laboratories strictly protected from outside influences, and workers trained by complex and special methods before anything can be observed that they are willing to accept as revealing the irrevocable causal laws of nature. Anything that makes ordinary natural occurrences differ from laboratory events must be cleared out of the way, and ignored as though it did not exist. The "clearing out" is valid enough, but the total ignoring of what has been put in the discard not rarely vitiates the conclusions drawn as a result of this "cooking" of the sum of the facts, and constitutes that common vice of the intellect, the misuse of abstraction.

Surely, when we have banished from our thoughts everything outside a scientific laboratory, what a mutilated and poverty-stricken universe there remains for our contemplation! Is it not surprising, then, that we should find distinguished scientists who really believe that there is nothing in the mind and intellect of man that cannot be described in terms of, and as being no more than the expression of, the activities of neurones: in short, in terms of the sodium-potassium pump, or the bloodless dance of action potentials? For them, as I have said before, the sonnets of Shakespeare, the *Primavera* of Botticelli, and the untold goodness and heroism of unknown thousands of human souls, are no more than the fruit of reverberating circuits and feedback mechanisms in the brain. I am not joining these self-confessed robots in their chill and ephemeral paradise. Of course, not all scientists live out their lives in blinkers like this, but it seems to me that those who tend to monopolize the literature on the brain-mind problem, and have such an inordinate influence on the young, do have these simply reacting neural dispositions—I must use this term for men who deny the concept of mind.

It is because I reject this outlook that I ask your indulgence to hear a point of view rarely put before you. I realize that to do this in a scientific institution is to put one's foolish head in a lion's den, but every point of view is entitled to an occasional ventilation. First let me say that it is the mind of *man* I am concerned with, and not with the feeble glimmerings that the anthropoid can show or the popular and cheaper rat, whose learning processes, such as they are, we commonly and unscientifically assume to be exactly the same as our own. Aristotle defined man as a rational animal, and the definition stands, even though there are irrational elements in man, and he is not continuously rational. Even the thought of the scientist is colored emotionally, and the notion that reason acts in an emotional vacuum is a high abstraction. Nevertheless, man is a rational animal. This rational element in man distinguishes him from all other animals, even though he shares their animality. Of a man it may be said, not only *what* he is but *who* he is—he has personality. His hallmarks are self-conscious activity, the faculty of abstract thought: that is, of forming concepts apart from their embodiment in particulars; he has conscience and a moral sense, the capacity to know and to seek perfection, and he enjoys the entertainment and communication of thought and feeling by articulate speech. Man is aware of his innate limitations and dependence: that is, he is imbued with natural religion.[2] This is why concentration upon the animal element in man to the exclusion of his rational element is illogical, unscientific, and intellectually disastrous. Moreover, I submit, this nature peculiar to man is not amenable to analysis by the disciplines of natural science: its study belongs to philosophy and theology.

It is from these premises, which transcend the natural sciences, that I start, and it may well be that some of you have parted company from me already. At least, I beg that you may listen to me. What I have to say will be a change from the confident, reiterated, and bleak pronouncements of those who believe that there is nothing in the human mind and in the soul than the biophysical activity of neurones; that to speak of mind is merely to talk of neurophysiology in a different language, but not to talk about something else; that philosophy, which is the study of the ultimate causes of things, is a mere linguistic exercise of which the adequate textbook is the dictionary, and that it has no basis in experience considered in abstraction.

I am not presuming to discuss this problem as a theologian or as a philosopher, which I should have no right to do, but, if you will allow me, as a physiologist, seeking to discover how far my science will take me to the frontier of the mind, whether the activities which express the mind in action can be described in the language of physiology, or require the qualitatively different language and ideas of psychology, and whether the theory of knowledge, of how we know, can be adequately discussed in the language of psychology, or needs a philosophical language—which operates on a higher level of abstraction than does that of the natural sciences and psychology. My answer is going to be that these three things: abstract or conceptual thinking, sensory experiences, and the activity of neurones—however complex the last may be—are three distinct and irreducible categories, each with its own language and concepts.

Speaking purely as a physiologist I am logically restricted to the language of physiology in which is discussed—for my present purpose —the dynamic properties of the nervous system, and these alone. I am not, *qua* physiologist, qualified to discuss human actions or human ideas. These are the field of psychologist and philosopher. I think this standpoint is absolutely essential to clear thinking, but it is not generally held, and so we find experimental psychologists and disciples of cybernetics using what I shall call "double talk" in which conceptual thinking and sensations are described in cybernetic and biophysical metaphors; while in a single paper on, let us say, consciousness, we may find the writer using the language of anatomy, physiology, psychology, and philosophy indiscriminately as though they were a single language, and a single universe of discourse were in question.

I give you a simple example from a recent monograph upon *Brain: Memory and Learning* (Ritchie Russell),[3] an excellent monograph on its clinical side, where the writer says, "The traditional reasons for separating mind from brain seem to be disappearing, and in the same way the separation of psychology from brain physiology has become somewhat artificial." Again we read, "Consciousness is simply the occurrence of cerebral alertness." From the first quotation, I submit that we must wholly dissent. As Hughlings Jackson said, "There is no more a physiology of the mind than there is a psychology of the brain," while the equating of consciousness with "cerebral alertness" is a pure tautology, and the sentence would mean as much or as little if we put it back to front and made it read, "cerebral alertness is simply the occurrence of consciousness."

What precisely is cerebral alertness? "Alertness" is not a word in the grammar of physiology. Head's term, "vigilance," is also coming into use in the same sense. Head never defined it, and its modern users do not do so. They cannot, for it is indefinable in the language of physiology in which they seek to put it. Even worse hybrids than "cerebral alertness" or "spinal vigilance" are to be found unrebuked in our literature: for example, the proposition that some cell groups in the brain stem can be the "seat of wisdom and the place of understanding." We cease to talk sense when we confuse our categories in this fashion.

As I have said, I adhere to the Aristotelian and Thomist views of man as a compound of matter and form: that is, as the union of the corporeal and the spiritual: this union in man differing from that in animals, in that the soul in man is able to exist apart from matter (cf. Maritain [4]). Yet I must not presume to discuss theology and philosophy, and I drop back for the purposes of this talk—to the somewhat more negative attitude which has been propounded by those two great scientists, Hughlings Jackson and Sherrington. In their written works, neither of these men concedes the notion of the soul as understood in the sentence I have just uttered. Indeed, by those who knew him, Jackson is said to have been an agnostic in religion, while Sherrington, at the date of his Gifford Lectures,[5] also denied the concept of an immortal soul—though I have my own doubts as to whether this was his final judgment in his last years.

However, this is not to the purpose, but what is germane is that both men explicitly rejected the notion that mind could be accepted as something within the realm of physiology or physics, or, as Sherrington put it, within the energy system. They thought the two irreducible. This issue, then, is not solely or inevitably one of religious belief. It was in both these men the expression of their conviction that mind could not be accounted for in terms of neural activity, even though the latter was a necessary condition of the former. The relationship between the two is not one of identity, it is not even a symmetrical one, for while mental action involves neural action, neural action does not always involve mental activity. Jackson adopted the doctrine of psychophysical parallelism, not as a doctrine, but as a convenient working hypothesis only, in his consideration of the nervous system. Sherrington saw nothing more strange in man considered as essentially dual than in man conceived as not dual. Sherrington has been called a Cartesian, but this was not strictly true, for Descartes confessed to no ignorance, while Sherrington's dualism was based simply upon his inability to equate brain and mind, and his rejection, or, more probably, his unawareness, of the hylomorphism of Aristotle and Aquinas.

It took some courage for both these men, that is, Jackson and Sherrington, openly to avow this outlook, for in Jackson's time the nineteenth-century positivists with their abounding confidence in the finality of science as they knew it, and their ignorant contempt of metaphysics, were firmly in the saddle, while today the amazing developments in neurophysiology that we owe to the electronic recording techniques now available have once more filled some scientists with a naïve optimism that we are almost on the brink of identifying brain with mind. Grey-Walter,[6] for example, thinks that it is only a question of careful observation and patience before we can observe as electrical discharges the thoughts of our own brains. Electrical discharges are not thoughts, and never can be the whole explanation of thought. They are not even entitled in a strictly rational terminology to be called "information" as they now frequently are called.

Let us, indeed, reduce the electrical discharge from the neurone to its proper place. It is no more than a single expression—revealed by a particular piece of apparatus—of the sum of the vital processes within the neurone, which, like any other living cell, has its own private life over and above its specific function as an impulse conductor. The neurone has its own metabolism, respiratory, and enzyme activities of which electronic recording tells us nothing directly. In other words, the electrical discharge just happens to be what we have been able to fish up out of the depths of the neurone's life processes, with the particular electronic net we are using, and we may not assume that there are no other fish in the sea.

It is refreshing in this climate of the cybernetic and biophysical concepts of a mind substitute, so eagerly pressed upon us by the "angry young men" of science, to find Adrian, in his obituary of Sherrington, written for the Royal Society, commenting as follows: "I personally believe that his neo-Cartesian doctrine of the duality of mind and brain will be eventually regarded as one of his greatest conceptual achievements. Sherrington realized," Adrian continues, "that his philosophical writings had come at a time of an unfavorable climate of opinion, but despite the misunderstandings of the critics, he continued indomitably to believe that man is both matter and spirit and that spirit is supreme." However firm one may feel in one's own convictions upon issues such as this, which have exercised the minds of men since the dawn of history, it is still comforting to feel that one is in good company in holding them, and that in due course our angry young men may grow up to realize that they have not solved the riddle of the mind and of *how* we know, despite their batteries of equipment, their mathematics, and their statistics. They may not be willing to look back upon the history of thought on this subject in times past. It would perhaps be easier for them to appreciate the difficulties of their search if they had a greater historical sense than they commonly display, and its lack may explain why some of them do not grow up. Our Peter Pans of science are always with us.

It seems to me, then, that both Jackson and Sherrington halted at the frontier between brain and mind. Insofar as they were natural scientists, concerned with nature as perceived, I think they were right to do so. This may seem an odd conclusion to those who accept that psychology and psychiatry belong to the natural sciences. Insofar as psychology deals with the physiology of the special senses, it is really physiology, but insofar as it deals with human motives and actions, I believe it does not belong to natural science, but is related to historical science. I cannot fully develop this theme at the moment, but those who wish to see its exposition will find this in the work of an English historian and metaphysician, Collingwood, in his book *The Idea of History*. He presents a case that demands

an answer, and I have summarized it in a Linacre Lecture in 1950.[7]
Thus, both Sherrington and Jackson are in a class apart from those
of the present time who deny the concept of mind and tell us that
feedback mechanisms in the cortex can know universals: that is,
are capable of conceptual thinking.

Whitehead, to whom I have already referred, in his volume of
lectures entitled *Modes of Thought,* reminds us that "Mentality
involves conceptual experience: that is, the entertainment of possibilities for ideal realization in abstraction from physical realization."
It involves the entertainment of alternatives, and "in this entertainment mentality reaches its highest development and becomes the
entertainment of the ideal, and shows itself in several species, such
as the sense of morality, the mystic sense of religion, the sense of that
delicate adjustment which is beauty, the sense of necessity for
mutual connections that is understanding, and the sense of dis-
crimination of each factor. All this produces the history of mankind
as distinct from the narrative of animal behaviors."

Yet all this, we are told, can be achieved by the activities of nerve
nets, which can know universals and thus can take over the business
of what Aristotle and Aquinas knew as the active intellect. I cannot here go into the arguments by which these cybernetic hypotheses
are illustrated. They will be found in the volume of essays entitled
Perspectives of Neuropsychiatry,[8] but I do go on to say that the
arguments are vitiated because it is perfectly clear that the writers
are profoundly unfamiliar with the history of the term universal:
a long and difficult history from Greek to medieval times. How,
indeed, should biophysicists know their Greek or scholastic philosophy, and how rash of them to have borrowed this term from a discipline not their own.

Here, again, I cannot develop this thesis, but my views upon it
may be found in *Brain,* 1953, in my Hughlings Jackson Lecture.
Yet a really distinguished name of our time attaches to the notion
that mind is no more than brain, and brain no more than physics
and mathematics can define, namely, that of Lashley, a man of great
physiological insights, but no friend of the science of ultimate
causes. Lashley expressed the view—speaking in the Hixon Symposium [9]—that "our common meeting ground is the faith to which
we all subscribe, I believe, that the phenomena of behavior and

mind are ultimately describable in the concepts of the mathematical and physical sciences." I see no grounds upon which I should be invited to join in this act of faith, as Lashley—perhaps with unconscious irony—calls it. My deepest intuitions tell me that physics and mathematics are singularly inadequate to subsume the human mind, and I surmise that it is not the mathematicians who hold this lofty notion of the powers of mathematics, but rather those biologists who think that an equation is an explanation.

As far as I can discover from my limited studies in comparative anatomy and animal physiology, there is no evidence that the neural processes in the brain of man differ in any qualitative fashion from those in lower animals that possess a nervous system. Are our reverberating circuits, our synaptic potentials, our feedback mechanisms in any sense different in quality from those of animals? They are more extensive and more complex, but not different in kind. In man as in the humble squid the nerve impulse originates and goes on its way owing to the same sodium-potassium exchange, the same order of electrical activity. Yet how different are man's conceptual powers from any other creature in the animal world. Here again I turn to Whitehead (*loc. cit.*), who says: "When we come to mankind, nature seems to have burst through another of its boundaries. The conceptual entertainment of unrealized possibility becomes a major force in human mentality. The life of a human being receives its worth, its importance, from the way in which unrealized ideals shape its purposes and tinge its actions."

Thus, the most we dare claim for neuronal circuits in action is that they integrate the ceaseless and changing flux of afferent impulses from the receptive periphery, and the constant activity within what Herrick calls the neuropil: that is, the synaptic fields of the cortex and the brain stem. They cannot and they do not provide conceptual knowledge as such, nor include any appreciation of the true universal. Here no nerve networks, however complex, can serve, for we pass out of the material world, in which alone they function, and find ourselves in an immaterial world of ideas. The bridge between the two necessarily implies the existence of nonmaterial faculties capable of effecting the transformation.

Thus it is that from sheer philosophical and psychological necessity, traditional commonsense philosophy from the early Greeks to

Aquinas has accepted the existence in man of an essential immaterial element, capable of such transformation and setting him above the merely animal. This element has been variously named as psyche, entelechy, anima, or soul. They recognized that, for the soul's functioning as an essential element in the hylomorphic human person, it needs sense data of which the brain is no more than the collecting, integrating, and distributing mechanism.

If, then, as I submit, we cannot invoke nerve nets and their activities as able to know universals, the first property of the active intellect, then we must either abandon the quest for an account of mind that shall explain its place in man's nature, or look elsewhere for it than in the concepts of physiology, physics, or mathematics. We must abandon the assumption that the human person is nothing more than a focus for the hurrying to and fro of molecules and their constituent postulated elements, or his mind no more than a bloodless dance of action potentials.

We have seen one scientist making his act of faith that ultimately the problem of mind will find its solution in the concepts of physics and mathematics. Each of us has the inalienable right to make his own act of faith, and mine is this: that these concepts are of their nature inadequate to subsume the activities of the human mind; to think that by additional knowledge they can become so is wishful thinking; and, finally, I believe that we shall have to return to the ancient concept of the soul: as an immaterial, noncorporeal part of the human person, and yet an integral part of his nature, not just some concomitant component, but something without which he is not a human person.

I subscribe to the belief that man's mind and soul are not to be wholly interpreted in terms of nerve impulses, but that there are values in his life, religious, ethical, and aesthetic, not to be comprehended in terms of action potentials. I am not ready—when I view the unceasing flux of scientific knowledge and opinion—to confine the universe within the procrustean bed of those proximate causes, different for every generation, which seem to so many scientists all that there is to be sought. We all know the nursery tale of Simple Simon who went fishing for whales in his mother's pail. I am happy not to find myself in the ranks of those scientific Simple Simons who believe that with better hooks, lines, and baits, pitched into the same pail, they will fish out from it the answer to the riddle of the soul and the mind. The whale isn't in the pail! I cannot put more succinctly and clearly my own personal view of the universe in which I have lived, and of the natural scientist's strictly limited role within it.

We live in at least two worlds, the world of the humanities and the world of science. The former cannot be reduced to the latter. Perhaps I may end by quoting from Sir Gavin de Beer a cruel parody in which we get the report of a committee of scientists upon a symphony concert. It runs as follows:

1. For considerable periods the four oboe players had nothing to do. The number should be reduced and the work more evenly spread over the whole of the concert, thus eliminating peaks of activity.

2. All the twelve first violins were playing identical notes. This seems unnecessary duplication. The staff of this section should be drastically cut: if a large volume of sound is required, it could be obtained by means of electronic amplifier apparatus.

3. Much effort was absorbed in the playing of demi-semiquavers. This seems an excessive refinement. It is recommended that all notes should be rounded up to the nearest semiquaver. If this were done it would be possible to use trainees and lower-grade operatives more extensively.

4. There seems to be too much repetition of some musical passages. Scores should be drastically pruned. No useful purpose is served by repeating on the horns a passage which has already been handled by the strings. It is estimated that if all redundant passages were eliminated, the whole concert time of two hours could be reduced to twenty minutes and there would be no need for an interval.

I should spoil this fable if I said any more.

In conclusion, I should like to guard against a misunderstanding that my remarks may cause, and, indeed, have caused in the past when I have voiced such sentiments as you have heard from me today: namely, the erroneous conclusion that I think the study of the functions of the nervous system a useless pursuit, and that I deprecate the efforts of those scientists who so ably and so tirelessly continue to seek for a fuller understanding of these functions. I yield to no one in my respect and admiration of good work and good workers in this field. Yet to cherish these sentiments need not allow one to forget the necessity of the use by anatomists and physiologists of precise and appropriate terminology, or the need for consistently used and logical principles of interpretation in scientific observation.

We have the right to ask for a terminology in physiological writings that is precise and physiological, and free from admixture—witting or unwitting—of terms from two other disciplines, philosophical or psychological, as though they belonged to the grammar of physiology; free also from the easy recourse to popular terms of no precise or constant reference, used to fill up gaps in scientific knowledge and to conceal their existence.

No reader of the relevant literature would deny that these standards of scientific language do not universally obtain today. The departure from them confuses thinking and expression and leads us unwittingly to the seeking of false goals far beyond the proper scope of natural science, and to the engendering at times of an absurd intellectual pride: and by that sin fell the angels.

References

1. A. N. Whitehead, *Modes of Thought* (London: Cambridge University Press, 1938).

2. A. J. E. Cave, *Proceedings of the Linnean Society*, London, Vol. CLXIII (1952), 1.

3. W. R. Russell, *Brain: Memory and Learning* (Oxford: Clarendon Press, 1959).

4. J. Maritain, *Introduction to Philosophy* (London: Sheed and Ward, 1946).

5. C. S. Sherrington, *Man on His Nature* (London: Cambridge University Press, 1940).

6. W. Grey-Walter, *Arch. Internaz. Stud. Neurol.*, Firenze, Vol. I (1952), 409.

7. F. M. R. Walshe, *Humanism, History and Natural Science in Medicine* (Edinburgh: E. and S. Livingstone, 1950).

8. D. Richter, *Perspectives in Neuropsychiatry* (London: H. K. Lewis, 1950).

9. K. S. Lashley, *The Problem of Serial Order in Behavior* (New York: John Wiley & Sons, Inc., 1951).

CHAPTER 9

Is the Concept

of Self Necessary?

GORDON ALLPORT

We come now to a question that is pivotal for the psychology of growth: Is the concept of *self* necessary? While there is a vast literature in philosophy devoted to this issue from the points of view of ontology, epistemology, and axiology, let us for the time being bypass such discussions. For it is entirely conceivable that a concept useful to philosophy or theology may turn out to be merely an impediment in the path of psychological progress.

Since the time of Wundt, the central objection of psychology to *self*, and also to *soul*, has been that the concept seems question-begging. It is temptingly easy to assign functions that are not fully understood to a mysterious central agency, and then to declare that "it" performs in such a way as to unify the personality and maintain its integrity. Wundt, aware of this peril, declared boldly for "a psychology without a soul." It was not that he necessarily denied philosophical or theological postulates, but that he felt psychology as science would be handicapped by the *petitio principii* implied in the concept. For half a century few psychologists other than Thomists have resisted Wundt's reasoning or his example.[1] Indeed we may say that for two generations psychologists have tried every conceivable way of accounting for the integration, organization, and striving of the human person without having recourse to the postulate of a self.

In very recent years the tide has turned. Perhaps without being fully aware of the historical situation, many psychologists have commenced to embrace what two decades ago would have been considered a heresy. They have reintroduced self and ego unashamedly and, as if to make up for lost time, have employed ancillary concepts such

Gordon Allport, *Becoming* (New Haven, Conn.: Yale University Press, 1955), pp. 36-62.

as *self-image, self-actualization, self-affirmation, phenomenal ego, ego-involvement, ego-striving,* and many other hyphenated elaborations which to experimental positivism still have a slight flavor of scientific obscenity.

We should note in passing that Freud played a leading, if unintentional role, in preserving the concept of ego from total obliteration throughout two generations of strenuous positivism. His own use of the term, to be sure, shifted. At first he spoke of assertive and aggressive ego-instincts (in a Nietzschean sense); later for Freud the ego became a rational, though passive, agency, whose duty it was to reconcile as best it could through planning or defense the conflicting pressures of the instincts, of conscience, and of the outer environment. With the core concept thus preserved, even with stringently limited meanings, it was easier for dynamically inclined psychologists, including the neo-Freudians, to enlarge the properties of the ego, making it a far more active and important agent than it was in the hands of Freud.

There still remains, however, the danger that Wundt wished to avoid, namely that the ego may be regarded as a *deus ex machina,* invoked to reassemble the dismembered parts of the throbbing psychic machine after positivism has failed to do so. The situation today seems to be that many psychologists who first fit personality to an external set of coordinates are dissatisfied with the result. They therefore reinvent the ego because they find no coherence among the measures yielded by positivistic analysis. But unfortunately positivism and ego-theory do not go well together. Bergson has criticized the use of "ego" in this face-saving way by likening the process to the dilemma of an artist. An artist, he says, may wish to represent Paris— just as a psychologist may wish to represent personality. But all he can do with the limitations of his medium is to draw this and then that angle of the whole. To each sketch he applies the label "Paris," hoping somehow that the sections he has ablated will magically reconstitute the whole.[2] Similarly in psychology we have a state of affairs where empiricists, finding that they have gone as far as possible with analytic tools and being dissatisfied with the product, resort as did their predecessors to some concept of self in order to represent, however inadequately, the coherence, unity, and purposiveness they know they have lost in their fragmentary representations.

I greatly fear that the lazy tendency to employ self or ego as a factotum to repair the ravages of positivism may do more harm than good. It is, of course, significant that so many contemporary psychologists feel forced to take this step, even though for the most part their work represents no theoretical gain over nineteenth-century usage. Positivism will continue to resent the intrusion, and will, with some justification, accuse today's resurgent self-psychologists of obscurantism.

The problem then becomes how to approach the phenomena that have led to a revival of the self-concept in a manner that will advance rather than retard scientific progress.

A possible clue to the solution, so far as psychology is concerned, lies in a statement made by Alfred Adler. "What is frequently labeled 'the ego,'" he writes, "is nothing more than the style of the individual." [3] Life-style to Adler had a deep and important meaning. He is saying that if psychology could give us a full and complete account of life-style, it would automatically include all phenomena now referred somewhat vaguely to a self or an ego. In other words, a wholly adequate psychology of growth would discover all of the activities and all of the interrelations in life, which are now either neglected or consigned to an ego that looks suspiciously like a homunculus.

The first thing an adequate psychology of growth should do is to draw a distinction between what are matters of *importance* to the individual and what are, as Whitehead would say, merely matters of *fact* to him; that is, between what he feels to be vital and central in becoming and what belongs to the periphery of his being.

Many facets of our life-style are not ordinarily felt to have strong personal relevance. Each of us, for example, has innumerable tribal habits that mark our life-style but are nothing more than opportunistic modes of adjusting. The same holds true for many of our physiological habits. We keep to the right in traffic, obey the rules of etiquette, and make countless unconscious or semiconscious adjustments, all of which characterize our life-style but are not *propriate*, that is, not really central to our sense of existence. Consider, for example, the English language habits that envelop our thinking and communication. Nothing could be of more pervasive influence in our lives than the store of concepts available to us in our ancestral tongue and the frames of discourse under which our social contacts proceed.

And yet the use of English is ordinarily felt to be quite peripheral to the core of our existence. It would not be so if some foreign invader should forbid us to use our native language. At such a time our vocabulary and accent and our freedom to employ them would become very precious and involved with our sense of self. So it is with the myriad of social and physiological habits we have developed that are never, unless interfered with, regarded as essential to our existence as a separate being.

Personality includes these habits and skills, frames of reference, matters of fact and cultural values, that seldom or never seem warm and important. But personality includes what is warm and important also—all the regions of our life that we regard as peculiarly ours, and which for the time being I suggest we call the *proprium*. The proprium includes all aspects of personality that make for inward unity.

Psychologists who allow for the proprium use both the term "self" and "ego"—often interchangeably; and both terms are defined with varying degrees of narrowness or of comprehensiveness. Whatever name we use for it, this sense of what is "peculiarly ours" merits close scrutiny. The principal functions and properties of the proprium need to be distinguished.

To this end William James over sixty years ago proposed a simple taxonomic scheme.[4] There are, he maintained, two possible orders of self: an empirical self (the *Me*) and a knowing self (the *I*). Three subsidiary types comprise the empirical Me: the material self, the social self, and the spiritual self. Within this simple framework he fits his famous and subtle description of the various states of mind that are "peculiarly ours." His scheme, however, viewed in the perspective of modern psychoanalytic and experimental research, seems scarcely adequate. In particular it lacks the full psychodynamic flavor of modern thinking. With some trepidation, therefore, I offer what I hope is an improved outline for analyzing the propriate aspects of personality. Later we shall return to the question, Is the concept of *self* necessary?

The Proprium

1. BODILY SENSE. The first aspect we encounter is the bodily *me*. It seems to be composed of streams of sensations that arise within the organism—from viscera, muscles, tendons, joints, vestibular

canals, and other regions of the body. The technical name for the bodily sense is *coenesthesis*. Usually this sensory stream is experienced dimly; often we are totally unaware of it. At times, however, it is well configurated in consciousness in the exhilaration that accompanies physical exercise, or in moments of sensory delight or pain. The infant, apparently, does not know that such experiences are "his." But they surely form a necessary foundation for his emerging sense of self. The baby who at first cries from unlocalized discomfort will, in the course of growth, show progressive ability to identify the distress as his own.

The bodily sense remains a lifelong anchor for our self-awareness, though it never alone accounts for the entire sense of self, probably not even in the young child who has his memories, social cues, and strivings to help in the definition. Psychologists have paid a great deal of attention, however, to this particular component of self-awareness, rather more than to other equally important ingredients. One special line of investigation has been surprisingly popular: the attempt to locate self in relation to specific bodily sensations. When asked, some people will say that they *feel* the self in their right hands, or in the viscera. Most, however, seem to agree with Claparède that a center midway between the eyes, slightly behind them within the head, is the focus. It is from this cyclopean eye that we estimate what lies before and behind ourselves, to the right or left, and above and below. Here, phenomenologically speaking, is the locus of the ego.[5] Interesting as this type of work may be, it represents little more than the discovery that various sensory elements in the coenesthetic stream or various inferences drawn from sensory experience may for certain people at certain times be especially prominent.

How very intimate (propriate) the bodily sense is can be seen by performing a little experiment in your imagination. Think first of swallowing the saliva in your mouth, or do so. Then imagine expectorating it into a tumbler and drinking it! What seemed natural and "mine" suddenly becomes disgusting and alien. Or picture yourself sucking blood from a prick in your finger; then imagine sucking blood from a bandage around your finger! What I perceive as belonging intimately to my body is warm and welcome; what I perceive as separate from my body becomes, in the twinkling of an eye, cold and foreign.

Certainly organic sensations, their localization and recognition, composing as they do the bodily *me*, are a core of becoming. But it would be a serious mistake to think, as some writers do, that they alone account for our sense of what is "peculiarly ours."

2. SELF-IDENTITY. Today I remember some of my thoughts of yesterday; and tomorrow I shall remember some of my thoughts of both yesterday and today; and I am subjectively certain that they are the thoughts of the same person. In this situation, no doubt, the organic continuity of the neuromuscular system is the leading factor. Yet the process involves more than reminiscence made possible by our retentive nerves. The young infant has retentive capacity during the first months of life but in all probability no sense of self-identity. This sense seems to grow gradually, partly as a result of being clothed and named, and otherwise marked off from the surrounding environment. Social interaction is an important factor. It is the actions of the other to which he differentially adjusts that force upon a child the realization that he is not the other, but a being in his own right. The difficulty of developing self-identity in childhood is shown by the ease with which a child depersonalizes himself in play and in speech.[6] Until the age of four or five we have good reason to believe that as perceived by the child personal identity is unstable. Beginning at about this age, however, it becomes the surest attest a human being has of his own existence.

3. EGO-ENHANCEMENT. We come now to the most notorious property of the proprium, to its unabashed self-seeking.[7] Scores of writers have featured this clamorous trait in human personality. It is tied to the need for survival, for it is easy to see that we are endowed by nature with the impulses of self-assertion and with the emotions of self-satisfaction and pride. Our language is laden with evidence. The commonest compound of self is *selfish*, and of ego *egoism*. Pride, humiliation, self-esteem, narcissism are such prominent factors that when we speak of ego or self we often have in mind only this aspect of personality. And yet, self-love may be prominent in our natures without necessarily being sovereign. The proprium, as we shall see, has other facets and functions.

4. EGO-EXTENSION. The three facets we have discussed—coenesthesis, self-identity, ego-enhancement—are relatively early developments

in personality, characterizing the whole of the child's proprium. Their solicitations have a heavily biological quality and seem to be contained within the organism itself. But soon the process of learning brings with it a high regard for possessions, for loved objects, and later, for ideal causes and loyalties. We are speaking here of whatever objects a person calls "mine." They must at the same time be objects of *importance*, for sometimes our sense of "having" has no affective tone and hence no place in the proprium. A child, however, who identifies with his parent is definitely extending his sense of self, as he does likewise through his love for pets, dolls, or other possessions, animate or inanimate.

As we grow older, we identify with groups, neighborhood, and nation as well as with possessions, clothes, home. They become matters of importance to us in a sense that other people's families, nations, or possessions are not. Later in life the process of extension may go to great lengths, through the development of loyalties and of interests focused on abstractions and on moral and religious values. Indeed, a mark of maturity seems to be the range and extent of one's feeling of self-involvement in abstract ideals.

5. RATIONAL AGENT. The ego, according to Freud, has the task of keeping the organism as a whole in touch with reality, of intermediating between unconscious impulses and the outer world. Often the rational ego can do little else than invent and employ defenses to forestall or diminish anxiety. These protective devices shape the development of personality to an extent unrealized sixty years ago. It is thanks to Freud that we understand the strategies of denial, repression, displacement, reaction formation, rationalization, and the like better than did our ancestors.

We have become so convinced of the validity of these defense mechanisms, and so impressed with their frequency of operation, that we are inclined to forget that the rational functioning of the proprium is capable also of yielding true solutions, appropriate adjustments, accurate planning, and a relatively faultless solving of the equations of life.

Many philosophers, dating as far back as Boethius in the sixth century, have seen the rational nature of personality as its most distinctive property. (*Persona est substantia individua rationalis naturae.*) It may seem odd to credit Freud, the supreme irrationalist of our age, with helping the Thomists preserve for psychology the emphasis upon the ego as the rational agent in personality, but such is the case. For whether the ego reasons or merely rationalizes, it has the property of synthesizing inner needs and outer reality. Freud and the Thomists have not let us forget this fact, and have thus made it easier for modern cognitive theories to deal with this central function of the proprium.

6. SELF-IMAGE. A propriate function of special interest today is the self-image, or as some writers call it, the phenomenal self. Present-day therapy is chiefly devoted to leading the patient to examine, correct, or expand this self-image. The image has two aspects: the way the patient regards his present abilities, status, and roles; and what he would like to become, his *aspirations* for himself. The latter aspect, which Karen Horney calls the "idealized self-image," [8] is of especial importance in therapy. On the one hand it may be compulsive, conpensatory, and unrealistic, blinding its possessor to his true situation in life. On the other hand, it may be an insightful cognitive map, closely geared to reality and defining a wholesome ambition. The ideal self-image is the imaginative aspect of the proprium, and whether accurate or distorted, attainable or unattainable, it plots a course by which much propriate movement is guided and therapeutic progress achieved.

There are, of course, many forms of becoming that require no self-image, including automatic cultural learning and our whole repertoire of opportunistic adjustments to our environment. Yet there is also much growth that takes place only with the aid of, and because of, a self-image. This image helps us bring our view of the present into line with our view of the future. Fortunately the dynamic importance of the self-image is more widely recognized in psychology today than formerly.

7. PROPRIATE STRIVING. We come now to the nature of motivation. Unfortunately we often fail to distinguish between propriate and peripheral motives. The reason is that at the rudimentary levels of becoming, which up to now have been the chief levels investigated, it *is* the impulses and drives, the immediate satisfaction and tension reduction, that are the determinants of conduct. Hence a psychology of opportunistic adjustment seems basic and adequate, especially to

psychologists accustomed to working with animals. At low levels of behavior the familiar formula of drives and their conditioning appears to suffice. But as soon as the personality enters the stage of ego-extension, and develops a self-image with visions of self-perfection, we are, I think, forced to postulate motives of a different order, motives that reflect propriate striving. Within experimental psychology itself there is now plenty of evidence that conduct that is "ego involved" (propriate) differs markedly from behavior that is not.[9]

Many psychologists disregard this evidence. They wish to maintain a single theory of motivation consistent with their presuppositions. Their preferred formula is in terms of drive and conditioned drive. Drive is viewed as a peripherally instigated activity. The resultant response is simply reactive, persisting only until the instigator is removed and the tension, created by the drive, lessened. Seeking always a parsimony of assumptions, this view therefore holds that motivation entails one and only one inherent property of the organism: a disposition to act, by instinct or by learning, in such a way that the organism will as efficiently as possible reduce the discomfort of tension. Motivation is regarded as a state of tenseness that leads us to seek equilibrium, rest, adjustment, satisfaction, or homeostasis. From this point of view personality is nothing more than our habitual modes of reducing tension. This formulation, of course, is wholly consistent with empiricism's initial presupposition that man is by nature a passive being, capable only of receiving impressions from, and responding to, external goads.

The contrary view holds that this formula, while applicable to segmental and opportunistic adjustments, falls short of representing the nature of propriate striving. It points out that the characteristic feature of such striving is its resistance to equilibrium: tension is maintained rather than reduced.

In his autobiography Raold Amundsen tells how from the age of fifteen he had one dominant passion—to become a polar explorer. The obstacles seemed insurmountable, and all through his life the temptations to reduce the tensions engendered were great. But the propriate striving persisted. While he welcomed each success, it acted to raise his level of aspiration, to maintain an over-all commitment. Having sailed the Northwest Passage, he embarked upon the painful project that led to the discovery of the South Pole. Having discovered the South Pole, he planned for years, against extreme discouragement, to fly over the North Pole, a task he finally accomplished. But his commitment never wavered until at the end he lost his life in attempting to rescue a less gifted explorer, Nobile, from death in the Arctic. Not only did he maintain one style of life, without ceasing, but this central commitment enabled him to withstand the temptation to reduce the segmental tensions continually engendered by fatigue, hunger, ridicule, and danger.[10]

Here we see the issue squarely. A psychology that regards motivation exclusively in terms of drives and conditioned drives is likely to stammer and grow vague when confronted by those aspects of personality—of every personality—that resemble Amundsen's propriate striving. While most of us are less distinguished than he in our achievements, we too have insatiable interests. Only in a very superficial way can these interests be dealt with in terms of tension reduction. Many writers past and present have recognized this fact and have postulated some principles of an exactly opposite order. One thinks in this connection of Spinoza's concept of conatus, or the tendency of an individual to persist, against obstacles, in his own style of being. One thinks of Goldstein's doctrine of *self-actualization*, used also by Maslow and others, or McDougall's *self-regarding* sentiment. And one thinks too of those modern Freudians who feel the need for endowing the ego not only with a rational and rationalizing ability but with a tendency to maintain its own system of productive interests, in spite of the passing solicitations of impulse and environmental instigation. Indeed the fortified ego, as described by neo-Freudians, is able to act contrary to the usual course of opportunistic, tension-reducing adaptation.

Propriate striving distinguishes itself from other forms of motivation in that, however beset by conflicts, it makes for unification of personality. There is evidence that the lives of mental patients are marked by the proliferation of unrelated subsystems, and by the loss of more homogeneous systems of motivation.[11] When the individual is dominated by segmental drives, by compulsions, or by the winds of circumstance, he has lost the integrity that comes only from maintaining major directions of striving. The possession of long-range goals, regarded as central to one's personal existence, distinguishes the human being from the animal, the adult from the child, and in many cases the healthy personality from the sick.

Striving, it is apparent, always has a future reference. As a matter of fact, a great many states of mind are adequately described only in terms of their futurity. Along with *striving*, we may mention *interest*, *tendency*, *disposition*, *expectation*, *planning*, *problem solving*, and *intention*. While not all future-directedness is phenomenally propriate, it all requires a type of psychology that transcends the prevalent tendency to explain mental states exclusively in terms of past occurrences. People, it seems, are busy leading their lives into the future, whereas psychology, for the most part, is busy tracing them into the past.

8. THE KNOWER. Now that we have isolated these various propriate functions—all of which we regard as peculiarly ours—the question arises whether we are yet at an end. Do we not have in addition a cognizing self—a knower, that transcends all other functions of the proprium and holds them in view? In a famous passage, William James wrestles with this question, and concludes that we have not. There is, he thinks, no such thing as a substantive self distinguishable from the sum total, or stream, of experiences. Each moment of consciousness, he says, appropriates each previous moment, and the knower is thus somehow embedded in what is known. "The thoughts themselves are the thinker." [12]

Opponents of James argue that no mere series of experiences can possibly turn themselves into an awareness of that series as a unit. Nor can "passing thoughts" possibly regard themselves as important or interesting. To whom is the series important or interesting if not to *me*? I am the ultimate monitor. The self as *knower* emerges as a final and inescapable postulate.

It is interesting to ask why James balked at admitting a knowing self after he had so lavishly admitted to psychology with his full approval material, social, and spiritual selves. The reason may well have been (and the reason would be valid today) that one who laboriously strives to depict the nature of propriate functions on an empirical level, hoping thereby to enrich the science of psychology with a discriminating analysis of self, is not anxious to risk a return to the homunculus theory by introducing a synthesizer, or a self of selves.

To be sure, the danger that abuse might follow the admission of a substantive knower into the science of psychology is no reason to avoid this step if it is logically required. Some philosophers, including Kant, insist that the pure or transcendental ego is separable from the empirical ego (that is, from any of the propriate states thus far mentioned).[13] Those who hold that the knowing itself is not (as James argued) merely an aspect of the self as known, but is "pure" and "transcendental," argue, as Kant does, that the texture of knowledge is quite different in the two cases. Our cognition of our knowing self is always indirect, of the order of a presupposition. On the other hand, all features of the *empirical self* are known directly, through acquaintance, as any object is known which falls into time and space categories.[14]

While their metaphysical positions are directly opposed, both Kant and James agree with their illustrious predecessor, Descartes, that the knowing function is a vital attribute of the self however defined. For our present purpose this is the point to bear in mind.

We not only know *things*, but we know (that is, are acquainted with) the empirical features of our own proprium. It is I who have bodily sensations, I who recognize my self-identity from day to day; I who note and reflect upon my self-assertion, self-extension, my own rationalizations, as well as upon my interests and strivings. When I thus think about my own propriate functions, I am likely to perceive their essential togetherness, and feel them intimately bound in some way to the knowing function itself.

Since such knowing is, beyond any shadow of doubt, a state that is peculiarly ours, we admit it as the eighth clear function of the proprium. (In other words, as an eighth valid meaning of "self" or "ego.") But it is surely one of nature's perversities that so central a function should be so little understood by science, and should remain a perpetual bone of contention among philosophers. Many, like Kant, set this function (the "pure ego") aside as something qualitatively apart from other propriate functions (the latter being assigned to the "empirical me"). Others, like James, say that the ego *qua* knower is somehow contained within the ego *qua* known. Still others, personalistically inclined, find it necessary to postulate a single self as knower, thinker, feeler, and doer—all in one blended unit of a sort that guarantees the continuance of all becoming.[15]

We return now to our unanswered question: Is the concept of self necessary in the psychology of personality? Our answer cannot be categorical since all depends upon the particular usage of "self" that is proposed. Certainly all legitimate phenomena that have been, and can be ascribed, to the self or ego must be admitted as data indispensable to a psychology of personal becoming. All eight functions of the "proprium" (our temporary neutral term for central interlocking operations of personality) must be admitted and included. In particular the unifying act of perceiving and knowing (of comprehending propriate states as belonging together and belonging to me) must be fully admitted.

At the same time, the danger we have several times warned against is very real: that a homunculus may creep into our discussions of personality, and be expected to solve all our problems without in reality solving any. Thus, if we ask, "What determines our moral conduct?" the answer may be, "The self does it." Or, if we pose the problem of choice, we say, "The self chooses." Such question-begging would immeasurably weaken the scientific study of personality by providing an illegitimate regressus. There are, to be sure, ultimate problems of philosophy and of theology that psychology cannot even attempt to solve, and for the solution of such problems "self" in some restricted and technical meaning may be a necessity.

But so far as psychology is concerned, our position, in brief, is this: all psychological functions commonly ascribed to a self or ego must be admitted as data in the scientific study of personality. These functions are not, however, coextensive with personality as a whole. They are rather the special aspects of personality that have to do with warmth, with unity, with a sense of personal importance. In this exposition I have called them "propriate" functions. If the reader prefers, he may call them self-functions, and in this sense self may be said to be a necessary psychological concept. What is unnecessary and inadmissible is a self (or soul) that is said to perform acts, to solve problems, to steer conduct, in a transpsychological manner, inaccessible to psychological analysis.

Once again we refer to Adler's contention that an adequate psychology of life-style would in effect dispense with the need for a separate psychology of the ego. I believe Adler's position, though unelaborated, is essentially the same as the one here advocated. An adequate psychology would in effect *be* a psychology of the ego. It would deal fully and fairly with propriate functions. Indeed, everyone would assume that psychology was talking about self-functions, unless it was expressly stated that peripheral, opportunistic, or actuarial events were under discussion. But as matters stand today, with so much of psychology preoccupied (as was Hume) with bits and pieces of experience, or else with generalized mathematical equations, it becomes necessary for the few psychologists who are concerned with propriate functions to specify in their discourse that they are dealing with them. If the horizons of psychology were more spacious than they are, I venture to suggest that theories of personality would not need the concept of self or of ego except in certain compound forms, such as *self-knowledge, self-image, ego-enhancement, ego-extension.*

The Fusion of Propriate Functions

In distinguishing various functions of the proprium—bodily sense, self-identity, ego-enhancement, ego-extension, rational activity, self-image, propriate striving, and knowing—I hope I have not implied that any concrete instance of becoming may be explained by one and only one function. The fact is that at every stage of becoming a fusion of these functions is involved.

Take, for example, the acquiring of *self-insight* or *self-objectification,* one of the most important characteristics of maturity in personality. Here obviously is a condition where the knowing aspect of the proprium is engaged. It catches a glimpse of the rational processes, including those devoted to ego-defensiveness. At the same time the rational processes are evaluated in terms of the sense of importance (propriate striving). The self-image and the ideals of resident in the extended ego play their part. It is not unlikely that the tangled process will arouse one's sense of humor, if one has it. Humor is a remarkable gift of perspective by which the knowing function of a mature person recognizes disproportions and absurdities within the proprium in the course of its encounters with the world.

In this particular case, the knowing function receives heavy emphasis, for the illustration happens to deal with the *cognition* of propriate states. But in other instances, the rational (or rationalizing) function may be more deeply involved, as in acts of insightful problem solving, where the person is not primarily self-conscious but is simply finding a solution to some riddle of importance to him. In other instances, self-assertion, acts of love, or carrying through a propriate purpose are in the ascendancy. But in all cases the functions are inextricably interlocked. The locus of the act is the person.

One common error in psychology is to center attention upon only one propriate function and attribute to it all, or nearly all, of the process of becoming. Thus Nietzscheans would fix upon the lust for power (self-assertion), Thomists upon the rational function, psychoanalysis upon the striving (particularly that portion that is not accessible to the knowing function). Some psychotherapists are occupied chiefly with the self-image (what the knowing function makes of the remainder of the proprium). We have already noted that some psychologists are concerned only with the coenesthetic components. Scholars interested in culture and personality deal primarily with the function of ego-extension, for their task is to account for the process of socialization. The truth of the matter is that all functions are important, and to center upon a portion of becoming that depends upon one function alone is to deliver a one-sided picture of growth in human personality.

But it is better to deal with propriate funcitons one-sidedly than not to deal with them at all. We have already seen that a large part of modern psychology, following the lead of Hume, denies that self or ego, in any sense whatsoever, forms a problem for the psychology of becoming. Habits and perceptions are treated as though they had separate existences, or else only the most inadequate "glue" is provided to account for the continuity and structure in personal development.

Critique

Let us consider one suggestion made by psychologists who decline to recognize any special problem in accounting for propriate activity. The suggestion is that the concept of *emotion* suffices to our need. In place of "ego-involved acts" is it not sufficient to speak merely of "emotional acts?" [16] It is argued that psychology has always admitted more warmth and more self-consciousness under conditions of emotional arousal. Therefore in speaking of propriate versus peripheral behavior, we may be dealing merely with emotional versus nonemotional behavior.

The proposal, I fear, is far from adequate. Propriate states are by no means always agitated states. A sense of worthwhileness, of interest, of importance is not what we ordinarily call emotion. Each lasting sentiment in personality is a propriate state, but only on occasion does a sentiment erupt into emotion. An Amundsen planning for decades to fly over the North Pole is constantly ego-involved but rarely agitated. It is true that all propriate striving is felt to be important and laden with value—in this sense it is an affective state; but the sense of warmth and importance makes for efficiency and unity, not for the disruption and distintegration that often accompany emotional excitement.

There is considerable experimental evidence that bears on this matter. In the course of learning, for example, we know that high intensities of emotional excitement tend to narrow the field of learning, to reduce the effectiveness of cues, and to diminish the range of similarity and transfer.[17] Propriate involvement, on the other hand, increases the breadth of learning, of transfer effects, as well as the ability of the individual to perceive and organize all relevant information into the system as a whole.[18] Thus, the experimental effects of emotionality and of propriate involvement may be precisely opposite. We cannot, therefore, permit the two conditions to be confused in our theory of becoming.

The distinction is apparent in yet another way. We sometimes experience emotions without viewing them as having appreciable personal significance. A loud noise may evoke startle and bring in its train widespread visceral disturbance, without at the same time engaging to any appreciable extent our propriate functions. Pain suffered in a dentist chair is intense but may be less ego-involved than, let us say, a mild reproach from a friend. According to Bettelheim the most acute suffering in concentration camps, with its many poignant emotions, was often regarded as ego-alien, as something happening to one's body but not to one's person.[19] Even if we doubt that intense emotional experience can ever be totally devoid of a sense of self-involvement, we must at least concede that there is far from perfect correlation between them, and that therefore we should regard emotionality and the proprium as separable phenomena.

I have pressed this point because I wish to show that an adequate psychology of becoming cannot be written exclusively in terms of stimulus, emotional excitement, association, and response. It requires subjective and inner principles of organization of the sort frequently designated by the terms self or ego. Whether these labels are employed is less important than that the principles they imply be fully admitted in accounting for the development of personality.

The position I have attemped to defend is vulnerable to attack from precisely the opposite direction. Personalists will say that at every step our exposition has *assumed* the existence of a self or ego. Is not "proprium" a mere synonym for self? When one speaks of person, individual, life-style, is not the self lurking therein? Can there be continuity in becoming without a continuing substance? When we speak of a sense of importance, who is the appraiser, if not the self?

These questions are clearly legitimate, and in a limited sense the implied accusation is justified. If we are accused of offering only a somewhat novel and differentiated doctrine of the self, we shall not deny the charge—provided the following novelties (as contrasted with most personalistic conceptions) are noted:

1. Person and personality are far broader conceptions than proprium. As we shall soon see, personality includes besides propriate functions a wide variety of adjustive activities, characteristic of the person and rendering the human organism the unique unit that it is. Many doctrines of self are so inclusive as to blur these distinctions.

2. Our position is that at birth we start with an organism (or individual) which develops unique modes of adjusting to and mastering the environment; these modes constitute personality. The earlier modes cannot involve propriate functions, though by the age of two or three they begin to do so.

3. The proprium is not a thing; it is not separable from the person as a whole. Above all it is not a homunculus. Proprium is a term intended to cover those functions that make for the peculiar unity and distinctiveness of personality, and at the same time seem to the knowing function to be subjectively intimate and important. The person is thus an individual organism capable of propriate activities, including, of course, the function of knowing.

4. The proprium develops in time. While we may grant that

each human being has a disposition (capacity) to develop a proprium, we stress the interlocking and emergent aspects of development rather than an unchanging nuclear self. Learning and socialization are major problems in the psychological view of becoming, whereas they recede into vagueness in most personalistic philosophies.

5. It is entirely conceivable, indeed probable, that an acceptable philosophy or theology of the person may logically require the concept of self to indicate the considerations of value and ontology important to a system of thought. It is partly to allow for this contingency that we have introduced the concept of proprium. It is a device to avoid trespassing upon, and confusion with, philosophical concepts that deal with somewhat different matters than does the psychological study of personality.

References

1. Until about 1890 certain American writers, including Dewey, Royce, James, continued to regard self as a necessary concept. They felt that the analytical concepts of the new psychology lost the manifest unity of mental functioning, but for the ensuing fifty years very few American psychologists made use of it. Mary Whiton Calkins being a distinguished exception; and none employed "soul." See G. W. Allport, "The Ego in Contemporary Psychology," *Psychological Review*, Vol. L (1943), 451-478; reprinted in *The Nature of Personality: Selected Papers* (Cambridge: Addison-Wesley Publishing Co., Inc., 1950).

2. H. Bergson, *Introduction to Metaphysics* (New York: G. P. Putnam's Sons, 1912), p. 30.

3. A. Adler, "The Fundamental Views of Individual Psychology," *International Journal of Individual Psychology*, Vol. I (1935), 5-8.

4. *Principles of Psychology* (New York: Holt, Rinehart & Winston, Inc., 1890), Vol. I, chap. x.

5. E. Claparède, "Note sur la localisation du moi," *Archives de psychologie*, Vol. XIX (1924), 172-182. Another school of thought has placed considerable stress upon the total body-image. Its variations are said to mark changes in the course of development. Schilder, for example, points out that in experience of hate the body-image itself contracts; in experience of love it expands, and even seems phenomenally to include other beings. See P. Schilder, *The Image and Appearance of the Human Body*, Psyche Monograph (London: K. Paul, Trench, Trubner Co., 1935), p. 353.

6. Cf. G. W. Allport, *Personality. A Psychological Interpretation* (New York: Holt, Rinehart & Winston, Inc., 1937), pp. 159-165.

7. The term "proprium" was a favorite of Emanuel Swedenborg. He used it, however, in the narrow sense of selfishness and pride, a meaning that corresponds here fairly closely to "ego-enhancement." See his *Proprium*, with an introduction by John Bigelow (New York: New Church Board of Publication, 1907). I am grateful to Professor Howard D. Spoerl for his clarification of this matter.

8. Karen Horney, *Neurosis and Human Growth: The Struggle Toward Self-realization* (New York: W. W. Norton & Company, Inc., 1950).

9. Cf. G. W. Allport, "The Ego in Contemporary Psychology," *Psychological Review*, Vol. L (1943), 451-478.

10. Raold Amundsen, *My Life as an Explorer* (Garden City, N. Y.: Doubleday & Company, Inc., 1928).

11. Cf. L. McQuitty, "A Measure of Personality Integration in Relation to the Concept of the Self," *Journal of Personality*, Vol. XVIII (1950), 461-482.

12. *Principles of Psychology*, Vol. I, chap. x.

13. Kant's position on this matter is summarized in the following pronouncement: "One may therefore say of the thinking I (the soul), which represents itself as substance, simple, numerically identical in all time, and as the correlative of all existence, from which in fact all other existence must be concluded, that it *does not know itself through the categories*, but knows the *categories* only, and through them all objects, in the absolute unity of apperception, *that is through itself.*" *Critique of Pure Reason*, trans. M. Müller (London: Macmillan & Co., Ltd., 1881), p. 347.

14. For a fuller discussion of this matter see F. R. Tennant, *Philosophical Theology* (London: Cambridge University Press, 1928), Vol. I, chap. v.

15. P. A. Bertocci, "The Psychological Self, the Ego, and Personality," *Psychological Review*, Vol. LII (1945), 91-99.

16. O. H. Mowrer, "The Law of Effect and Ego Psychology," *Psychological Review*, Vol. LIII (1946), 321-334.

17. D. A. Prescott, *Emotion and the Educative Process* (Washington, D.C.: American Council on Education, 1938).

18. G. W. Allport, "The Ego in Contemporary Psychology," *Psychological Review*, Vol. L (1943), 451-478.

19. B. Bettelheim, "The Individual and Mass Behavior in Extreme Situations," *Journal of Abnormal and Social Psychology*, Vol. XXXVIII (1943), 417-452.

PART FIVE

Sources

# of Religion

Religion is generally understood as rooted in spirit itself or in a belief in spirit. The whence and why of such a universal phenomenon continue to intrigue specialists in a number of fields who often feel that *their* findings have the answer to many of the ageless questions that surround this subject. The guesses, the speculations—Frazer, Tylor, Comte, Freud, Durkheim, Feuerbach, and Marx—have been going on long enough to permit Henri de Lubac's summary in terms of the most popular *fallacies*. De Lubac is not alone in his somewhat negative survey of the field. Milton Yinger, whose book *Religion, Society, and the Individual* has a helpful classification of theories about the origin of religion, writes:

> It is now generally agreed that a scientific theory of the origin of religion is impossible. It seems clear that religious beliefs and practices reach back in the history of man tens of thousands of years; and the story of their origins has to be built out of the flimsiest of archaeological, philological, and anthropological evidence, filled out with psychological and sociological guesses.*

Although de Lubac, one of France's greatest theologians and a man of wide-ranging mind, demonstrates well the fallacies involved in a too-facile dogmatizing on the origins of religion, the opinions he discusses undoubtedly deserve attention for the insights they give on this problem. Monotheists, Christians, cannot afford to ignore them completely. Religion, even though of the spirit, and further, for many, rooted in revelation, still remains a human activity, and

* Milton Yinger, *Religion, Society, and the Individual* (New York: The Macmillan Company, 1957), p. 51.

the effect of man's psychology, history, economics, government, racial background, and the like on his religion provides material for much disturbing thought. For example: Does religion ever perform the function of explanation about the universe, or is this a usurpation by religion? To what degree are fear, family, and especially father involved in religious faith? Does the childhood feeling of helplessness persist into adulthood and account for the persistence of religious beliefs in grown men? Is religion more rootedly rational or emotional? What does atheism mean to the monotheist? Is it in any way a commentary on monotheism itself?

CHAPTER 10

The Origin of Religion

HENRI DE LUBAC

So many are the theories about the origin of religion that a considerable volume might be written on the subject. But a very few lines would do equally well, for all we know of the matter, with scientific certainty, amounts in reality to very little indeed. There is no room here to review the numerous theories—confused jumbles, for the most part, of observations and hypotheses, explanations and judgments of value—that have been propounded in the course of the last hundred years: we have had naturism, for instance, manism, and totemism; animism and preanimism; magism and premagism; neonaturism, sociologism and how many others! These various systems all tend to overlap, or else split up into innumerable combinations; the most prominent have had their short-lived triumph, their subsequent decline, and their spasmodic renewals in rejuvenated form. What will be more helpful here, after calling attention to the fallacies common to most of these theories, will be to indicate shortly the principal conclusions—and these, incidentally, are for the most part negative—that in the light of our present knowledge we are entitled to draw.

Common Fallacies

The Psychic Activity of Primitive Man

One first fallacy, important to mention because it is still very common, is that it is possible to know what primitive man really felt about religion.

The two chief roads leading back to our origins are ethnology

Henri de Lubac, "The Origin of Religion," in God, Man and the Universe, Jacques de Bivort de la Saudée, ed. (New York: P. J. Kenedy and Sons, 1953), pp. 195-202, 210-216.

(aided by folklore) and prehistory. But the more progress that is made in these two sciences—by investigation and discovery, or by perfecting methods of procedure—the more it becomes evident that our remotest past remains still inaccessible.

The most truly primitive among the "primitives"—the special department of ethnology—are primitive only in a very relative sense. "We no doubt know a number of things regarding the social status of contemporary or past savages, but of absolutely primitive human society we know nothing." [1] Everywhere we turn, we find cultures already complex, due to possibly very long evolution and probably also to a mingling with other cultures. And even when a particular people might be a retarded example of what was the original culture of all, we may be sure it would reveal it in an unrecognizable form. For spiritual elements are not preserved like fossils: whether it be due to some congenital impotence or to unfavorable circumstances, geographical or other, a people that fails to progress regresses; if the state of infancy is not replaced by maturity, it turns to infantilism, which is another form of senility. It is therefore as well to mistrust easy formulae: such as that which describes Africa as the "preserving-box of primitive humanity," or Australia as the "museum of the human past." It is advisable to recall Joseph Huby's warning: "Neither the Pygmies, nor the Australian aborigines of the southeast, nor yet the Bantus, teach us anything certain about the mentality of the first man." [2]

As for prehistory, however plentiful and interesting the evidence now at its disposal, it stops far short of the earliest age of mankind. If we are to believe Henri Breuil,[3] hundreds of thousands of years must have elapsed between this first age and the appearance of those races of which we now have any knowledge. What, for instance, do we know of the Chellean man, beyond his existence from the fact that he shaped stones? What information do we get from the Heidelberg jawbone about the mentality of the man who owned it?

An Insoluble Problem

And so, for all our inductions and hypotheses, the problem of absolute origins finds no solution here. However ancient the human stratum, attained or reconstructed with the aid of ethnology, we can never assert positively that it stands for what was really primitive humanity; similarly the earliest prehistoric evidence for traces of psychic activity in man will always have behind it a still immense past that remains shrouded in darkness.

The Myth of the Primitive

There is a second fallacy that still deceives many. It consists in imagining that important results can be obtained by jumbling together a whole string of observations about very different peoples so as to make a kind of composite picture. This method, or rather absence of method, is the weakness of most systems constructed during the past century. On the grounds that ethnology is the science of peoples without histories, it has too long been thought justifiable to treat it as a simple natural science, without any concern for historical considerations. There has been too great a tendency to regard the primitive—"that great proletariat of the history of religions" [4]— as a homogeneous mass; it is, indeed, only as a concession to clarity that the subject has been summarily divided into sections. Thus Frazer, dealing with "the worship of the sky in Africa," divides his work into four parts: East Africa, the valley of the Congo, South Africa, and West Africa.[5]

Arbitrary Schemes

On this principle, if the ethnologist attempts more than an account of the actual facts and seeks to introduce any order of succession—distinguishing, for instance, the origins of religion from its subsequent evolution—he is reduced to being guided by psychological probabilities; and these, as we shall see, are more often than not dependent on his own ideology. First came Auguste Comte, with his famous "law of the three states": theological, metaphysical, and positive. Then, after others, the more complicated scheme of Lubbock, itself subjected to a number of modifications: atheism, fetishism, totemism, shamanism, anthropomorphism, and theism. For Frazer, the whole of man's religious history is explainable as a progress toward the abstract and general: science and religion are the two great hypotheses about the universe, the materialist hypothesis and the spiritual hypothesis, both of which have advanced side by side by a process of gradual simplification and unification: "Just as the materialist hypothesis has reduced innumerable aspects of matter to a single substance, hydrogen, so the spiritual hypothesis has reduced a host of spirits to one unique God." [6]

Historical Schools

Since about the beginning of this century, there have appeared new schools of thought in strong reaction against this subjective method. In spite of profound differences in inspiration, method, and results, these have one thing in common, an insistence on including history in ethnology. Declining to isolate any cultural element from the whole that must explain it, they seek to discover by the most objective criteria possible, the connections between the cultural units already distinguished, the order in which they occur, and their mutual dependence. Therefore all these schools can be described as historical: the German school that produced the first manifestoes in favor of the "historico-cultural method" (Batzel, Frobenius, Graebner, Ankermann); the Austrian school that sought to apply greater rigor to the method and widen the importance of the results obtained (Schmidt, Gusinde, Kippers, Schebesta); the English school, more and more "diffusionist" (Maitland, Rivers, Elliot Smith); and the American school, more chary of wide generalizations and more keenly alive to convergence in phenomena (Boas, Dixon, Goldenweisser, Radin, Lowie). France, here, is not so strongly represented: perhaps, as M. Georges Montandon suggests, because the Latin genius is more inclined to shrink from the idea of heterogeneous cultures. Actually French reaction against the classical views of ethnology has tended (less happily) to follow in the track of Durkheim's sociology.

Rationalist Ideology

The ideology behind the work of most theorists in ethnology has usually been made up of two principal elements: a belief in uniform and continuous progress, and a belief that the ideal to which it tends is rationalism. Therefore, on the one hand, it was taken for granted that religion must have begun with some very crude and rudimentary idea, to arrive little by little, under the combined influence of mental and social development, at superior forms such as monotheism. On the other hand, the only true progress would have to be the elimination of all religion, or at any rate what men have always understood by religion, and its replacement by an adult and fully conscious rationalism.

The various systems of this type might have very different starting-points. For classical ethnology, it lay in discovering some error, some too hasty hypothesis, made by reason as yet ill-equipped with experience. According to others, religion was the product of an activity entirely different from any rational activity: Durkheim talks of a collective thought, reaching its paroxysm in phases of hysterical exaltation in the whole assembled clan; M. Lévy-Brühl (whose theory is sometimes stated in an exaggerated form) calls for the intervention of a "primitive mentality," producer of "mystical" ideas, which would be repressed, if not wholly eradicated, by civilization. But whatever the explanation of man's first steps in the immense field of religion, it is assumed that everything essential depends on these steps; that all the rest must be judged by them; that no really new value comes into being by the way, and that the numerous changes supervening in religious forms are only variations of the same initial datum. If the latter is false or inconsistent, so must be all the rest. Thus we come back to Auguste Comte's old idea, of an age that has at last become positive or, as M. Brunschvicg remarked recently, of the arrival of *homo sapiens*, banishing *homo religiosus*. The way of thinking presupposed by religion corresponds, at this rate, to a stage of infancy; religion is therefore no more eternal than—to take an example from the history of human societies—is the modern phenomenon of the nation in arms; it has survived for a long time in its inevitable decline, but a day will come when natural science, explaining everything by positive laws, will finally and once and for all make an end of it.

The Fallacy of the "Elementary"

This is not the place to criticize the metaphysics underlying such theories. It is enough to point out, on the phenomenological level, the nature of the particular fallacy they imply. It is assumed that the judgment of science about the nature of primitive religion—presuming, incidentally, such a judgment possible—would be an assessment of the value of religion itself, both in its essence and in the variety of its historical forms. It is therefore thought possible to resolve the problem of religion simply and solely in the light of ethnology. So Tylor, for instance, starting with the savage's idea of the soul—derived from a childish interpretation of things like dreams and swoons—saw even in the great historical religions nothing else but transformed animism, tainted (one might say) with the same original weakness as primitive superstitions about nature spirits or the souls of the dead. So, too, Loisy (more subtle than usual) thought he could see in all sacrifice a purely magical operation; hence his conclusion that "the idea of satisfaction by means of sacrifice, however moralized in certain cults by attenuation and refinement, is never anything, fundamentally, but a magical guarantee." [7] Hence too the epithet, deliberately chosen by Durkheim, when he entitled his well-known work: *Elementary Forms of Religious Life*. As editor of Hamelin, he knew very well that the *"elements* of representation" are its essential principles and (one might also say) its permanent categories; similarly the "elementary" forms of religion would be not only those that were primitive and rudimentary but also its essential and constituent forms.

Bankruptcy of Crude Evolutionism

So paradoxical is this view that there are few who succeed in maintaining it consistently. Hence we have seen many an instructive "repentance": from the "positivist religion" of Auguste Comte to Durkheims's paradox, that "if religion is often accompanied by a certain frenzy, such a frenzy is not without grounds," or M. Lévy-Brühl's somewhat timid rehabilitation of obscure spiritual forces that baffle all criticism.[8] Evolutionism has been so much oversimplified that it is now out of favor, even in the study of material life. It is recognized as a fallacy, and many psychologists, historians, and philosophers—independently and often at variance with each other—are now in process of reacting very strongly. Anxious to understand the fact of religion for what it is, they reject the primacy, still more the monopoly, of either ethnology, sociology, or economics. Whether for the origins of religion or its subsequent manifestations, they decline to confuse order of appearance with causal connection. They hold that in the religious sphere, as anywhere else (perhaps more than anywhere else), every novel form of life or thought has a right to be judged on its merits; that in the spiritual history of man, the unchanging principle may well undergo superficial disguises and complications, but in addition to these there are genuine "discoveries"; that "what is transformed or sublimated is in reality something new" (L. Brunschvicg); that the great personalities in religion—prophets, founders, mystics, and reformers—have an anything but negligible part to play; hence any judgment, passed on what is presumed to be the starting-point, does not necessarily hold good for the final goal.

Moreover, here, as everywhere else, it is a fact of common experience that humble, barely differentiated beginnings are a poor indication of what they spring from. The latter can mostly be judged only in the light of later developments. This is true even of biological species, particularly the human race. "The scientific solution of the human problem," as Pierre Teilhard de Chardin observes rightly, "is not to be found in the study of fossils, but in a closer consideration of contemporary man, his properties and potentialities, which make it possible to foresee the man of tomorrow" [9]—and also, retrospectively, throw light on the man of the past. Where social institutions are concerned, this is recognized expressly by Durkheim himself: "To gain a proper understanding of an institution, it is often a good thing to see what it becomes in the advanced stages of its evolution, for sometimes its true meaning appears most clearly when it has reached its fullest development." [10] It is strange to read this in the very book that professes to explain spiritual realities, and even the essence of contemporary Christianity, by the totemism of the Aruntas!

Underlying Philosophies

And lastly there is a fourth fallacy to note, no less general than the others. It was customary, not so long ago, to make the empirical study of its distant past the sole criterion for judging religion. Now there is a confusion of the opposite sort, though it is nearly always combined with the other. What it amounts to is that the study of religion, though supposed to be empirical, is completely dominated by dogmatic ideas that serve to dictate the conclusions to be reached. What is supposed to be a factual explanation arrived at objectively is really, subconsciously, the construction of a theory. Religion's so-called "historical" and "psychological" origins are both treated alike, and they are both explained in the light of a philosophy that has been drawn from wholly extraneous sources.

The procedure, admittedly, is not wholly illegitimate; nor is it entirely unavoidable. The scientific datum is never a bald fact; between the theory and the experiment (or what takes its place) there is always a mutually profitable interaction; and here if anywhere it is true that no method can boast of being purely objective. But the fact should be allowed for. Now it could be shown how, all through the nineteenth century, the various theories propounded about the origin of the idea of God followed parallel variations in contemporary philosophy and "spiritual tendencies." Traditionalism, associationist psychology, Spencerian evolutionism, Burchner's materialist dynamism, Marxism, and the sociology of Durkheim, each found in turn its faithful image in descriptions of the origin and evolution of religion. Several instances of this were shrewdly noted by Schmidt. Perhaps he could have given yet another, though not so striking as the rest, in the very doctrines he promulgated himself.

The "A Priori" of Leninist Marxism

No theory succumbed to this latter fallacy so completely as did Leninist Marxism. On its fundamental theory of historical materialism, it set out to explain the origin of religion as "a fanciful reflex, arising in the social consciousness from a feeling of imperfection and impotence," a feeling itself produced by the inadequate technical equipment of primitive man. No explanation could be more narrowly doctrinaire, even when Marx's thought is correctly interpreted.[11] Yet those who propound it never hesitate to declare that "Leninist Marxism studies the given facts and draws its deductions from them alone."

Summing Up

The belief that science can penetrate to the actual beginnings of humanity; the belief that it is possible, by psychological induction, to decide at the present day which peoples are the most primitive, which the most primitive forms of religion we are in a position to observe; the belief that the primitive or rudimentary is necessarily the essential and fundamental; and finally the belief that we are pursuing science pure and simple when we are really applying a philosophical theory—these, in varying degrees, are the four great fallacies still so widespread today among students of comparative religion that it has been worth our while to draw special attention to them.

We are throwing no stones at the victims of these illusions, sometimes very distinguished scholars. It was only to be expected that a science, still young, should have entertained hopes that have since proved chimerical. Nor was it possible, in its very first phase, to be already in possession of a tried and sure method. Born in the century of evolutionism, it tended to adopt instinctively, along with sound intuitions, a number of crudely oversimplified theories. Finally, like all other branches of positive learning, it needed time to rid itself of metaphysics, subject, of course, to the necessity of returning to metaphysics later, but by this time, consciously and without confusion of method. Nevertheless, in spite of so many theories that proved fragile, this new science has made progress, but its achievements will not be decisive till it is free of the illusions that are incompatible with maturity. It is only necessary to note what they are, to realize that it is not in the field of ethnology or prehistory, nor on the scientific question of origins, that the decisive battle about religion is to be fought. This is not perceived by Leninist writers; these, quick as they are to criticize the theories of "bourgeois rationalism" and its superficial ideology, still believe that the study of "primitive religion" will provide them with the "key" to the religious problem.[12]

[We omit two sections of de Lubac's original essay: "Some Important Points" and "Is the Idea of God the Product of Slow Evolution." These sections contained some of the negative conclusions of anthropology. The section that follows remains comprehensible without these omitted sections.]

The Relations Between Social and Religious Development

What we have just seen makes it possible to define, at any rate partially, the relations that exist between social and religious development. Numerous and important as they are historically, they really belong to two quite distinct histories. These do not always cover the same ground, any more than they coincide with the history of technical achievement. Marxism, however, has attempted to revive here the theory of a great many "bourgeois" sociologists, by stressing the economic behind the political factor. The following, for instance, is its explanation of monotheism.

The Marxist Theory of the Development of Monotheism

It was the great empires of antiquity (we are told) that led up to it, the gods being celestial shadows of their rulers. The victorious king of Babylon would impose his god Marduk on the peoples he had vanquished. But it was commerce that contributed most to the spreading of the idea of a single divinity. The merchant voyager, uprooted from his home, pressed the claims of his own god wherever he went, so that such a god came to be regarded as present everywhere. Thenceforward, since he could no longer have human form, men made him a pure spirit. In the great cosmopolitan cities he merged easily into other gods. "So the idea was formed of a universal god, abstract in nature, himself a reflection of an abstract man and the controller of the fortunes of the market." [13] Such was already the God of primitive Christianity; above all it was the god of the capitalist age and of economic liberalism.

Monotheism therefore, like religion itself and every form of civilization, would be a simple reflection of economic life, or—to use the classic term—its "superstructure." And it would be no less malign, no less oppressive, than the cruder religious forms that preceded it. With changes in social relations, produced by economic progress, with the constantly altering forms of exploitation, religious ideas may well change also. But religion goes on justifying violence and oppression; it is always sanctioning this or that exploitation as something instituted by God Himself. It began when men were first divided into classes, with the exploitation of man by man. When this comes to an end, religion will end too.

Its Partial Truth

In spite of some details that it is hard to take seriously, we must own that not everything in this theory is false. Or at any rate that there are plenty of facts to make it plausible. Accordingly as man is hunter, tiller of the fields, or shepherd, his whole religious system will have different characteristics. The historico-cultural schools were careful to stress this law. As the human group, first a modest tribe, becomes successively a city-state, then a nation, then an empire, there occur a whole series of parallel transformations in the myths it believes in and the rites it observes. It is therefore perfectly true that we find in these a reflection of social conditions—which are not independent of economic conditions—and that in consequence they tend to reinforce these conditions. But to be entirely fair, it should also be noticed how, along with social abuses, religion, even of this kind, sanctions the very principle of society itself; and how it therefore contributes, perhaps more than anything else, to ensure social cohesion and so to enable man to live and survive, which is surely the first condition of progress.

But there is something else, and it is the thing that is really essential. Like rationalism, Marxism is (so to speak) *quantitatively* right—rather as determinism is right in that part of human action that bulks largest and is most obvious. But the thing that really counts is often what occupies materially less space; and this, even if it is perceived, before it can be properly appreciated must be regarded from the inside. Where religion is concerned, the ethnologist, the sociologist, and the pure historian can never get further than the superficial view.

But, in spite of everything, there are certain great facts too striking to be overlooked by anyone who is willing to open his eyes. What of this worship of a featureless god, the reflection of a commercial and banking age? And monotheism, the result of unity effected by temporal powers? How then are we to explain the history of India, where lofty forms of worship and very profound systems of religious philosophy grew up in the midst of a primitive economy and a society politically amorphous? And what of the first precepts of the Jewish decalogue? (The question of its date is of no concern here.) "Listen, Israel! I am the Lord thy God. Thou shalt not defy Me by making other gods thy own. Thou shalt not carve thyself images . . . I, thy God, the Lord Almighty, am jealous in My love!" [14]

The Two Kinds of "Monotheist" Religion

It does not require any meticulous examination to distinguish in our Western history two kinds of "monotheist" religion, closely interwoven as they are in many respects.[15] The first, at any rate in part, is certainly the result of social development, accompanied by progress in philosophical thinking: little by little, as a reflection of what takes place on earth, pantheons became established; they acquired their organization, their hierarchies; the very multitude and medley of gods suggesting the unity of the divine; finally the chief of the divine society became magnified into a supreme god, the other gods being merely his servitors. So it was—with numerous variants in the process—with Babylon; with the Achemenid Empire; with the Hellenic world; with the Roman Empire. An advantage politically? And for civilization and thought? It was indeed, and sometimes a very considerable advantage. But was this progress properly religious? Not always, by any means. And if anthropomorphism was left behind, the only thing that replaced it, as a rule, was an abstract divinity or a deified Nature. But there is a second kind of monotheism in which the unique God proclaims a fierce exclusiveness: "There is no God but God." This is not the result of any syncretism, whether political or intellectual. It is impossible to discuss it in terms of integration or concentration, but rather of opposition and negation. It is not brought about by evolution, but imposed by revolution.[16] It is a God that calls for conversion and the breaking of idols. What we had before, at best, was a complacent Principle, justifying the practice of polytheism, consolidating the imperious supremacy of the flesh, yet always in itself the possession of a tiny élite of philosophers. Now we have a Being, by no means abstract though wholly spiritual; an intransigent Being, claiming all worship for himself, requiring to be recognized by all; a transcendent Being, above and beyond all cities on earth, even the city of the world.

It is only this second monotheism that has any dynamic power. This alone makes for religious progress, springing as it does from a radical transformation in religious ideas and in the religious life. When it encounters the other, it first has to vanquish it, then afterwards utilize it for its own self-expression, for its completion and expansion, while at the same time bringing fulfillment to this other also. It never makes its appearance in the great unified states after any mighty conquests, nor yet as the result of deep speculation or great economic changes. Insofar as it is possible to judge from hopelessly inadequate sources, the religion of Zoroaster, "the least pagan of pagan religions," came to birth in a very remote province of Iran, certainly far from the cultural center of Babylon, and before the era of open syncretism, brought about in Babylon itself by the conquests of Cyrus. Judaism and Islam also defy every theory of religious development that has recourse only to factors extraneous to religion.[17] Israel was a small people, intellectually undistinguished, its economy rudimentary, its civilization far less brilliant than that of its great neighbors that one after the other were constantly overwhelming it. The Arabs, before the Hegira, had hardly any unity. The idea of God—we see it now in its loftiest manifestations as we did before in its humblest forms—shatters and overruns all social as well as intellectual boundaries. "The Spirit," we are tempted to say, "blows where it wills."

Religion Not an Accomplice of Oppression

It blows indeed! And while the first of the two monotheisms—very imperfectly named—serves to support a greater social order, wealthier no doubt, but possibly also more tyrannical as well (we have only to call to mind the "solar monotheism" of Aurelian), the second, and the only true one, that of the "Living God," becomes for human consciousness the principle of enfranchisement, and against social abuses of every sort a permanent vindication of justice. It is so at least, and in the highest degree, in the faith that Christianity inherited from the Jews. Renan compared the prophets of Israel to socialist orators. In this he strangely reduced their stature. What socialist orator ever uttered words like the "roaring" of Amos, the shepherd chosen by Yahweh to proclaim his menaces to those who "ground in the dust the poor man's rights [. . .] shouldered aside the claim of the unbefriended"? [18] Religious reformers as they were, they were also social reformers—and for that very reason. For them, Yahweh was the All-Powerful; but his power was not at the disposal of the mighty of this world: it was wholly for the furthering of justice, even as his sanctity was for the furthering of all moral goodness.

True enough—"whenever a religion yields to social complacency, whenever it represents the economic conditions prevailing at the moment as the fulfillment of the designs of Providence for society, it provides grounds for the reproach"—that the Marxists level at it. This fault, as we are well aware, is common enough even among

Christians. But the most conservative of Christians is bound to admit, provided he is loyal to the inspiration of his faith, that Christianity imposes on man "a constant progress in charity, to be translated into the organization of economics and society" (Yves de Montcheuil). Far from reflecting the conditions that exist, it is rather a principle of their renewal, of their perpetual transformation. If this is not always immediately apparent to the historian, it is because it operates far below the surface of things, where it can be recognized only by long reflection.

Conclusion

The idea of God, in its objective expression, depends strictly on the double analogy by which we apprehend everything in the natural world, namely, the sensible and the social. Yet in spite of this it makes its appearance among men as something spontaneous and peculiarly itself. All the attempts to account for its "genesis," or to explain it as a "reduction," invariably come to grief in one place or another. It does not immediately follow, admittedly, that the idea conceived corresponds to a real Being or that religion itself has an absolute value. Nor are we called upon to demonstrate it here— any more than we are to define the boundaries and relations between "natural knowledge" of God and "revelation." By way of conclusion, it will be enough to emphasize that the certain facts of religious history, though too meager and obscure to be scientifically satisfying, seem to lend themselves naturally to a Christian interpretation (we do not say they demand it), and are most readily intelligible in the light of Christianity.

In a humanity made in the image of God, but sinful, compelled to a long and groping ascent, yet from its very awakening inspired by a summons from above, it is only to be expected that the idea of God should be constantly arising, yet also be in constant danger of being stifled. Two main tendencies are always felt, the one due to the conditions in which the intellect has to work, the other to moral deviation at the source: there is the tendency to confuse the Author of Nature with Nature itself, through which He is obscurely revealed and from which we must borrow images before we can think of Him; and there is the tendency to forsake a God, too exacting and sublime, and turn to subordinate deities or simple fictions. Analogies tend to harden, and until such time as knowledge appears to have made decisive progress, God is still conceived as an individual with human passions, or else as an abstraction without effective influence. The better sometimes changes to the worse, and the great force in man that makes for perfection may become enslaved to ends that are wholly profane.

Hence the need for purifying, constantly renewed. To this process of purifying, ever since the distant times of Xenophanes, even atheist thought has had something to contribute—for the greatest atheists are not always those who think and call themselves godless. But it is a still blind perspicacity that would be for rejecting God because man has deformed His image, or religion, for the abuses that man has made of it. Just as religion began as itself, so too, as itself it must be constantly purified: even monotheism, as we have seen, was created out of a negation, but it was a fertile negation. Moreover, after the wildest negations, man returns to worship in one form or another: it is not only his essential duty but the deepest need of his being. God is the pole by which man is forever attracted; even those who think to deny Him, involuntarily bear witness to Him, since they merely apply, as the great Origen says, "to anything sooner than God their indestructible idea of Him."

Perspective

All being grist to its mill, modern atheism has pressed into the service of its denial both the history of religion and religious ethnology. It has not often been able to do so without much tampering with the facts. At the very least it has selected them, often interpreted them arbitrarily, and applied to the origins and evolution of religion explanatory principles drawn from its own unbelief. But does it not itself, in spite of this, bear witness to the faith? It has been said of atheism that "the more assertive it is, the more clearly we see in its features traces of past religious experiences. . . . A man wills to be not religious, but the very volition makes him religious. He may flee the face of God, he will never escape Him." [19] The ethnologist who wrote these words shows that the so-called primitive mentality is really, in its deepest roots if not in the forms in which it clothes itself, something inalienable, genuinely valid, and part of the mental structure of all of us; and he goes on to observe that this part of ourselves is undergoing in our day an irrepressible revival. The man of the twentieth century, he concludes, "is in process of discovering the reality of his gods, and even, sometimes, that of his God." So humanity's great problem, now that it has at last emerged from an age of unreal and stifling rationalism, is whether it will impotently succumb to this new invasion of its gods "of flesh and blood"—as Greece of old was all but submerged by the dark orgies of Dionysus —or whether by dint of an effort of enlightenment it will find once more the God Who made it in His own image and Whose loving hands have never abandoned it.

References

1. James G. Frazer, *The Scope of Social Anthropology* (London: Macmillan & Co., Ltd., 1908), pp. 163-164.

2. *Recherches de Science religieuse* (1917), p. 352.

3. Leçon d'ouverture au Collège de France, *Revue des Cours et Conférences*, Vol. XXX (December, 1929).

4. The phrase is Söderblom's.

5. James G. Frazer, *The Worship of Nature* (London: Macmillan & Co., Ltd., 1926).

6. *Ibid.*, pp. 9-10.

7. *Essai historique sur le Sacrifice* (Paris, 1920), p. 319; cf. pp. 531ff.

8. *Nouvelle Revue Française*, Vol. I (September, 1933), pp. 453ff.: "Just when we perceive most clearly the distance that separates this mentality from our own, it inspires us with an interest that is more than curiosity. The description and study of its essential features arouse a distant echo in ourselves, like a faint vibration of the secret fibers of our being. May we not have here, in what we describe as primitive mentality, certain active tendencies and ways of behaving in the very depths of ourselves, defying analysis, not reducible to clear conceptions, and not yet drawn from the shadows by any of our systems of logic and psychology? In modern society, these elements of the mental life, more affective than intellectual, have been respected, controlled, and disciplined by the progress of criticism and reflection. But they have not been eradicated. Granted it were possible they might be, would it be altogether desirable?"

9. An important discovery in human palaeontology, the *Sinanthropus Pekinensis, Revue des questions scientifiques*, July 20, 1930. Cf. Yves de Montcheuil, *Mélanges théologiques* (Paris: Aubier, 1946).

10. *Les formes élémentaires de la vie religieuse*, p. 137.

11. The point is contested, notably by Henri de Man, who refers chiefly to the early writings of Marx: "According to the fundamental conception of social facts which was Marx's starting-point, material conditions determine man quite as much as man determines his social conditions. He maintained this position mainly in what he wrote when he was young: it merely recognizes the reality of life, with its double aspect of a process at once material and spiritual. Polemical necessity, imposed by the circumstances of the time, led him in his later writings to dwell more on the first of these aspects and emphasize the material de-

termination of society. Most materialists, since, have continued to misplace the accent, so that the dialectical doctrine of a mutual reaction between the material and the spiritual in man's struggle with his environment has become the materialist doctrine that facts of the spiritual order have purely economic causes." *L'Idée Socialiste* (1935), p. 16. However that may be, the fact remains that Marx himself never understood religion.

12. Lucien Henry, *Les origines de la religion*, p. 139. See pp. 25 and 68 for the author's criticism of the ideas of Salomon Reinach and Frazer.

13. *Ibid.*, p. 37.

14. Deuteronomy 5.

15. We ignore here the monotheisms that remained purely philosophical. These call for entirely different treatment.

16. On this see R. Pettazzoni, *La formation du Monotheisme*, Revue de l'histoire des religions, Vol. LXXXVIII.

17. Not that it is suggested, by any means, that it is not a fact that every durable religion must have its roots, and depend for its birth, on conditions not wholly of the religious order. This is no paradox to the Christian, who knows the importance, even in revealed religion, of the idea of "the fullness of the times."

18. Amos 1:2, 2:7, 4:1, and so forth.

19. G. van der Leeuw, *L'homme primitif et la religion* (Paris: Alcan, 1940), pp. 167-168, 194-195.

PART SIX

The Value

# of Man's Religion

Once the inquiring mind of the Westerner has recognized the prevalence of religion, a few questions naturally arise about the meaning of religions other than the Judaeo-Christian. Can any religion claim to be unique? We have here two essays by committed Christians on what they consider to be Christianity's relation to man's religious history and patterns. Influenced by Carl Jung, the late Gerald Vann, English Dominican and spiritual writer, believed that the myths of man's religions preserve not necessarily any historical truth but a deeper truth which in Christianity is both mystery and history. His lucid essay leads to other questions about the relation of revealed religion to man's psychology, a problem answered in contrasting ways in recent Christian theology (see especially the works of Karl Barth, Martin D'Arcy, Jean Daniélou, and Paul Tillich). Is there some correspondence between what revealed religion says God does and what man *naturally* aspires to? Or is any seeming correspondence really but an example of wishful thinking on the part of man? In another direction—what does the nonconceptual nature of symbols and myths tell us about man who uses them?

In his essay the Oxford scholar on non-Christian religion, R. C. Zaehner, leads us through the tangled forest of Hindu and Buddhist religion. To some degree he illustrates Vann's argument in his comparison of Christianity and Hinduism and Buddhism. This highly informative essay also gives us a truly revealing distinction of world religions. In regard to Hinduism and Buddhism specifically, he presents in an easily digested way some rather esoteric material and protects us from the simplifications and generalizations that Westerners make so readily and presumptuously in this area. (Because of the vastness of this area it remains advisable for the student to refer to some of the books listed in the suggested readings for this part). Zaehner's short and intensive essay makes it possible for the student to discuss with some intelligence the great problems and questions that come to mind when comparing the world religions. *All* seem tempted to discuss them, but without specific knowledge such discussion is unlikely to be relevant. Given the background provided by this essay, we can ask these questions: Can the Christian see in non-Christian religion any providential activity? Or again, what significance is there in the rather common affirmation of the superiority of non-Christian religion over Christianity? If there is such superiority, in what exactly does it consist? Does Eastern religious teaching on the body-soul relationship enshrine important truths? In the West itself, are the Greek (Platonic) and Semitic notions of man complementary or in conflict? Concerning this last question, the insights afforded by both non-Christian religion and Tielhard de Chardin could be most illuminating.

CHAPTER II

Relearning Symbols

GERALD VANN

It may be helpful to approach the subject of the place of symbols in Christianity from the consideration of two sets of difficulties or disabilities which seem to affect many Catholics nowadays in the Western world.

First, Catholics are often accused of not reading the Old Testament. If this is true, and by and large it seems to be, it is important for us to discover why it is so; and the likely explanation seems to be that to a great extent we have lost the clue to the reading of the book, we have forgotten the "language," the idiom, in which it is written.

Again it seems undeniably true to say that the modern Catholic, however deep and vivid his belief in the efficacy of the sacraments, often finds little meaning if any in their ritual, the ritual for instance of the baptismal waters; whereas it is clear that in the days of primitive Christianity this same ritual had on the neophyte an immensely vivid impact.

Secondly, many Catholics nowadays seem to feel that the formulas, the propositions, in which the Christian faith is stated and propounded to them in creed or catechism have about them a certain unreality: they seem so dry, so technical, so remote from ordinary everyday speech and everyday reality, that they may easily come in the end to seem meaningless: the dogmatic formulas, the definitions of faith, so remote and so dry as to be unreal; the moral principles, so neat and tidy as to seem lacking in validity.

Now these two sets of facts may at first sight seem contradictory; but in reality they are complementary.

Gerald Vann, O.P., "Relearning Symbols," *Worship*, Vol. XXIV, No. 10 (November, 1960), 588-596.

Two Different Languages

To say that we have forgotten the "language" of the Old Testament means that we tend to approach the Old Testament as though it were a history textbook written in the idiom of the twentieth century, the idiom of the modern scientific historian.

But it is not. Whether we like it or not, the fact is that God wrote His book in the language not of scientific prose but of poetry, the language not of formulas but of pictures or images; if we lose the clue to those pictures we lose the clue to the book; and this is what does in fact seem to have happened.

The same is true of our approach to the Church's sacramental ritual, which again is a question of communicating truth and reality to us not only through formulas but through pictures: the picture, for instance, of life found through death, through a going down into the waters of darkness.

And it seems at least likely that our feeling of unreality when confronted with the precise formulations of Christian doctrine in creed or catechism or theological textbook is partly to be explained by this same loss of the other language, the complementary language of Bible and ritual, the language of poetry.

It is necessary to stress this idea of the two different languages being in fact complementary. The Church tries to teach us, to communicate reality to us, simultaneously in the two ways, through the two different kinds of language; and each way, each language, is essential to us.

Without the "prose" we should easily fall a prey, as the history of mysticism or religious enthusiasm makes clear to us, to all sorts of doctrinal vagaries, perhaps to some form of pseudo-mysticism. But without the "poetry," the doctrinal formulas do of their very nature tend to seem abstract, arid, and therefore unreal; and nowadays there is precisely a danger that these formulations may seem to the Catholic to be all that God, that Christ, that the Church, have so to speak to offer us, and that they are in themselves the objects of religious faith.

Sometimes it has to be pointed out that we do not believe in a creed: we believe through a creed.

The fact is that we cannot express the Inexpressible in concepts, in words; we cannot confine the Infinite Unknowable in concepts or in words. Formulas are an essential guide; but sooner or later we find ourselves brought up short against a wall of mystery. Beyond this wall we cannot be led by the language of theological or doctrinal formulas.

But we can sometimes be led further in another way, the way of nonconceptual awareness or apprehension, the way precisely not of prose but of poetry, of picture-language. And it is this language that is used for the most part in the Bible, and by Christ in His teaching, and by the Church in its sacramental ritual.

It must be stressed at once that to speak of "poetic" language in this context does not imply anything abstruse or highly intellectualized; on the contrary, it means something extremely simple.

This is the language, these are the pictures, used for example by Christ in his parables, those simple stories which can be understood by any human being of any age or race. This is the language, these are the simplicities, of folklore, of fairly tales, even of the humble nursery rhyme, as well as of the mighty visions of the greatest poets and artists. But how does this language take us further than the language of prose?

Variety of Signs

First let us distinguish three different things. There is the conventional sign, such as the signs used in algebra or the road signs with which we are all familiar; these are not "signs" at all in the sense in which the word is used, in the Fourth Gospel, of the miracles of our Lord; they are simply pointers, decided upon by convention, to some utilitarian end.

Secondly, there are the individual symbols, images, metaphors, which are so to speak invented and utilized by this or that individual poet in order to communicate his vision: these are of their nature, being personal and invented, limited in scope, and may well be obscure to a reader unacquainted with the individual poet's background or world of thought.

Thirdly, there are symbols which are universal, the heritage of humanity as a whole; these are the images through which, as

Kerenyi says, "the world speaks." These are the images which are to be found through all human history, in all ages, among all peoples, such as water, tree, fire, wine, oil, rebirth, and the story of the hero and his dark journey.

It is with this third type of image, the universal symbols, that we are concerned here.

These, which are the heritage of humanity, lie very deep in human nature. The individual, invented symbol can contain and therefore communicate only what the inventor puts into it; the universal and so to speak "innate" symbol has a vastly greater content than that of any individual conscious mind, and indeed contains elements for which no verbal expression would seem to exist.

These are not just illustrations of some proposition, used to make the proposition intellectually clearer, as is the case when we make use of similes. These are of themselves the vehicle of communication, and the communication is a deep one, first because the images do communicate a reality for which no words, no concepts exist; secondly, because they are of their nature ambivalent; they are paradox as the teaching and imagery of Christ in the Gospels is paradox; thirdly because, being the language of poetry, they appeal not just to the head but to the heart: more accurately their appeal is to the whole of man's psyche and indeed the whole of man's personality.

Once one has grasped the clue to them, once one has relearned the idiom in which they are stated, they can never seem arid and unreal as can formulations of doctrine: they are immensely real because like life itself they are untidy; they have in them the untidiness and the richness of paradox. More than that, appealing as they do to the whole personality, and not only appealing but also healing precisely because of their total appeal, they at the same time evoke a total response.

We are perhaps too accustomed to thinking of faith in terms of an intellectual assent to propositions, from which it is an easy step to thinking of faith as belief in rather than through a creed; the communication of divine reality through this image-language evokes quite a different response: a total personal commitment, the kind of response which is envisaged by St. John in the Fourth Gospel when he speaks of faith as the one "work" which God demands of us.

The Universal Story

Now these universal symbols or pictures are elements in a universal story-picture: a story which, always substantially the same, appears in endless variety of detail in the different ages and races of mankind.

This is the story which provides the background to our Lord's mysterious words to Nicodemus, the words concerning death and rebirth. It tells of the hero who must leave behind him his home, must sacrifice rest and security, and go forth adventuring, embark on an arduous and perilous journey, go down into darkness, often into the dark waters of the sea or deep caverns beneath the sea, and there meet and do battle with an adversary—a dragon, a wild beast, an evil king—and often endure death at the end of his *agon*, his struggle, so as to win for himself a new life, a life which he is then empowered to take back, as the boon or treasure he has won, to his people.

This journey from death to life, from dark to light, is to be found everywhere; it is, we might say, the pattern of reality as a whole as we know it.

We find it in nature: every day the sun-god dies in the evening, goes back to his ocean-mother, goes back to the dark womb of the sea, in order to be born anew next day at dawn; every year after the high summer is over, the year falls and in winter dies, to be born again in the following spring.

In human mythology, art, poetry, folklore, fairytale, in ballads and nursery rhymes, in fiction and fantasy, and last but not least in dreams, this same pattern and these same images are to be found; they are to be found in the stories with which the Old Testament is full: the stories of Adam, Noah, Abraham, Jacob, Joseph, David, and a host of others; then in the New Testament the same pattern, the same story, the same symbols, are lived out in the life and death and rising again of our Lord, and stated again and again in His teaching; and then finally, deriving from that life and that teaching, the same pattern is found in the daily life of the Church, in its sacramental ritual, its daily bringing of life to humanity.

Myths Versus Historical Facts

Here we must pause to dispose of a common but needless and indeed dangerous timidity which Catholics sometimes feel when mythology is mentioned in the same breath as Christian reality. If we couple pagan myth and Christian mystery together, are we not making the latter as "unreal" as the former?

No: myth is defined simply as a "sacred iconograph," that is to say, an image communicating sacred or religious reality. Inasmuch as the communicating of truth is concerned, it makes no difference whether the image is taken from what we would normally call real history or from some purely fictional story: the lesson, the communication, remains the same.

In the Old Testament, for example, it makes no difference to the vividness or validity of the lesson of Job or Tobias whether these men are historical figures or imaginative creations. In the Gospel the same is true of, say, the prodigal son or the Pharisee and the publican in the temple.

But the story of the life and death and rising again of Christ is an entirely different matter: this is absolutely inescapably *history*; the events described for us are historical happenings brought about by the emotions and passions of human agents on certain definite dates and in certain definite places; and because the events described concern the Christ who is God-made-man, God Himself entering into the historical, the cosmological, process, their historicity is indeed essential.

That historicity is in fact as obvious and inescapable in the case of the Christ-story as is the fantasy-character of the pagan-mythological statements of the same theme.

Nevertheless in all cases the theme does state the same essential facts about human nature. In pagan mythology we are shown man's yearnings for life; in the Old Testament stories we are shown more than that; we are shown not merely yearnings but hopes, hopes based on definite God-given promises; in the New Testament we are shown the fulfillment of those hopes (and *a fortiori* the fulfillment of all the yearnings of humanity) in the life-history of the God-man who, unlike the heroes of the myths, lived out the pattern Himself in brute fact in His own life, in order that we in our turn might then be empowered to live out the same pattern in our different ways ourselves.

Hence it is that the sacraments re-present the same pattern, the same theme of life through death and light through darkness, the same baptismal theme of rebirth or renewal; and in so doing apply, effectively, Christ's living-out of the pattern to ourselves, to our own lives.

The Christ-life ends not on Calvary or in the tomb or even in the moment of rising into new life or ascending into glory, but only at the moment of Whitsuntide, the coming to humanity of that boon of life, the Holy Spirit, which is the direct *result* of all that Christ had lived and experienced and done. And the sacraments are simply the ways in which that boon of life is now brought to us daily, over and over again, through the instrumentality of the Church.

Need of Rediscovery

If then we find the Old Testament boring, the sacramental rituals unintelligible, it is because we have so largely forgotten this language in which they speak to us; but we have forgotten the language because the world we live in has long been accustomed to think no communication valid unless it is couched in the language of reason, of science: it is a world whose heritage is the impoverished aftermath of rationalism, empiricism, and ·*scientisme*.

But now at last we are belatedly coming to realize that just as we cannot *escape* from nonconceptual thought, from the language of symbol—for if we attempt to repudiate it in our conscious thinking, our waking moments, it returns to us in the field of imagination and fantasy or in the life of dreams—so also we can not *afford* to despise it or attempt to exclude it from our conscious lives, for without it we are doomed to remain incomplete, unintegrated, unbalanced, neurotic.

And as modern Western man must recover the world of symbol in general if he is to recover his sanity and the fullness of his psychic life, so the Christian must recover the world of symbol if he is to acquire a fuller and more vital awareness of the meaning of Christian truth, of God's self-revelation.

Therefore it is a matter of the utmost urgency for us to become familiar once again with the great universal symbols—the water, the wood, the fire, the wine, the oil, the tree—and to see these once again as elements in the basic and universal story-symbol of rebirth, the paradox-theme of life won through death, joy through sorrow, strength through weakness, greatness through nothingness, light through darkness, wisdom through a childlike "learned ignorance" (*docta ignorantia*), and eternal youth, freedom, vitality, and gaiety through the humble acceptance of our temporal disabilities, our disintegrated state, the shackles and enfeebling frailties and fatigues and pains which are sin's legacy.

These we must learn and assimilate from the stories and histories of the Bible, that "theme-with-variations" given us by God Himself; in particular and above all we must see them fully and finally lived out in actual fact in the Christ-life, and thence coming to us here and now, in the re-presentation of that Christ-life, through the Church's sacramental system.

To do that is to find Bible and ritual alike springing to life; it is to find in Bible and ritual alike the thrill and excitement of a fresh discovery: for all those details in the Old Testament stories which historically speaking are insignificant and therefore boring now thrill and throb with life since we see them not just as historical fact but as picture, as symbol, as elements in this constantly stated and re-stated life-pattern.

And the pattern becomes thrilling for us because, being the universal life-pattern, it reveals itself to me as the pattern of—and the clue to—*my* life, my struggles, my *agon*, my joys and sorrows, my problems, my distresses, my quest for God, my glimpses of God, my journey to God.

But then there is the further thrill of finding this same pattern repeated everywhere: a thrill which perhaps in some way resembles the vital experience of the saints in their awareness of God's omnipresence, finding all things in God and God in all things: for this new discovery means finding the pattern of the baptismal rebirth, the pattern of the quest for life through death, endlessly stated and restated in the world's art and literature and story and fantasy and dream.

Why Important

To modern man the ritual of baptism or of the Mass might seem strange indeed, the unintelligible language of a strange sect, and the statement of its truths in the theological formulas might equally well seem unreal and fantastic; but how can this be so when the same truths are stated in and through the same symbols, the same pictures, by humanity as a whole, whether in the sometimes dim, sometimes distorted, adumbrations of paganism or in the prefiguring of the Old Testament?

This is indeed one of the chief ways in which pagan myth and ritual are of importance to us: that they show us the *universality* of the truths and facts of which the Bible and Christian ritual speak to us; they show us the *naturalness* and humanness of the Christian supernatural ideals of holiness.

They show us that "the world" does indeed speak through these Christian symbols, but that now, since the symbols communicate not merely an imagined myth-pattern but an historically lived-out theandric experience and activity, they voice not just a vague yearning, or even a far-distant hope, but the humble yet exultant conviction of fulfillment, a fulfillment given to us and realized in us by God through His Christ.

But there is a second way in which these nonscriptural parallels are of importance to us: they can revitalize Christian images which, known to us perhaps from early childhood, have become too familiar and have therefore lost something of their meaning or at least of their vividness.

We can find new light for our understanding of Genesis, for instance, if we study the Babylonian creation-myth; we can gain new insight into the Christian allusions to Christ as Sun or as Fire if we know something of the pagan poetry of sun-worship from ancient Egypt and elsewhere; we can find new meaning in the story of Jonah and the whale if we compare it with its many extrabiblical parallels; and in general we can better understand the dark journey which is the pattern for each one of us if we add to its many biblical presentations those other presentations of it that we find in myth and poetry and folklore and in the rituals of other religions.

CHAPTER 12   Christianity and

the World Religions

R. C. ZAEHNER

Israel and India

          Ease of communications brings all men together:
but the contiguity of bodies does not necessarily entail the cross-
fertilization of minds, and the mere fact that we can now move
round the world at incredible speed does not mean that we are
any better equipped to appreciate the ideas and cultures of other
lands. Indeed it can be argued that the enormous development of
the tourist traffic in Europe has done more to emphasize national
peculiarities than to promote international good will: mere physical
contact between nations does not necessarily lead to better understanding.

That there is need for better understanding, however, few would
deny; and it is only since the last war that Europeans have come
to realize it. For it is quite certain that the last war put an end to
European supremacy forever; and Europeans, so long the master
race, will now have to learn the hard way how to get on on equal
terms with peoples they had previously dominated. Morever, their
recent attainment of freedom has given the Asiatics a new self-
confidence and a new faith in their ancient civilizations.

Christianity benefited greatly from the imperialist expansion of
nominally Christian powers, and Christian missions have made most
progress where European political power has been strongest. With
the retreat of Europe from imperialism all that has changed, and
the newly liberated peoples of Asia see Christianity not so much

R. C. Zaehner, "Christianity and the World Religions," *Blackfriars* (July-
August, 1960), pp. 256-271.

as a rival religion to be judged according to its own merits as the religion of their late masters who so often seemed to behave in a singularly un-Christian way. For them Christianity means the religion of the white man, and on that account it is regarded with deep suspicion. Morever, Asia is very different from Africa, and the missionary task for Christians there is immeasurably more difficult.

Most of Africa (except those parts which had already embraced Islam) only knew religions of the most primitive kind, many of them riddled with witchcraft; and it was therefore easy for Christianity to advertise itself as something immeasurably higher and more worthwhile: there was no serious competition from other higher religions. Asia, however, is the cradle of religion, just as Europe is the cradle of science, and not one of the world religions has originated outside Asia. But there are two peoples which stand out from all the others for the immense contribution they have made to the religious life of the world—Israel and India.

Of the world religions, only one arose independently of either the Hebrew or the Indian religious tradition—Confucianism: and most people would agree that Confucianism is rather a system of social ethics than a religion. Because China was so poor in religious ideas of her own it was possible for the Buddhists to spread throughout the Celestial Empire without meeting serious opposition on the purely religious plane. So it can be said that man's religious heritage derives overwhelmingly from the Hebrews and the Indians. Israel and India are the two peoples which have given the world the faiths by which they live.

Similarity of Form

Moreover, in both traditions we meet with a similar pattern of religious development. In both cases you begin with what was originally a national religion, in the one case Judaism, the religion of the Jewish people, and in the other, Hinduism, the religion of the Hindus, that is, the religion of the Indian people. Both peoples gradually develop throughout the centuries a canon of scripture, and after the completion of the canon both give birth to national heresies which very soon were to become international faiths. Judaism gave birth to Christianity and Hinduism to Buddhism. Again, about 600 years after Christ a new religion was to arise in the Arabian desert which saw itself as the completion of the full Jewish heritage in both the Old and New Testaments: this was Islam, the religion preached by the prophet Mohammed. Similarly in India, again perhaps some 600 years after the death of the Buddha, a new form of Buddhism arose, the Mahayana, which was so different from the older Buddhism as almost to constitute a new religion. Thus, in each of the two religious traditions we start with a strictly national religion, which gives birth to two international or universal faiths. Nor does the parallel stop here, for in each case, beside the main stream flowing from the original source—Israel or India as the case may be—we find a minor subsidiary stream of the same type of religion originating in lands far removed from the main center. Parallel to the Jewish stream is the religion of the prophet Zoroaster which arose in Iran, and parallel to the Indian is Taoism which arose in China. So akin to their own religion did the Jews feel the monotheism of the Iranian prophet to be that their own prophet Isaiah did not hesitate to refer to Cyrus as the "Lord's anointed." So too, when the Buddhists reached China, they very soon saw that there was much in Taoism that was akin to their own religion.

The patterns between the historical development of the two great religious streams in the Far and Near East are, then, strangely alike; but the similarity is all of form, not of content. The development is similar, but the message is completely different: for some of the Oriental religions are so different from our own that few Westerners would understand in what sense they could be regarded as religions at all.

Notion of Religion

No completely satisfactory definition of "religion" has, perhaps, ever been made, but at least in the West we consider that worship of God is an important element in it, and if God is to be worshipped "in spirit and in truth," then, it would seem, we must have some sort of conception of what sort of Being God is. Hence the necessity of revelation. Here, however, we immediately run into difficulties, for how can we be sure that any particular revelation is a true revelation?

Take the Jewish revelation first. Jews, Christians, and Moslems all agree that the Old Testament is a direct revelation of God to man. The Jews, however, maintain that it is the only such true and direct revelation. What Christians consider to be God's final revelation in Jesus Christ, because Christ is not a mere prophet, but the Incarnate Word of God, the Jews reject out of hand as being a heresy because Christ did not conform to their own idea of what the Messiah should be, nor did the idea of an Incarnate God enter into their way of thought at all. So we find the One Truth divided: with the coming of Christianity we no longer have one true religion, we have two, the older one denying all validity to the new. Finally we have yet another revelation in Mohammed, who claimed to be the Seal of the Prophets among whom Jesus was his immediate predecessor. Islam, moreover, denies the Incarnation, and—although the Koran is ambivalent on this point—Moslem tradition has always denied the Crucifixion and the Resurrection, that is to say, it makes nonsense of the whole doctrine of the Atonement. So we find ourselves faced with three religions, all springing from one stem, each of which claims to be uniquely true. This is, obviously, not a very satisfactory state of affairs. It has, moreover, made for intolerance, persecution, and religious war; and it is only recently that we have grown to be a little ashamed of the Crusades, which do not now appear so very different from the ideological wars of today.

How do matters stand in India? There we enter into a totally different climate of opinion—the whole *way* of thinking is different. The parent religion, Vedic Hinduism, is about as different from Judaism as it is possible to be. The sacred book is known as the Veda (meaning "knowledge" or "wisdom"), and this is thought to have been revealed to sacred seers in immemorial antiquity. It is composed of three main strata, of which the last is by far the most important. The earliest part of this enormous storehouse of sacred texts is the Rig-Veda, which consists of over a thousand hymns extolling a number of deities, many of whom obviously represent natural phenomena; only toward the end of the tenth and last book of the Rig-Veda do we find anything resembling monotheism, but this too remains undeveloped. Then what to us seems a very strange phenomenon occurs: interest in the gods as such diminishes, and overriding importance begins to be attached to the ritual as such. The sacrificial ritual is believed to be possessed of immense magical power of itself, quite independent of the deity or deities to whom it is offered; and the welfare of the gods themselves now depends on the correct perform-ance of the ritual: the priest then becomes more important than the god to whom, in theory, the sacrifice is offered. All idea of a supreme, personal, creator God vanished, and instead another con-cept assumed ever-increasing importance, *brahman*, which can best be translated as "sacred power." I have not the space to trace the development of this concept in early Hinduism, but must now pass straight on [to] the third stratum of the Veda, the Upanishads.

Though the whole of the Veda is supposed to be equally sacred, in practice it is the Upanishads, the end of the Veda or Vedanta, which really constitutes the sacred book of the Hindus. Very roughly speaking, it can be said that the Upanishads occupy the place in Hinduism that the New Testament occupies for Christians.

Quest for Immortality

The Upanishads are philosophical in content and are comparable to the earliest type of Greek philosophy in which the philosopher strives to discover the origin of the universe, that is, that one change-less thing from which all change arises and into which it must again dissolve. What they are looking for is a changeless, absolute something that has its being outside space and time, change and causality. This they call *brahman*. Their search for *brahman*, however, is not con-fined to the outside universe; it is also conducted within the human being himself. These ancient seers are not only looking for the deep ground of the universe, they are also looking for their own immortal souls; they are looking both for the immortal substrate of the world and for the immortal substrate of their changing psycho-physical organism. In the event, once they had found the one, they assumed, rashly perhaps, that they had found the other.

Yet, when all is said and done, the main preoccupation of the Upanishads is not so much a quest for the unknown God as the search for an immortal state of being in which, it was thought, the soul, at its deepest level, lived.

Now, parallel with the speculations of the Upanishads went the practice of Yoga which seems to have been practiced in India long before the arrival of the Aryans more than a thousand years before Christ. Yoga is a technique the object of which is to gain complete control of body and mind, through which, the Yogin maintains, man can pierce through to the immortal substrate of his own soul; and in this connection it is very important to know what we mean by the world "immortality." It does not mean "life everlasting" as usually understood by Christians; it does not mean just going on living forever and ever, least of all the "pie in the sky" variety of Christian heaven. It means conquering death by escaping into a form of existence which death cannot attack. The idea is not unfamiliar to Christianity, for Christ Himself says that Satan can slay the body, but he cannot slay the soul, but the Yogin would understand this saying in a different way. For him everything that is conditioned by space and time is subject to birth and death; but what has its being outside space and time cannot be subject to the power of death. His technique is designed to enable man to realize his own true being which inhabits a world, if such we can call it, where either space nor time have any meaning; and where there is no time, of course, there can be no death.

The ultimate aim of all the myriad forms of Hinduism is described by the word *moksha*, which is best translated as "liberation," and by "liberation" is meant liberation from mortal life as we understand it here and now. Indian religion is through and through mystical, and until quite recently it has attached very little importance to this world: it stands poles apart from the Judaic idea of a personal God leading his people through history toward a historical consummation at the end of time. For the Indian, history has no importance whatever.

Historically, however, the Yoga technique was based on a philosophy that was basically atheist, the so-called *Samkhya*. According to this philosophy, reality was two, not one. There were two orders of existence, two eternities. There was the eternity of time without beginning and without end on the one hand, and there was the eternity of timeless and spaceless substances on the other. Timeless being was, however, not an unfractionable Absolute as in the rival philosophy of the Vedanta, it consisted of an infinity of pure essences or souls which, in a manner that is never explained, become enmeshed in this world of space and time. There they are imprisoned, and the goal of man's religious striving must be to escape once and for all from matter and return to his true timeless existence where he is isolated from all that is not his own eternity forever and ever. To show how completely different is this Indian scheme of things from anything we are accustomed to call religion in the West, it should be mentioned that in the classical Yoga system, the existence of a God who controls the universe is admitted, and up to a point he is a God of grace, for he can and will help souls still in the bondage of matter back to their eternal home; but that is all, for once the soul is released, not only is it liberated from time, space, and matter, it has no contact with any other spiritual substance and therefore no contact with God. This, then, is a type of mysticism that is quite foreign to the Christian variety, for in Christian mysticism the ultimate goal is regarded as being union with God: it is usually spoken of in erotic terms, for according to St. John God *is* love. Such terminology would be unthinkable to the Samkhya-Yoga: its aim is not union with anything at all, it is disunion from all that is not man's own eternal self.

Buddhism

Buddhism broke from the Brahmanical orthodoxy because the Buddhists did not recognize the authority of the Veda as a sacred book and because they regarded the whole of official Brahmanism, with its interminable sacrifices, as so much mumbo-jumbo. Early Buddhism was consciously atheistical, that is to say, while it was perfectly prepared to admit the existence of the Brahmanical gods as inhabiting another and no doubt a better world, it was not prepared to bow down and worship them, for the gods themselves were subject to space and time and were bound—at the end of millions of years, maybe—themselves to die and be reborn again. As to whether there was a supreme God, creator of heaven and earth, the Buddha was prepared to keep an open mind. Whether there were many gods or only one or none at all was, for him, simply irrelevant: it was not part of the religious life.

What then for the Buddha was the religious life? Religion, for him, had only one purpose, and that was to enable man to make good his own deliverance from this world of space and time. Nothing else mattered. The source of the human malaise, the Buddha considered, was impermanence. Like all Indians of his time he accepted, not as an article of faith but as a simple fact of existence, the doctrine of transmigration. Our existence stretches back to all pre-eternity and will stretch forward to an eternity without end of more or less miserable lives, sometimes in human form, much more often not, unless the Gordian knot is at some point deliberately cut, and we quietly drop out of space and time, never to be heard of again. This must be the aim of all our striving—to pass away utterly from all our purely human occupations into the timeless peace of *nirvana*. To achieve this state is alone important, and everything not connected with it is irrelevant. More irrelevant than most things is to believe that there is a God or gods who are supposed to be able to help you to achieve your passage to nirvana, for the salvation of every man is in his own hands. "Work out your salvation with diligence," are traditionally the last words the Buddha addressed to his disciples on earth. All the Buddha claimed to be able to do was to point the one sure way that would ultimately bring man to his true goal, which is nirvana, but each individual had to apply the Buddhist precepts for himself. Belief in God was, if anything, a hindrance rather than a help.

On the subject of what nirvana was, the Buddha was purposely vague. It is the "unborn, not become, not made, not compounded," the "stopping of becoming," the "destruction of old age and death"; above all it is the "immortal or deathless," a state beyond time and space in which death can have no possible meaning.

Now, to experience timeless immortality is considered by some to be the essence of all mystical experience; and for the Buddha it was certainly the only experience that was supremely worthwhile. Christian mysticism, however, has rarely spoken in these terms, but in terms of an overwhelming mutual love between God and the soul: and I have heard Buddhists argue that this is simply to express in Christian terms an experience which is of its nature ineffable. Christians speak in this way because for them God *is* love as He is also the Eternal; the taste of eternity, therefore, is interpreted as direct experience of the one Eternal Who, for Christians, is God. But, when all is said and done, according to the Buddhists, the experience must be the same, and any rationalization of it must be more or less false. We shall be returning to the validity or otherwise of this argument later.

Israel and Islam

Indian religion, and particularly Buddhism, represents one type of religion—the mystical, the type of religion that seeks the kingdom of God within you. The opposite type is represented above all by Israel and Islam. The contrast between the two types of religion was great enough to make the partition of the subcontinent of India almost inevitable—for Islam is everything that Hindusim is not, and conversely Hinduism is everything that Islam is not. The two seem mutually incompatible.

Now when we turn from India to the Middle East, a very different picture meets our eyes. For the Jews of the Old Testament God was an ever-present reality. God alone is the Eternal, but He is the Eternal manifesting Himself in history, and His relationship to man is that of a lord to His servant, and man's correct attitude to God is "I hear and I obey." Mysticism is not only wholly foreign to the Old Testament: as understood in India it is foreign even to the so-called Jewish mysticism of the Middle Ages, for the Jewish mystics, though sometimes ready to admit that communion with God is possible, are very reluctant indeed to speak of union; and the Buddhist conception of nirvana would seem not only incomprehensible to an orthodox Jew, but also perhaps blasphemous. As a neo-Calvinist scholar has put it, "It is to repeat the Fall," it is the original sin recorded in the second chapter of Genesis, to try to be "like gods," to seek to be immortal in total independence of God. The Old Testament Jews were acutely conscious of the presence of God as an objective fact: He taught them, rewarded, and punished them here in this life, and because He was so real to them as the controller of their destiny and their guide both in their individual lives and, on a larger canvas, in the history of their nation, they never gave any thought to the immortality of their own souls. For them this was as irrelevant as was the existence of God to the early Buddhists. Moreover, when they did finally come to the idea of the immortality of the soul it was through their contact with the Zoroastrians in the Babylonion captivity.

Though their conceptions of God as omnipotent, omniscient Lord, Who creates the universe out of nothing and communicates with man through prophets, were very similar, the Jews and Zoroastrians differed in one important respect. God's revelation to the Jews is a revelation to a nation, a gradual revelation to a historical community who regarded themselves as God's chosen people. In Zoroastrianism revelation is to one prophet only, and the content of the revelation is, therefore, very much concerned with the individual and his destiny. So it was the prophet Zoroaster who first proclaimed a life after death, and not only did he claim this, he affirmed that at death the soul of each individual soul would be called to judgment at the Bridge of the Requiter, there to receive his lot of weal or woe in accordance with his good or bad deeds on earth.

We have seen that in the Samkhya philosophy in India reality is regarded as being dual: there is a material world which is governed by change, and there is a spiritual world which is changeless. So too with man: he is not a single being; he is an uneasy mixture of two diametrically opposed elements—soul and body. The soul is immortal because it cannot change since it has its being outside time, but the body is mortal; it is subject to birth and death, and then rebirth and redeath forever and ever. By his body man belongs to the animals, by his soul he is pure spirit, what we would call an angel. The combination of these two elements in one organism is regarded as being a disaster for the angelic half of man, and it can have no goal but to escape from the animality of the body. And this escape must be radical, for it means an escape not only from the body but also from the mind since, according to the Samkhya, mind has a material origin quite as much as body.

In the West very similar views were held by Plato and the Gnostics, but this had originally been no part of Jewish thinking nor was it accepted by the prophet Zoroaster. For both the Jews and Zoroaster man was a single unfractionable being, and the union of body and soul was essential to his very nature. Thus the idea of the survival of the soul after the death of the body entered very late into the Jewish way of thinking and was almost certainly derived from Zoroastrianism. Zoroaster, however, though he accepted the Jewish view of man, nevertheless believed in the survival of the soul, but he did not believe that this was its final destiny. God, indeed, would judge the soul at death, and the soul would go on to either heaven or hell in accordance with the kind of life it had led on earth, but that was not the end of the story. At the end of time there would be a final conflagration in which all evil would be destroyed and all things made new. There would be a new heaven and a new earth, the bodies of all men would be resurrected, and the whole human race would enter into life eternal in body and in soul to live forever in eternal bliss.

Thus it will be seen that between Judaism and Zoroastrianism on the one hand and the Indian religions on the other there is the sharpest possible difference of opinion on what constitutes man's good. For the Indians "liberation" means deliverance from matter and time; for the Jews and Zoroastrians it means deliverance from evil; and for them, evil is most certainly not, as it is for the Indians, identical with matter or with life on this earth.

So it will be seen that there is an absolute gulf fixed between the two great religious traditions: and the reason that this is so is that they are rarely talking about the same thing. For the Jews the one vital fact of life is the Lord God and man's true relation to Him; the fate of the individual soul is not thought to be of great consequence in this context because the soul in any case is only one aspect of the whole man, and a man ceases to be a man once soul and body part company. For the Indians the only good worth striving for is the realization here and now of the deathlessness and timelessness of one's own individual soul; whether there is one god or many or none at all is not felt to be important, and what happens to the body and the mind which is dependent on it cannot be of the slightest consequence to the soul.

Indian Developments

Basically then there is no point of agreement between the Jewish (and Mohammedan and Zoroastrian) point of view and the Indian. The situation, however, is not quite as hopeless as this rather stark confrontation would suggest. For Indian religion did not stand still.

So far we have laid all our emphasis on the Samkhya-Yoga and Buddhist aspects of Indian religion, but there were other developments. We have seen that the sages of the Upanishads were looking not only for the immortal and timeless soul in man but also for the immortal and timeless ground of the whole universe: either through

Yoga techniques or quite spontaneously, they found the first, and this they then proceeded to identify with the second. *Because* they had been able to realize the eternity of their own souls, they then concluded that this eternal within them must be the same as the changeless Eternal One which they were convinced was the source and origin of all things. Thus because they *had experienced* the soul as eternal, they concluded that it must be *the* Eternal: they concluded that the soul is God, the changeless essence that gives rise to all this world of change. They thus identified what is a purely psychological condition with a metaphysical construction; or, to put it another way, they identified a state of mind in themselves in which time had been transcended with the Great Being that transcends all things including time. And from this again they concluded that all things in essence are one, and that thus God is All, and since the soul is also identical with God, the soul is also All. So did the pantheistical trend which is so strong in Hinduism begin.

Vedanta

This form of Hindu pantheism is usually known by the name of Vedanta, which is still the predominant philosophy of India. In the last analysis, however, it appears to rest on a confusion of a purely psychological experience with a metaphysical system which really has nothing to do with it. Neither the Buddhists nor the Samkhya-Yogins drew any such conclusion: the Buddhists drew no metaphysical conclusions at all. According to the Samkhya-Yogins, however, all that you could say positively about the experience was that on the achievement of "liberation" you were conscious only of having passed out of space and time into a condition of absolute peace in total isolation from all things both material *and spiritual*: you were eternally alone in and with your own immortal soul: there is no suggestion of union or fusion with anything else whatever. There can, I think, be no doubt that as far as the actual experience goes, the "isolation" of the Samkhya-Yoga is identical with the realization of oneself as the unqualified One of the Vedanta: the Vedanta merely gives the experience a metaphysical interpretation which the psychological facts hardly warrant.

It need hardly be said that the Vedanta does nothing to bridge the gap between the Indian and the Hebraic points of view: on the contrary it widens it, for whereas Buddhism is totally unconcerned with God, the Vedanta reintroduces the idea of God, but not as the personal Lord of the universe but as the impersonal ground of the universe with which the soul is identical. In the religion of the Old Testament there is an unbridgeable gulf between the Creator and the creature, and the creature must approach its Creator in fear and trembling, whereas in the Vedanta creature and creator are one. Such a view is, for a Jew or a Moslem, sheer blasphemy.

Vishnu and Siva

The Vedanta, however, is only one aspect of Hinduism and, as far as popular religion is concerned, not the most important. For while these esoteric theories were being evolved, popular religion was developing on very different lines. As we have seen, the old gods gradually lost their importance, and in Buddhism nothing was put in their place. But in popular Hinduism two gods gradually emerged as the one true God for their devotees: these were Siva and Vishnu, personal gods who were, for their worshippers, the supreme source of the universe, accessible to man and willing to help him. Of the two, Vishnu is the more interesting from the Christian point of view, for he is a god who becomes incarnate in this world "for the protection of the good, for the destruction of evildoers, and for the establishment of the religious law."

The incarnation of Vishnu as Krishna, the charioteer of the mythical hero Arjuna, is the subject of the last and greatest of the Hindu sacred writings, the Bhagavad-Gita; and the main message of the Gita seems to be this. The older doctrine of the identity of the human soul with *brahman* is accepted, but the word *brahman* seems to be used in a different sense. In the passages in which the soul is said to become Brahman, *brahman* seems to mean little more than a timeless state of existence. Moreover, Krishna, as the incarnation of Vishnu, claims to be higher than Brahman, he is the personal God beyond the Absolute, and must be worshipped as such. Moreover, worship and mystical experience are not incompatible, as they must be in the Vedanta system, for if you *are* God, there can plainly be no point in worshipping yourself: indeed, according to the classical Vedanta, once you have achieved liberation, you must cease to observe all religious rites because they are now pointless. The theology of the Gita changes all this: to realize oneself as Brahman means no more than to realize the eternity of one's soul, to realize that because it has its being outside time it cannot die. This realization can only be achieved by giving up all the things of this world, by detaching oneself wholly from all that is not eternal: only so can liberation be won. But once it is won, this is not the end: on the contrary, this represents only the initial stage of purification by which the soul is freed from all the dross of this world and is thereby enabled to enter into communion with *the* Eternal *par excellence* because it is now sufficiently like Him to make such communion possible. Man's goal is no longer the total isolation of his own eternal essence; it is the active participation of that essence in the love of God who is other than he and the only true object of worship. How the realization of the eternity of the soul which, before the Gita, had been the almost exclusive concern of Indian religion, is to be brought into relation with the loving worship of a personal God, is brought out in the last chapter of the Gita:

> By giving up self, . . . force, pride, lust, anger, and acquisitiveness, with no thought of "mine," at peace, so is a man fitted to realize his eternal essence [to realize himself as *brahman*]. Become eternal, his soul all stilled, he grieves not, nor does he desire. Feeling equanimity towards all creatures, he receives the highest love of me. By his loving devotion he comes to know me, how great I am and who. Then, once he has known me as I am, he forthwith comes to me. . . .
>
> Think on me, worship me, sacrifice to me, pay me homage: so shalt thou come to me. I promise thee truly, for I love thee well. Give up all things of the law, turn to me only as thy refuge. I will deliver thee from all evil. Have no care.

So does Krishna, the Incarnate God, summon his devotee to share in his life. This is no longer an arid isolation of the soul within itself, nor is it to delude oneself that one is either God or the "All"; it is an invitation first to realize yourself as you really are, that is, eternal and in that respect *like* God, and having become like God, to love Him who is your eternal exemplar and to enter into Him.

Thus the Bhagavad-Gita completely changed the whole orientation of philosophical Hinduism. Much the same was to happen to Buddhism. The Buddha, of course, had made no claims to deity because he had no belief in God: he had merely claimed to be the "Supremely Enlightened One." Yet only a few centuries after his death his later disciples had transformed him into a triune God, the source and origin of the universe who yet became incarnate in the sixth century B.C., much as Vishnu had done in Hindu legend, "for the establishment of the religious law."

Mahayana and the Bodhisattvas

This, however, was not the most important transformation of the original doctrine that the later Mahayanists brought with it. Despite the ethics of total unselfishness that the earlier forms of Buddhists had taught, the Mahayanists realized that there was, in fact, something inherently selfish in the earlier ascetic ideal. The goal of every man was his own salvation, his own escape into nirvana, not his neighbor's, and this, the Mahayanists thought, was to set at naught the Master's compassion. So in place of the earlier ideal they set that of the Bodhisattvas, those saintly beings who postponed their own nirvana in order to enable their fellow men to enter it before them: they "radiate great friendliness and compassion over all beings, and give their attention to them, thinking: 'I shall become their savior, I shall release them from their sufferings.'" Or more fully the new faith is expressed in the following words:

> However innumerable beings are, I vow to save them. However inexhaustible the passions are, I vow to extinguish them. However innumerable the *dharmas* are, I vow to master them. However incomparable the Buddha-truth is, I vow to attain it.

So does the Bodhisattva gladly accept the task of taking upon himself the suffering of the whole world in order that his fellow men may enter the peace of nirvana; and it seems strange that once the ideal of the Bodhisattva had been created, the Mahayana Buddhists should not have thought that union and communion with such a being was a more worthwhile goal than the featureless and empty peace of nirvana.

Yet both the Hindu God Vishnu in his incarnation as Krishna and the Bodhisattva ideal of the Mahayana Buddhists prepare the way for the Incarnation of God in Christ. For in Christ the good news brought by Krishna that God loves man and the more tragic self-sacrifice of the Bodhisattvas meet. Thus in the historical person of Christ the hopes of Indian religion which always expresses itself in myth are fulfilled. Christ can be regarded as much as the historical Bodhisattva as the historical Messiah.

A Historical Religion

For Christianity, rooted as it is in Judaism, is and remains an historical religion. The world process is not conceived of, as it is in India, as being cyclical; it is not an endlessly repeated process of emanation and reabsorption into the Deity: it has a starting point, a middle, and an end. The starting point is the creation of man and his Fall, and the Christian doctrine of the Atonement is not comprehensible at all except against the background of the Fall: and it is important to know just what we mean by the Fall. According to Catholic doctrine the Fall was the result of the disobedience of Adam, who may be taken as representing the whole human race in the legend; and by disobeying God man asserts his will to live independently of God; he denies his creatureliness and denies that he has need of God. The result of this rebellion not only wrecked the harmony that had previously existed between man and God, it also wrecked the harmony of man's own being. Body and soul were henceforth to be at war, and physical death is therefore seen as being the direct result of original sin: for God is the source of all life, and once man has declared his independence of God, he cuts himself off from the source of his own life. But, according to the legendary account in Genesis, the soul of man is of the breath of God and to that extent divine. The soul, then, cannot die, and must continue to live on after the death of the body: but this does not mean that it thereby returns to God; it does not, because it has rejected God. What then can it do?

Fallen man, separated as he now is from God, looks at himself, and sees that there is something seriously wrong with him: he is not a united whole, he is half immortal and half mortal, half angel and half beast. There is thus no cure for him except to realize himself as wholly angel: he must slay the beast. This is what all mysticism tries to do, and it is the secret of the Buddha's Enlightenment. At his Enlightenment the Buddha realized that he had conquered death, he had freed forever his immortal part from his mortal frame; and this, he thought, must be man's ultimate good; and given the human condition as he actually found it, he was right. Man, as he now exists, *is* an unnatural amalgam of an immortal soul and a mortal body, and the highest good he can achieve by his own efforts is to shake off that part of him which is mortal: this the Buddha and other Indian sages did, but the Buddha did not obscure the nature of this liberation with unwarrantable metaphysical claims; he did not claim that the timeless being he enjoyed was the totality of all divine life as the Vedantins did. He merely confirmed by his own experience what the prophet Zoroaster claimed to know by divine revelation, namely, that man's soul is immortal and timeless and therefore indestructible. He experienced what Christian doctrine was later to assert, that the soul is as certainly immortal as the body is mortal.

Indian religion takes man as it finds him, a duality: and for this duality there can be no salvation except the final disjunction of the immortal half from the mortal one. Neither Judaism nor Zoroastrianism, however, was prepared to accept this duality as final. The soul and the body, they felt, were mutually dependent, the body being the means by which the soul expressed itself. Immortal life could never be complete until the body came to share in it: so, Zoroaster maintained, God would create a new heaven and a new earth in which men would enjoy eternal beatitude in body as well as in soul. The same idea is graphically expressed by St. Paul in the Epistle to the Romans: "For we know," he says, "that the whole creation groaneth and travaileth in pain together until now. And not only they, but ourselves also, which have the first fruits of the Spirit, even we groan within ourselves, waiting for the adoption, to wit, the redemption of our body."

Christ and the World Religions

Thus, seen against the background of both Indian religion and of the message of Zoroaster, the purpose of Christ's Incarnation, death, and Resurrection becomes a little more clear. God, by becoming man, confirms the Judaeo-Zoroastrian view that the body has a dignity of its own, and by dying and rising from the dead as man He demonstrates that man's ultimate destiny is immortality in body and in soul. The final climax of the Incarnation, however, is not the Resurrection but the Ascension; and this represents the final healing of the breach between man and God: man is taken up into heaven "and sitteth at the right hand of God the Father Almighty." In other words the link between man and God, broken by original sin, is restored, and it is possible for the old love affair between the two to be resumed. Christ's bodily Resurrection and Ascension, however, are only the "First fruits," the certain promise that at the end of time all men will rise from the dead. Seen against the background of Indian religion, however, Christ's Resurrection and Ascension have another significance. In Biblical terminology the crucifixion represents the slaying of the "old Adam" and the Resurrection represents the birth of the "new Adam"; in Indian terminology it is the destruction of the lower soul and the realization of the timeless, immortal soul; but at the same time it is more than this, for as the Mahayana Buddhists realized, the realization of one's own immortality is not enough; there is still a remnant of selfishness even in nirvana, and this too must be crucified: only then, as the Bhagavad-Gita teaches, can the grace of God flow in. The isolation of the immortal soul is indeed the furthest point man can reach by his own unaided efforts; he cannot proceed beyond this without the grace of God, and this further leap into the divine is enacted in the Ascension of Jesus Christ, the Man-God, to the Father. Thus salvation, for the Christian, does not mean "isolation" within an immortal essence as it does for the Samkhya-Yogin, but a close union and communion with God in a mutual outpouring of love, and not only with God, but with all other souls. This is the doctrine of the Communion of Saints.

Thus it would seem that all the highest insights of the more ancient religions meet in Christianity. By dying for His friends Christ demonstrates the total quality of God's love for man as foreshadowed in the Bhagavad-Gita and the Bodhisattva doctrine of Mahayana Buddhism; by ascending to the Father He shows that the destiny of the human soul, now that the rift between God and man has been healed, is no longer to be sought in isolation but in loving communion with God; and by the whole drama of the Incarnation and Resurrection He confirms the prophecy of Zoroaster that in the last days man will be resurrected in body as well as in soul, and that he will live, as it was God's intention that he should, a harmonious whole within the greater whole of the totality of God's universe, communing forever with his Maker, God.

PART SEVEN

The Justification

and Meaning of Belief

Entering into the basic concerns of the existentialist philosophers about the meaning of life itself, Albert Dondeyne (author of a perceptive and comprehensive book called *Contemporary European Thought and the Christian Faith*) approaches the *problem of God*. Much of his essay argues a necessary preliminary, the possibility of knowledge of another kind of reality than that which is the subject matter of the natural sciences. Can we really know anything that is incapable of empirical verification? The many "nothing-but" reductions of reality that abound in our civilization and in the preoccupations of earlier writers in this volume are exposed in the fullness of their implications. Dondeyne casts considerable light on the problems intrinsic to the other essays. The essay deserves and probably requires several readings. It should direct attention to the possibility and meaning of philosophy. Though the author does not refer explicitly to the Anglo-American logical positivists and their variants, still what he has to say will be found to have application in regard to them. Some fundamental questions carry ahead the discussion in the essay: Is life worth living? Is there a purpose or power behind it? If there is a purpose or power behind it, can *it* be addressed as Thou?

As an aid to the recollection or open spirit that Dondeyne early postulates as necessary for his venture, we have prefixed three significant and parallel aids from a French Catholic and mathematical genius, Blaise Pascal; a Danish Protestant thinker, Søren Kierkegaard; and Albert Camus, non-Christian spokesman for many of our serious contemporaries.

Finally a distinguished theologian, Jean Daniélou, gives us a positive, wide-ranging, and very personal treatment of religious faith without abstracting it from man's psychology and today's milieu. Even though his essay terminates the book, it is meant to be, as Daniélou says, a beginning, not an end, the beginning of something this book only approaches. He and Dondeyne force the Christian reader or student to raise questions about his Christianity and the nature of commitment to Christ. What *does* Christianity mean? Do we, do I, actually have faith in Christ? Do I have a right to believe? Again, do I really know what it means to believe? Do I realize how faith shatters some very natural tendencies and set patterns of thought and explanation? Is faith realized at one moment, and is it then forever static? Is faith the result of good philosophical thinking and a certain amount of apologetic knowledge? Do I believe with the mind, the will, the feelings, the guts?

CHAPTER 13

Selections

BLAISE PASCAL

Weariness

Nothing is so insufferable to man as to be completely at rest, without passions, without business, without diversion, without study. He then feels his nothingness, his forlornness, his insufficiency, his dependence, his weakness, his emptiness. There will immediately arise from the depth of his heart weariness, gloom, sadness, fretfulness, vexation, despair.

* * *

Diversion

When I have occasionally set myself to consider the different distractions of men, the pains and perils to which they expose themselves at court or in war, whence arise so many quarrels, passions, bold and often bad adventures, and so forth, I have discovered that all the unhappiness of men arises from one single fact, that they cannot stay quietly in their own chamber. . . . On further consideration, when, after finding the cause of all our ills, I have sought to discover the reason of it, I have found that there is one very real reason, namely, the natural poverty of our feeble and mortal condition, so miserable that nothing can comfort us when we think of it closely. . . . Hence it comes that play and the society of women, war, and high posts are so sought after. Not that there is in fact any happiness in them, or that men imagine true bliss to consist in money won at play, or in the hare which they hunt; we would not take these as a gift. We do not seek that easy and peaceful lot which permits us to

From *Pascal's Pensées*, trans. by W. F. Trotter (New York: Dutton Paperback Series, 1958), by permission of E. P. Dutton & Co., Inc., and J. M. Dent & Sons, Ltd.

think of our unhappy condition, nor the dangers of war, nor the labor of office, but the bustle which averts these thoughts of ours and amuses us.

Reasons why we like the chase better than the quarry.

Hence it comes that men so much love noise and stir; hence it comes that the prison is so horrible a punishment; hence it comes that the pleasure of solitude is a thing incomprehensible. And it is in fact the greatest source of happiness in the condition of kings that men try incessantly to divert them, and to procure for them all kinds of pleasures. The king is surrounded by persons whose only thought is to divert the king, and to prevent his thinking of self. For he is unhappy, king though he be, if he think of himself.

* * *

Thus passes away all man's life. Men seek rest in struggle against difficulties; and when they have conquered these, rest becomes insufferable. For we think either of the misfortunes we have or those which threaten us. And even if we should see ourselves sufficiently sheltered on all sides, weariness of its own accord would not fail to arise from the depths of the heart wherein it has its natural roots, and to fill the mind with its poison. Thus so wretched is man that he would weary even without any cause for weariness from the peculiar state of his disposition; and so frivolous is he that, though full of a thousand reasons for weariness, the least thing, such as playing billiards or hitting a ball, is sufficient to amuse him.

CHAPTER 14

Selections

SØREN KIERKEGAARD

    . . . for worldliness means precisely attributing infinite value to the indifferent. The worldly view always clings fast to the difference between man and man, and naturally it has no understanding of the one thing needful (for to have that is spirituality), and therefore no understanding of the narrowness and meanness of mind which is exemplified in having lost one's self—not by evaporation in the infinite, but by being entirely finitized, by having become, instead of self, a number, just one man more, one more repetition of this everlasting *Einerlei.*

    Despairing narrowness consists in the lack of primitiveness, or of the fact one has deprived oneself of one's primitiveness; it consists in having emasculated oneself, in a spiritual sense. For every man is primitively planned to be a self, appointed to become oneself; and while it is true that every self as such is angular, the logical consequence of this merely is that it has to be polished, not that it is to be ground smooth, not that for fear of men it dare not be itself in its essential accidentality (which precisely is what should not be ground away), by which in fine it is itself. But while one sort of despair plunges wildly into the infinite and loses itself, a second sort permits itself as it were to be defrauded by "the others." By seeing the multitude of men about it, by getting engaged in all sorts of worldly affairs, by becoming wise about how things go in this world, such a man forgets himself, forgets what his name is (in the divine understanding of it), does not dare to believe in himself, finds it too venturesome a thing to be himself, far easier and safer to be like the others, to become an imitation, a number, a cipher in the crowd.

* * *

Reprinted from *Sickness Unto Death* by Søren Kierkegaard, trans. Walter Lowrie, by permission of Princeton University Press. Copyright 1941 by Princeton University Press.

Generally the need of solitude is a sign that there is a spirit in man after all, and it is a measure for what spirit there is. The purely twaddling inhuman and too-human men are to such a degree without feeling for the need of solitude that like a certain species of social birds (the so-called lovebirds) they promptly die if for an instant they have to be alone. As the little child must be put to sleep by a lullaby, so these men need the tranquilizing hum of society before they are able to eat, drink, sleep, pray, fall in love, and so forth. But in ancient times as well as in the Middle Ages people were aware of the need of solitude and had respect for what it signifies. In the constant sociability of our age people shudder at solitude to such a degree that they do not know of any other use to put it to but (oh, admirable epigram!) as a punishment for criminals. But after all it is a fact that in our age it is a crime to have spirit, so it is natural that such people, the lovers of solitude, are included in the same class with criminals.

CHAPTER 15

Selections

ALBERT CAMUS

There is but one truly serious philosophical problem, and that is suicide. Judging whether life is or is not worth living amounts to answering the fundamental question of philosophy. All the rest—whether or not the world has three dimensions, whether the mind has nine or twelve categories—comes afterwards.

* * *

Whether the earth or the sun revolves around the other is a matter of profound indifference. To tell the truth, it is a futile question. On the other hand, I see many people die because they judge that life is not worth living. I see others paradoxically getting killed for the ideas or illusions that give them a reason for living (what is called a reason for living is also an excellent reason for dying). I therefore conclude that the meaning of life is the most urgent of questions.

* * *

We get into the habit of living before acquiring the habit of thinking. In that race which daily hastens us toward death, the body maintains its irreparable lead. In short, the essence of that contradiction lies in what I shall call the act of eluding because it is both less and more than diversion in the Pascalian sense. Eluding is the invariable game. The typical act of eluding, the fatal evasion that constitutes the third theme of this essay, is hope. Hope of another life one must "deserve" or trickery of those who live not for life itself but for some great idea that will transcend it, refine it, give it a meaning, and betray it.

* * *

It happens that the stage sets collapse. Rising, streetcar, four hours in the office or the factory, meal, streetcar, four hours of work, meal,

Albert Camus, *The Myth of Sisyphus and Other Essays*, Justin O'Brien, trans., copyright 1960, by permission of Alfred A. Knopf, Inc., and Hamish Hamilton, Ltd.

sleep, and Monday, Tuesday, Wednesday, Thursday, Friday, and Saturday according to the same rhythm—this path is easily followed most of the time. But one day the "why" arises and everything begins in that weariness tinged with amazement. "Begins"—this is important. Weariness comes at the end of the acts of a mechanical life, but at the same time it inaugurates the impulse of consciousness. It awakens consciousness and provokes what follows. What follows is the gradual return into the chain or it is the definitive awakening. At the end of the awakening comes, in time, suicide or recovery. In itself weariness has something sickening about it. Here, I must conclude that it is good. For everything begins with consciousness and nothing is worth anything except through it. There is nothing original about these remarks. But they are obvious; that is enough for a while, during a sketchy reconnaissance in the origins of the absurd. Mere "anxiety," as Heidegger says, is the source of everything.

* * *

I come at least to death and to the attitude we have toward it. On this point everything has been said and it is only proper to avoid pathos. Yet one will never be sufficiently surprised that everyone lives as if no one "knew." This is because in reality there is no experience of death. Properly speaking, nothing has been experienced but what has been lived and made conscious. Here, it is barely possible to speak of the experience of others' deaths. It is a substitute, an illusion, and it never quite convinces us.

CHAPTER 16

The Existence of God
and Contemporary Materialism

ALBERT DONDEYNE

Presenting the issue between contemporary materialism and belief in God means conducting an argument. This argument we want to be as straightforward as possible, so here is an initial misunderstanding to clear up.

To the man in the street, especially if he is sincerely religious, the word "materialist" has an anything but flattering connotation. It suggests a person who is selfish and sensual, immersed in brute matter, incapable of lofty thoughts or any noble sentiments. Thus "materialism" comes to imply a certain *ethical behavior* associated with a materialistic conception of the universe.

Actually things are not so simple as all that. Contemporary materialism is not always, or necessarily, a flat denial of spiritual values. Marxism, materialist as it is, finds room in its vocabulary for mind and liberty: it demands freedom for humanity and its deliverance from material constraints. Is it possible, then, to call oneself a humanist and a materialist at the same time; to proclaim the primacy of freedom and of the human personality and yet deny the existence of spirit? In actual fact there is no contradiction.

And for the following reason: Human existence can be considered on two different levels.

In the first place we have the level of *immediate data* or, in modern terms, of the *phenomenological description of existence*. By that we mean the consciousness of our existence, such as appears directly in

Albert Dondeyne, "The Existence of God and Contemporary Materialism," *God, Man and the Universe*, Jacques de Bivort de la Saudée, ed. (New York: P. J. Kenedy & Sons, 1953), pp. 3-32.

the daily experience we have of it. This is a fact there is no denying. Man possesses a certain consciousness of his own being: he experiences himself as existing, and precisely in this experience of existing he appears to himself not as something inert and static, but as an inexhaustible urge, a being haunted and enlightened by values. Among these values there are some that directly concern the body, conferring physical well-being: of such is health, and all that makes for health. But there are values that transcend the corporal or biological: such is the joy of knowing, aesthetic emotion, unselfish love, freedom, a society governed by justice, and respect for the individual. These values we will call spiritual. Even more than the first, they make human existence appear as something "worthwhile," deserving to be loved and pursued, something for which it is worth working and striving. In short, at the level of immediate consciousness man is revealed to himself as "body and soul," as "animal endowed with reason," as "thinking reed," as "located freedom," as "consciousness-in-a-body," as "interiority and exteriority," as "for-self and in-self," as "spirit incarnate." All these expressions have been invented in the course of the ages to convey the native complexity of human existence, a complexity that is at once unity and tension between two different aspects at first sight contrary, the material and the spiritual aspect of our being. There has long been in existence a "spiritist" vocabulary; there can be no abandoning it now, for it corresponds to facts that it would be senseless to deny.

But man is not satisfied with merely registering facts and describing phenomena. He must explain and understand. He dreams of a definitive explanation of the universe. Accordingly as he sees in matter or spirit the ultimate foundation of things, what finally produces and explains the universe, he will be a materialist or a spiritist as the case may be; and that no longer in the phenomenal, but in the *scientific* and *metaphysical*, sense.

Now contemporary materialism is scientific and philosophical. It is a prolongation of science, professes to supply the ultimate explanation of things, and does not hesitate to offer itself as something imperatively demanded by truth and freedom. It considers belief in God as a myth without foundation, a hypothesis not merely useless but actually harmful to the progress of science and to the liberation of mankind.

Modern Materialism Is a Scientific
and Philosophical Materialism

Our purpose, here, is not to follow the history of materialism since Feuerbach, nor to examine in detail the forms and various shades it assumes today. All that is important is to understand the essence of contemporary materialism and wherein lies the source of its strength.

Materialism is philosophical when, as an ultimate and definitive explanation of things, the primacy is given to matter, this being regarded as the substratum, the very stuff and ultimate foundation of beings and of all the manifestations of existence. In materialism, matter and reality are ultimately synonymous. In this sense, Auguste Comte was right to define materialism as the tendency to explain the higher by the lower. But Feuerbach's definition perhaps throws more light on what is the essence of all materialism: "Matter cannot derive from intelligence, nor be explained by it; it is much rather the foundation of personality, without being itself founded on anything: spirit without nature is a mere abstraction, consciousness develops only by taking nature for its starting point. This doctrine is . . . materialist." [1]

But what are we to understand by matter? Surely not the idea of it held by Descartes, for whom matter was just amorphous and inert extension, inasmuch as the universe was only an immense vortex of material particles in motion. Modern science is not mechanist in the Cartesian sense. Matter is not inert; it is essentially energy, a field of force. Nor is it amorphous; it includes form, *Gestalt*, and consequently an indefinite potentiality of structure, from the constellation we call the atom to that infinitely complex organism, the human brain. Therefore, in the materialist language of today, the word "matter" takes on a much fuller meaning than with the mechanist materialists of the past; it is more like the common-sense view of matter. Common sense also is apt to identify matter with reality. By real, it understands sensible reality, what we see, touch, and feel, what we can verify as existing by the various data of our senses. The psychic and mental world, consciousness and the infinitely complicated play of feelings, thoughts and reasonings seem very fragile and unreal compared with the indestructible solidity of the material universe.

For common sense, thought will never be anything but an image, a reflection of that true reality, which is sensible and tangible matter.

At first sight the materialist conception of the world is surprising. It seems to conflict with reason: to explain the higher by the lower, the more by the less, would seem to be the reverse of sound logic and good sense. Actually the question is not so simple. The strength of contemporary materialism—it is perhaps also its weakness—lies in its close relationship with positive science. The very structure of scientific explanation, in the modern sense, is an analytical process of reducing the complex to the simple, the more to the less perfect. This is what we now have to examine more closely.

We must not confuse scientism with positive science. If it is true that we have seen the bankruptcy of the prophetic and flashy scientism of the second half of the nineteenth century, it would be wrong to speak of any failing on the part of science. Scientism and science are not the same thing. The prestige of science is still increasing.

It is important to understand the reasons for this. The growing prestige and authority of science are due to the intention and aim by which it is animated, and by the way it has succeeded in achieving its aim. This intention is none other than a very genuine insistence on truth and certitude, which science alone, in one sense at least, is capable of attaining. The reason is this: the desire for knowledge and truth that haunts the human spirit demands, within an inseparable unity, three things. (1) We must have an *objective* knowledge: capable, that is, of revealing the real, attaining things "in person," as they really are, not as we imagine them or as we would like them to be. The constant aim of true knowledge will be, as Heidegger says, to "unveil," to make manifest to us, "the existent itself . . . nothing else, nothing more, nothing beyond," in short "to let the existent be." [2] The man of science would say: "We must let the facts speak." (2) It follows that our desire for truth tends always to a *universally valid* knowledge, capable of creating agreement between different minds, susceptible of being verified and checked by others. (3) But this knowledge is at the same time required to be a knowledge that *explains* and *understands*. The human mind can never be content with merely recording facts, storing up data at random. Its final aim is to see clearly into facts, to grasp their how and why, to explain and understand. Comprehension always involves in some way "taking together," disclosing relationships, reducing the diversity of data to the unity of an idea or a law, or a system of ideas and laws, all logically coherent; in short, to introduce unity, order, and intelligible clarity into the infinite jumble of events that make up the universe. Hence the importance of hypothesis in building up knowledge. A hypothesis is first a mental construction, a work of the mind with a meaning for the mind. It is the light which the mind needs to see into facts. The mind, as it were, goes to meet the facts, armed with the hypothesis, so that the language of the facts may be a language it understands.

These three demands, it is important to notice, are all inseparably embodied in the desire for knowledge. Each appeals to the others. The intelligible unity that consciousness pursues (the how and the why, the rule and the law) must itself bear the mark of objectivity: it must, in some sort, spring from the facts themselves, be able to be verified and checked *in* the facts.

Now it must be granted that only science, in the modern sense of the word—science, that is, based on experiments methodically ordered, capable of being verified and checked at will—answers, and that in a wholly unique way, to the triple requirement we have seen to be at the heart of our desire to attain truth.[3] The enormous prestige of modern science is due to this.

Indeed its authority is so great that it is in a fair way to eclipse all other forms of knowledge, and to relegate them slightingly to the realms of dreaming, sentiment, or myth. Science's great temptation is to abuse its authority and play the dictator. It would take as its slogan: There is no truth but scientific truth. In so doing, science sets itself up as a philosophical conception of truth and the universe. Reality, it would say, is what positive science reveals, and it is *nothing but that*. That is how science comes to be transformed into scientific and philosophical materialism.

Why is this? What is this magic link between science and materialism? There is nothing magical about it. It is all indicated in what we have said already about the structure of science and the ideal of truth that it pursues. This ideal of science marks out its domain, and this domain can be nothing else than the external world in the broadest sense, namely, the world of bodies, including man. It is, in fact, only external observation, the grasping of external facts and events, that admits of experiment universally verifiable and capable of being checked. The internal psychic fact, as such, is something incapable of being checked. If we add to all this the fact that mathematical intelligibility means intelligibility in respect of quantity, namely, the external as such, it will be realized that exact science, in proportion as it approaches the ideal, assumes the form of mathematicized physics. Modern physics becomes the archetype of modern science. The sciences of life, in proportion as they transcend the stage of morphological description, turn to biochemistry. Psychology, in order to be scientific, becomes behaviorist, confining itself as far as possible to the study of outward behavior.[4] Sociology becomes positive and static. In short, the higher becomes in some sort reduced to the lower, and the process of reduction by analysis becomes the ideal of all explanation. The structure of mathematical physics is regarded as an example to imitate and an ambition to achieve, drawing the whole imposing array of modern sciences in its train. Moreover this ambition is no empty project. It has proved itself remarkably successful. Rules and laws are everywhere laid bare, relations of antecedent to consequence, of conditioning to the conditioned. The close connection between biology and physics becomes clearer every day. Thus, by many thinkers, materialism is quite naturally regarded as the philosophy of the future, as the only ultimate explanation of things that can be a true continuation of science. Man is now "just an aggregate of trillions of cells, each of them a collection of diverse molecules." [5] As far as thought is concerned, it is in the cells of the cerebral crust that "there occur chemical reactions and transformations of energy which account for what we call consciousness, of which we know nothing except that it is inseparably connected with these reactions and transformations." [6] As for the affirmation of God and the immortality of the soul, this very evidently loses all validity. The biologist will tend to look for some psychic origin for it, the sociologist will try to explain it by social or economic environment. Feuerbach would have it that it is due to our selfish desire for happiness.[7] Auguste Comte consigned it to the "theological age" of humanity, characterized by a childish mentality, prescientific and even prelogical. For Marx, faith in God and in survival is a product of the capitalist regime, being nothing other than the sentimental and imaginative compensation whereby a downtrodden, servile proletariat projects into the beyond the happiness of which in this life it is deprived: "Religion is the sigh of the creature overwhelmed by misfortune, the heart of a heartless world, the mind of an age without mind. It is the opium of the people." [8]

Such is modern materialism. Like every materialist conception of the world, there is something in it hard and humiliating to the human heart. Truly enough, as Rostand says, we must reverse the Shakespearean dictum and now say: "There are fewer things in heaven and earth than are dreamed of in all our philosophies." [9] But the choice between materialism and belief in God is not a question of sentiment. The prestige of contemporary materialism comes to it, when all is said, from its alliance with modern science. Is scientific truth really the only truth that counts, the only form of certitude of which man is capable? This is the crucial point on which our argument with the materialist must concentrate.

Before going further and entering the thick of the debate, we must be more precise about the second horn of the dilemma. We know now the nature of materialism. But what exactly do we understand by the "existence of God" or the "affirmation of God"?

The Religious Affirmation of God

The man of science, especially if he has no religion, sees theism simply as a hypothesis to be set parallel, or in opposition, to his own. It is not surprising that he finds the theist explanation a useless encumbrance and that he prefers the clarity of scientific materialism to the nebulous hypothesis of a creative God. Such a God always appears to him as a *deus ex machina*. Jean Rostand puts it very well: "We refine God away, we simplify Him, strip Him of His attributes, accept His silence and passivity. We agree that everything in this world takes place as though He never existed. All we ask of Him is that we keep His name." [10]

If this were the only meaning and significance of theism our argument with the materialist would lose much of its seriousness. Fundamentally a God who is postulated merely as a final explanation of the universe hardly concerns us. We scarcely care whether the world was set in motion by an "initial shove" given it by God, as Descartes believed, or whether physical movements are the effect of a transformation of energy that constitutes and defines matter. The universe of electrons, neutrons, and protons that gives us being may itself be given being and kept in existence by a creative God; but unless that God is a God-for-us, the fact represents no value or aim for us; it makes little difference to our situation in the world and sheds little light on the great agonizing question: is life, or is it not, worth the pains of living?

The affirmation of God that we have in mind at the moment has quite a different bearing. What we want to confront the materialist with is the affirmation of God in the full and customary sense of the word: namely, *faith in God* or the *religious affirmation of God*. The believer is not content with thinking of the world as created by a transcendent first cause; in the act of faith he cleaves to God Himself, he addresses Him directly, opens his heart to Him as to an Absolute Thou, in the hope that God will be his light, his truth, and his life, as He was for Abraham, Isaac, and Jacob, as He was for Jesus Christ. *"Deus, illuminatio mea et salus mea; quem timebo?"* cries the Psalmist: "The Lord is my light and my deliverance, whom have I to fear?" (Ps. 26:1).

It is not to the *concept* of God, or to the proposition "God exists," that the believer gives assent, but to God Himself. He affirms, he recognizes that God exists and that God is God; but his affirmation goes far beyond a conceptual and abstract enunciation; it is like a judgment of value proclaimed with his whole being, in an act of trust and self-surrender to a God regarded as the supreme value of all. Such an act of trustful adherence to Him would naturally have no meaning, should even be considered presumptuous and unseemly on our part, if on God's part there were nothing to correspond to Him, or, to be more precise, if God had not taken the initiative and constituted Himself man's light, truth, and life—in short, God-for-us-and-with-us. That is why the religious affirmation of God is in its very structure a dialogue with God, God being the first speaker, or as St. John says, "showing love for us first" (1 John 4:10).

This, then, is the affirmation of God we are thinking of at the moment. It is a religious affirmation, faith in God, recognized as a supreme value, as God-for-us. It is not the answer to a theoretical question about the ultimate structure of the universe, but to a vital, fundamental question, one that no man can ignore: What, when finally analyzed, is our existence worth? Nor can the answer to the question be found by means of scientific investigation. Philosophy itself, considered as the search for the final explanation of things, is also incapable of giving us the definitive answer. Actually, if God deigns, by a loving initiative of His own, to become God-for-us, it is for Him to make us know Him. The religious experience of humanity will here have the last word. This experience is a fact given us, one that deserves our attention just as much as a scientific fact, as much as aesthetic creation or moral grandeur: to refuse *a priori* to take it into consideration would be to give proof of a dogmatism that would have no place in a quest for true knowledge.

So the question to be examined narrows down to this: Is belief in God, as we encounter it in humanity, a mere chimerical play of the imagination, or can it be considered as founded in reason? Has man sound reasons for believing in God?

[NOTE:] It is desirable here to draw attention to the ambiguity of the term "reason" and its derivatives (rational, irrational, rationality, rationalism). Every science is marked by a type of rationality that is proper to it and constitutes its logical structure. Broadly, there are two basic meanings of the word "reason," corresponding to two quite different types of rationality. There is first of all the narrow, rationalist, and what one might call the Cartesian sense of the word. It allows no place to mystery. Descartes, in fact, understands by reason the faculty and domain of clear and distinct ideas, with the logical deductions they suggest. Geometry is its ideal form. Modern positive science, with mathematical physics at its summit, pays tribute to Cartesian rationality: it seeks clear facts, that can be discerned with precision, and aims at establishing between them relations that can be formulated mathematically. But the word "reason" also has a wide sense, one that we are willing to call *existential*. Reason means now the general exigence that is within us and the corresponding power to found and justify our affirmations and behavior. It is this exigence that makes us human beings, it is the basis of our freedom and personality. To act as a human being is to assume responsibility for one's actions and make them one's own; it is to affirm and act, knowing what one is doing and why. There are realities, truths, and values that we justly consider to be founded in reason because they thrust themselves upon us in a way there is no avoiding. Yet these wholly escape an *a priori* dialectic of the Cartesian sort, as well as scientific demonstration as it is understood today. Such, for example is our experience of existing as I-and-others-in-the-world, of the existence of others, and generally speaking of the world of values and acceptance of values. A man takes his revolver and kills someone. From the scientist's point of view there is nothing there but a sequence of physico-chemical processes. Was it an act of patriotism or a dastardly crime? Science cannot tell. Are we then to conclude that patriotism is merely an empty word not founded in reason? Reason in its wide, existential sense is not exclusive of mystery, namely the possibility of an existential reality transcending the clear and distinct idea, but yet having a meaning for consciousness. Naturally we are using the word reason in the wide sense when we talk of justifying faith in the eyes of reason.

The First Existential Question

"There is only one philosophical problem that is really serious," says Albert Camus, "and that is suicide. To decide whether life is worth living or not is to answer the fundamental question in philosophy." [11] Let us consider the problem.

In the eyes of the believer, the answer to this problem is faith. It goes without saying that this answer has no sense, and no value as an answer, for any but the person who asks the question. It is one that anyone can ask himself. It is one that he must ask. Or to be more precise, it is one which, by an act of faith in the mystery of being that is ourself, we must allow to arise in us, to develop without hindrance, and to become urgent. This is what we propose to do now.

It is no arbitrary problem. It is an existential question, one with all that is most profoundly human in us.

Man, after all, is a being who asks questions, as modern philosophy is never tired of assuring us. It is in this that man is distinguished from other beings, that he emerges from the universe of which he is a part and transcends the world of brute nature and animal life.

Inert matter asks itself no questions. A table is what it is; it is not perturbed about what it is, or about what it ought to be. Nor does the animal ask questions. It lives, uses its appetites and instincts, but without reflecting, without wondering about those appetites or instincts, what they are for or what they are worth.

Man, on the other hand, is able to reflect, to return upon himself, to view himself and the world from without; in short, to be astonished and ask questions. Questioning and reflection are very closely associated, not to say synonymous. It is out of reflection that there come to be born and matured our genuinely human actions, namely, our cognitions and all our acts that are clearly understood, that are motivated and deliberate.

But this reflection, with the motivated knowledge it engenders and the enlightened action it makes possible, is not only capable of diversity, according to the objects it chisels out in the external world, but it can also attain different degrees of depth. I can question the universe and adventure into it as a mathematician or a biologist, as a physician or an economist; but I can also return upon myself and ask what this "I" really is, busying itself with science and techniques, with economy and social activities. When I do so, I transcend my own particular worldly activities and investigations and turn my attention to the existential totality that supports and pervades them: I go in quest of first origins, of the profundity of being, of the final meaning of my existence as a whole. The question I ask myself is: What am I, after all, and what is my life worth?

This last question is inevitable, and it has several characteristics:

1. In the first place of all, it lies altogether beyond scientific investigation and our cultural projects for making the world more habitable. It springs, so to speak, from an existential region far deeper than the course of science and civilization, since it is inherent in my existence considered as a whole, which subtends and pervades all my projects, adventures, and particular tasks. It is not to be found in the field of scientific research or any particular worldly activity: not that it interferes with these, but it cannot be resolved by them.

This is a very important point. It follows from it that neither scientific progress nor the evolution of civilization can ever succeed in silencing the question of the ultimate meaning of our existence. It was the great illusion of Comte to suppose that one day science would make philosophy and religion superfluous, just as it was the mistake of Marx to suggest that a Communist organization of society would bring about of its own accord the extinction of the need for religion.

2. The question of the ultimate meaning of our existence as a whole has as its aim, very evidently, the throwing of light on this existence as a whole. In this respect it is something urged upon us in the name of enlightenment and freedom. What is freedom if not the power that is in us to assume control of our existence, to give it a deliberate meaning and become fully engaged with it. Far from hampering our freedom, the metaphysical and religious question

presents itself as something in us that our freedom needs, as an effort to give our freedom its full value and definitive development. As long as we are in ignorance about what our life is ultimately worth, we remain shrouded in darkness; in a very precise sense we are not truly free.

3. The question that engages us here is not one of pure speculation. It is the most practical question of all. It concerns the meaning, the ultimate value, of life. Now every quest for value is as it were the germ of a judgment of value; it presupposes an openness of the soul, a degree of willing acceptance in regard to the value sought.

What is true of judgment of value in general applies *a fortiori* to the search for the ultimate value of life, for the value of existence as a mysterious whole. Where the meaning of existence as a whole or as a mystery is stifled by the pressure, for instance, of a dissipated life or of daily care for immediate worldly projects, there will scarcely be room for a dialectic of the soul in relation to God, the ultimate and transcendent value.

It is of vital importance, therefore, that the sense of existence, as totality and mystery, should be allowed to arise in us spontaneously: this means the development of an attitude of the soul, what one might well call a certain *existential climate*, both spiritual and moral.

It is undoubtedly not easy to find the exact word to describe this climate. "Fidelity" might be used. It amounts, after all, to an act of fidelity to the mystery of being that is in us and all about us: to refuse the question of the ultimate meaning of existence is to turn a deaf ear to an appeal that surges up from the deepest intimacy of our being. "Recollection" has been suggested,[12] and this is well enough, provided it is not understood as a selfish falling back upon the self or an introspective analysis of consciousness, but rather as an act of self-opening to the mystery of the "All-Pervading," that which supports and nourishes our life, the source of that haunting need for the infinite and for unity. Others have spoken of a certain "sense of the sacred." [13] And it is, in fact, a matter of assenting and giving ear to a question that springs from the depths of our being, a question we do not frame for ourselves but find as something given—perhaps indeed a "gift." To listen to this question, to lend oneself to it, is in some sort already to perform a religious act.

It also follows, from all this, that the awakening in us of the sense of existence as a whole, and eventually of faith in God, is not unaccompanied by a great respect for humanity and a great faith in the moral consciousness. Where respect for the human person withers, where the human being is reduced to the rank of a *thing*, and where the moral consciousness becomes generally enfeebled, the sense of God is unable to develop. It is not without reason that philosophy and popular thinking have always shown a tendency to regard the testimony of moral consciousness, with the absolute character that belongs to it, as an appeal to God, as the symbol, above all others, of transcendence. If it is true that our life is ultimately nothing, if death delivers us once and for all to extinction, the moral difference between good and evil seems highly precarious and without foundation. Why, asks popular wisdom, should one prefer sacrifice to selfishness, duty to cowardice, if in the end it all leads nowhere?

To which it may be retorted that true moral grandeur asks not where it all leads; it is disinterested; expects no reward; duty is performed simply because it is duty, because it is sacred. That is certainly very true; but it may well be that here, as in many other cases, popular wisdom simply translates into very banal and earthy terms a truth that is far more noble and profound. The question may be asked: what is left to the intangible sacredness of duty if duty itself, in the last analysis and when all is said, is a simple secretion of the brain, an ordinary protoplasmic transformation? Dostoevsky's remark in *The Brothers Karamazov*, "If there is no God, everything is permissible," is a strikingly vigorous statement of the eternal question of the ultimate meaning of our existence.

We shall see now how this same question leads finally to metaphysics. Metaphysics, from all time, has been occupied with the problem of God. It has always been an approach to what we have called "the religious affirmation of God by faith."

The Metaphysical Approach
to the Mystery of God

We are not ourselves the whole of reality, we exist among other beings, made of the same stuff as they, joined by all the fibers of our being to the universe that supports and pervades us. Hence the question of the ultimate meaning and value of our existence appears inseparable from the problem of existent beings in general: the problem that philosophers have commonly regarded as actually defining metaphysical inquiry. What we have to ask ourselves is what it can teach us about the existence of God. Let us reflect first for a moment on the nature, possibility, and foundation of metaphysics. Contemporary materialism, in view of its close affiliation to positive science, generally sees in metaphysics merely a logical game of concepts, without foundation in experience. Is scientific truth really the only truth that counts, the only form of certainty and rationality that man is capable of possessing? This is the crucial point of the matter we are discussing.

Metaphysics, as its very name implies, certainly professes to transcend empirical fact. Does this mean that it is simply a dialectic in the air, without contact with experience? Most certainly not. But there is experience and experience.

Metaphysics takes for its starting point and foundation experience in the widest, the most inclusive sense: namely, the experience whereby I am aware of my existence as an I-and-others-in-one-and-the-same-world. It is in this sense that René Le Senne remarks: "Philosophy is the description of experience." [14] Science, on the other hand, by very reason of its so-called *objective* method, contrives to take something away from this all-pervading, existential experience. What it deals with is the world of *objective phenomena*, capable of being observed and checked by anyone, at any time: phenomena, that is, considered as events taking place, so to speak, *before* the consciousness, *exterior* to the consciousness. Even the interior psychic event, insofar as science cannot eliminate it completely—which it attempts to do, replacing it with exterior objective behavior—appears as a simple fact among others, an event taking place in the series of objective events. And what concerns the judgment of value, positive science also reduces to a simple objective event. All it is concerned to do is to note that in a certain society, in certain given circumstances, this or that judgment of value prevails, and it will try to discover why. The judgment of value itself it never studies *as such*, nor what it is that makes a value appear to the consciousness as a value; above all, it is careful to make no pronouncement on the question: What should we consider as truly and ultimately of value?

To take an example: A man picks up his revolver, shoots, and kills someone. For the biologist the act of killing a man is reduced to a sequence of physico-chemical processes, to be explained by physics and physiology according to certain laws. The act of shooting a bullet is called muscular contraction and relaxation, leading to an expenditure of energy. The trajectory of the bullet is calculated according to the quantity of energy released by the explosion of the powder. The death of the victim is simply the disorder effected by the projectile in the protoplasmic structure. This is all the biologist records. But the act we are concerned with had a *meaning*; it obviously represented a *value*. It might have been an act of heroism: a soldier risking his life to defend his country. Or it might simply have been a murder, committed through hatred, greed, or cowardice. Of this biology knows nothing; it ignores the judgment of value. Psychology, no doubt, and sociology would go a little further; they would explain the act by saying that motives must be taken into account; but these motives, for them, are only events, objective facts; the *value* of the motive as such—what is the making and basis of heroism as a value, of cowardice as a nonvalue—all this positive science ignores. So true is it that science effects a reduction in the totality given, that strictly speaking it could not even declare that a person was a *victim* of an *outrage*. For if these words have a meaning at all, they indicate a double judgment of value: to talk of a "victim" is to consider the protoplasmic whole, who was the object of the outrage, as *the body of someone*, as *a good, a value to and for himself*; while to speak of an "outrage" is to regard the other protoplasmic whole, the firer of the bullet, as the *author* of an act, namely, an agent endowed with freedom, or at least as one who, in certain circumstances, was capable of acting freely, of knowingly assuming responsibility for his acts.[15]

In short, objective science devotes no attention to the *meaning-for-consciousness* factor, or to the *object-and-value-for-consciousness* that affects the data of experience, and generally it ignores the mode of being, the sector of being, that is commonly referred to by the words "consciousness," "subjectivity," "immanent activity," "consciousness as intersubjective," "presence-to-the-self," "presence-to-the-world," "freedom." . . . Why should it ignore all this? Fundamentally because it never looks at this side of reality; because it withdraws from it by definition, as the very name of "objective" science clearly indicates. The object for science is therefore only an aspect, a sector of global experience, and the intelligibility attained by science is only a particular form of the total intelligibility man is capable of attaining: the intelligibility, that is, which he always exercises—in science as in everything else—by the very fact that he experiences his existence, everywhere and always, as an I-with-others-in-the-world.[16]

That is why the man of science would be wrong to reduce all being, as the materialist does, to matter, namely, to the world he finds at the end of his scalpel, under his microscope, or traced on his photographic plate. From the scientific point of view it would be to effect an extrapolation that scientific method forbids; from the philosophical point of view, it would be to commit an error rightly called by Le Senne the "detotalizing" of the totality: "We use this word," he says, "to describe the all too frequent operation of passing from the consideration of the whole, in its widest sense, to that of the whole deprived of one of its parts, while continuing to attribute to the mutilated whole the name and properties it had in its original condition." [17]

It will be remembered what Claude Bernard had to say about this:

> If we were to see intelligence return to a countenance and brain when given the oxygenated blood required for functioning, we should be wrong to see in this a proof that consciousness and intelligence are contained in the oxygen of the blood or in the cerebral matter. All we have to consider, here, is the conditions of a physico-chemical determinism that are necessary to the manifestation of vital phenomena as well as for the manifestation of mineral phenomena. It would be idle, therefore, to look for explanations here that would result in an absurd and meaningless materialism.[18]

Or we could put the matter in this way. There is a latent ambiguity at the heart of contemporary materialism, and it is thanks to this ambiguity that it exercises the potent influence it does on minds at the present day. The claim to be a materialist can mean two quite different things. It is either a question of materialism pure and simple, the reduction of mind to matter, namely, to the object of the physiological sciences: thought is simply the "superior product" of matter (*das hochste Produkt*, said Feuerbach, Engels, and Marx), a simple secretion of the brain, just like sugar and vitriol (according to Taine). Taken literally, this position is untenable, and in this sense materialism is a veritable contradiction *in actu exercito*: to affirm materialism true is obviously to transcend the manner of being that belongs to matter, in the physiological sense of the word; it is, to quote René Le Senne once more, "to detotalize the totality." But there is a second way of understanding the materialist position. Very often, it would seem, all the materialist means to say is this: In view of the close connection between mind and matter, there exists in the mysterious whole, commonly called the sensible material universe, of which we are ourselves a part, all that is necessary for thought to arise, to emerge at a given moment. But that, as Engels himself remarked, is no longer materialism; it is agnosticism,[19] and in fact a platitude. The question that immediately arises is: What, in that case, is the deep-seated structure, the existent "density" of the universe, if thought "emerges" in it? If matter is really the substratum of mind, is not this an indication that sensible matter is molded out of mind, or as the ancients used to say, informed by spirit? But the answer to this question is not within the province of positive science; it belongs to metaphysics.[20]

Metaphysics bases itself on experience just as science does, but the experience it utilizes is experience in the widest sense: the actual experience of our existence as an I-and-the-other-in-the-world. This existential experience is our participation in being, our human manner of having part, and taking part, in the being that supports and pervades us. It is thanks to this that we know ourselves to be present in being, and that the order of being becomes present to us with its true structure and meaning: it is revealed to us as an intersubjectivity of incarnate consciousness, bound together and separated by matter. Since all we do is to participate in being, doubtless its mysterious foundation is still hidden from us. But through this phenomenal visage of being it is possible for us to guess something of its hidden mystery, of the profound in-itself, of the ultimate meaning of things, just as when we decipher an old text or study a work of art we hope to discover the meaning once put into it by the author. This is what we propose to examine now.

There have been very few philosophers who, like Marx in the last century and M. Sartre today, have suggested that the affirmation of God is an absurdity, that God neither does nor could exist. As a general rule they are less self-assured. That is the wiser attitude. For if it is not easy, by natural reason alone, to arrive at absolute certitude about the existence of God, it is harder still to prove the nonexistence of God! After all, how could we ever be certain that God does not exist and never could?

A position very commonly adopted by philosophers is that of Kant in his *Critique of Pure Reason*. The idea of a Supreme Being, absolutely perfect, is a natural and inevitable idea. It springs spontaneously from our consciousness, owing to the fact that we are haunted by the ideal of perfect knowledge and perfect happiness, and we seek a foundation for the possibility of that ideal: unless God exists, this ideal is an empty word. But, it will be objected, the idea of God thus obtained is a problematic idea, a problem-idea. To be sure that there is a reality corresponding to this idea we have need of further data. For Kant, we know, it was the moral consciousness that justifies acceptance of the certitude of God; for others, it is religious revelation that comes, as it were, to fulfill—transcendently, no doubt, and in a manner beyond all expectation—the metaphysical concept of God, which is a sort of expression of a secret expectance of God. Fundamentally, the question of knowing to what extent natural reason is capable of attaining God is not absolutely essential to the justification of belief in God that we are pursuing here. Humanity's faith in God is not the work of philosophers; in this matter, as we have said, it is religious experience that must have the last word.

We believe, however, that it is possible to go further than Kant and that a metaphysical proof of God is possible. If this is to be satisfactory, we obviously need a full elucidation of the critical and metaphysical problems involved in any philosophical demonstration of God. It need hardly be said that such an elucidation is beyond the scope of this study. In what follows, therefore, the reader must see not a complete and technical proof, but rather the sketch and outline of a proof.

What we learn of existence from metaphysics is this:

1. We are acquainted first with the fundamental unity, the deep ontological kinship, that binds all beings together.

That being is fundamentally one, and that this unity is not a simple aggregate, is common ground in all philosophy, something that can be regarded as its fundamental postulate. Without this basic conviction, metaphysics as a science would be unthinkable and could never have aspired to be the investigation of "being in general";

which is as much as to say it would never have existed. To have different metaphysics for different sections of being would be to have no metaphysics at all.

Various names have been invented to describe and express this basic unity: Being, Absolute, Substance (in Spinoza's sense), Thought, Consciousness, Will, *Elan vital*, Act. And so too for defining the act by which we take account of such unity: we have had intellectual evidence, feeling, experience (as interpreted by M. Le Senne), assurance of being (Jaspers), intuition (Bergson), faith, and so on. Fundamentally it is all these things at once. It is with our whole existence and all the manifestations of our existence that we feel, understand, and experience at every moment the fact that we are inserted in being, that we are profoundly akin to all existent beings; every act of ours, whether it diminishes or expands our existence, is witness to the fact that we are not an isolated self-sufficient monad, but an existent-in-being, open to being, who to exist and be fully ourself stands in need of all other existent beings. Science itself, too, shows us that matter and mind are not in water-tight compartments. "The universe is in evolution," says Pierre Teilhard de Chardin, "and it evolves toward mind." Biology is a kind of basement to the spiritual life, and if it is true that matter separates minds, it serves also as a connective union between minds. More significant is the intersubjectivity of consciousness, as we see it in knowing and loving. Our knowledge is a knowledge in common, and genuine love of values draws us out from ourselves, for we see such values as universal and transindividual: the scientist who would keep his science to himself has no love for science and sins against truth; so too the artist, who cultivates his art for selfish ends, knows nothing of true aesthetic joy. "Value," as M. Le Senne remarks, "is contagious." [21] The true meaning of values projects us out of ourselves toward others, to the end that others may share the same values.

All this shows how far our existence is from being insulated. We are in being and being is in us; we *participate* in being in the double sense of *having* part and *taking* part.

2. Reflection on our human existence, insofar as it makes us an I-with-others-in-the-world, next enables us in some sort to measure the *density of being* we exercise, to recognize the *tenor* and *meaning* of our participation.

To participate is to be limited. To exist as an I-in-being, as none can doubt, is to be conscious of this limitation. But it is important that we should clearly understand the reason why. An old prejudice, deriving from German idealism but still very general today, makes of the existence of the not-I a simple limit to the I. This leads logically to considering all subjectivity, even perfect subjectivity, as an interiority imprisoned in the self: pantheist monism is the inevitable result. The real error here is taking as a point of departure a false description of the finite. The existence of a not-I is not simply a synonym for "limit-for-the-I." My knowledge is by no means limited or hampered by the fact that I have beside me another who knows things even better than I do. On the contrary, true knowledge always tends to impart itself to another. All value is contagious, as we said just now with M. Le Senne. To love the other for himself, to accept his existence for himself, to treat him as an end in himself, in short, as another for-self, involves for me no sort of diminution. The other is not primarily, as M. Sartre would seem to say, an enemy, someone who watches me, reduces me to the rank of an object, and steals away my world. If my subjectivity can be defined as a presence-to-self, an affirmation of the self, it is also, at one and the same stroke, an indefinitely possible affirmation of the other, as other and for-himself. The "profound will" or "will-to-be" that animates us, rightly called by M. Forest "an acceptance of being," is neither primarily nor necessarily a selfish acceptance "for the self," but a general acceptance for the "other-than-self," in short—if we may be allowed to anticipate for a moment—something like a participation in the creative omnipotence of God, Who wills all things to be. As subjectivity we are by no means a monad enclosed within itself and its mental images, but an existence open to the world, an indefinite possibility of *affirming the other in and for himself.* Therein lie our riches. We have infinity within us.

Yet we are all this in a manner radically and intrinsically finite. I am not the source either of myself or of the world; moreover, if I were the ultimate and complete foundation of my own being, I should be equally the foundation of the world and the beings that compose it, since I am bound to them by all the fibers of my being and have need of them to make me myself. We can express it in another way by saying that our existence, as presence-to-self and presence-to-the-world, seems thoroughly unnatural. We find our existence as a fact and we find the world as a datum imposed on us from without. Hence we are not clear to ourselves; the world for us is full of mysteries. We are finite through and through; even the infinite within us is there in a finite manner.

3. What have we left to do? Let us see if this participation we have described allows us to say anything about the mystery of being that supports us, penetrates us, and supplies our ultimate foundation. What now becomes the governing idea is the final condition of possibility or the *ultimate foundation*. Note, too, that the very description of participation suggested this idea. To exist in the manner of participation is obviously not to be the totality of being, or absolute, self-sufficing being; it means that the being is not itself its own foundation. Hence the idea of *source, Urgrund* and *Ursprung*.

How then are we to conceive the mystery of the being that supports us, our ultimate foundation?

We have already shown that this cannot be matter. To reduce being-as-whole to matter is to detotalize totality; it is to forget that matter is the object *before and for the mind*. Materialism that reduces mind to matter and identifies being-as-whole with matter is untenable.

It is the same with monist and pantheist spiritism, and for similar reasons. The idealist monism of the Great Consciousness, or the Great I, also detotalizes experience. It does indeed emphasize the priority of mind and the profound ontological unity of all existents in being. But it regards the unfathomable deep in which we exist either as an impersonal dialectic of corresponding ideas or as the identity of a great self-enclosed consciousness wherein all particular beings are but moments, the imminent contents of it. This means that monist spiritism conceives Being as analogous to the unity of the human consciousness, insofar as this latter bears, and unites within itself, an infinite diversity of moments, manifestations, and imminent contents of consciousness. But this is only a very restricted aspect of our subjectivity. Actually we are more than that. As we have shown well enough already, the density of being we exercise is richer in other respects. The human I, as it shows itself even in its cognitive life, but still more as it unfolds in love, has nothing in common with a subjectivity shut up within itself and enclosed in its immanent representations: it presents itself from the very outset as an affirmation of the other, as an effort to see the other in himself and for himself.

That is why the Absolute on which we are based cannot be conceived otherwise than in the same line as our own true spiritual being, namely, as a transcendent person, a superego, a freedom or a love capable of giving rise to other freedoms for themselves: in short, as a creative God.

This metaphysical affirmation of God is still only an attempt on the part of our minds to represent the mystery of the being that subtends us. In religious faith, man is not satisfied with representing to himself the world as supported by God; he "takes God seriously," *addresses Him as a person* in a gesture of confident hope. Now this confidence on man's part is not in vain: God has deigned to answer him. This answer is to be found in what we customarily call the religious experience of humanity. This becomes, here, an invaluable confirmation of the philosophic proof of God, while at the same time it supplies a definite answer to the question we started with: What is life ultimately worth?

The Religious Experience of Humanity

Is it true that God is with His saints and that in the lives of the saints He testifies to us that He is, and what He is?

For sanctity to take on the value of evidence for us, it is necessary, of course, that it should find us ready to listen to its language. If the modern world lives so far from God, might not the reason be that it lives so far from the saints and their wisdom? No wonder God is not found: He is not sought where He is, where He makes Himself manifest.

Which means that here, too, we must avoid an insulated conception of consciousness. We have all in us something of the rich man in the parable. Before we believe, we must have direct personal testimony coming straight to us from heaven: a private message for ourself alone. How many times have we heard it said: if God wants me to believe, let Him come and tell me so! It seems to be forgotten that God may have spoken, and especially that His word is a *sanctifying* word: consequently, to hear it, one must first begin by approaching the saints. Pascal expressed it in unforgettable terms: "God of Abraham, of Isaac and Jacob . . . , God of Jesus Christ. *Deum meum et Deum vestrum . . . He is found only by the ways taught in the Gospel.*"

The fact of sanctity, considered as a whole, as an imposing array of convergent data, is an authentic testimony to God as God-for-us-and-with-us. This testimony, in practice, assumes a double form.

There is first the experience of God in the depths of the soul: it has been given the name of mystical experience. Secondly, we have objective manifestation—proof that is sensible and, to some extent, capable of being checked—of God's providence for His saints: it is what, for want of a better word, we shall call the miraculous, reserving to later the definition of what we precisely mean by the term.

Mystical experience, in the religious sense, is a human fact, a state of consciousness with its own peculiar structure and content: it would be folly to attempt to deny it. Blessed John Ruysbroek, St. Bernard, Master Eckhart, St. John of the Cross, St. Teresa of Avila, Blessed Suso, and so many others are mystics, and their writings are mystical works. The latter have their source in an intuition, an existential experience distinct in kind from the other forms of intuition that are known to man. Einstein's scientific intuitions made him a great mathematician, not a religious mystic. The same can be said of Napoleon's military genius, of the aesthetic emotion of a Cézanne or a Beethoven. The fact that there is such a thing as false mysticism, mystical counterfeit, that disintegrates the personality, whereas the other, true mysticism, is one of the outstanding forms of intellectual and moral vigor, is no reason to discredit authentic mysticism. One might as well say there is no true greatness open to man because there is such a thing as megalomania.

If true mystical experience has nothing to do with its numerous counterfeits, it must also be distinguished from the paramystical phenomena—psychic or physiological—that sometime accompany it and generally anticipate its final development: such are mental and sensible visions, interior colloquies, ravishments, diminution, or complete obliteration of sensibility. The mystics themselves are the first to make the distinction, and they take great care to do so. It would even seem that some of the secondary phenomena are simply the repercussion, in the psychic and biological life, of the mystical experience properly so called. That, too, is why we speak of secondary or paramystical phenomena, to indicate that they have no effect on the central core of mystical intuition. It is not these that make the mystic, any more than the scientist's absent-mindedness makes scientific genius.

What is then the peculiar structure, the peculiar content, of the mystical experience as it appears, according to the testimony of the mystics themselves, to the consciousness of the person enjoying it?

One thing is entirely certain: mystical experience belongs to the domain of the *sacred* and *religious*. Mystical intuition is really a higher form of prayer. It is a prayer that unites the soul so intimately to God that it is spoken of as a direct *contact* of the soul with God, its transformation by God; it is something like an experience of the presence of God, felt as subsistent and creative Love, at once immanent and transcendent. Thus, for the mystic, God is no more a problem. He is the reality of realities. The mystic would doubt the existence of the world sooner than that of God.

But there still remains the question: What is it worth, this testimony of the mystics? Has it an objective and universal value? Like any other testimony, it could be invalidated for two reasons: lack of honesty in reporting the interior experience, or granted honesty, erroneous interpretation.

The good faith of the mystics is not in doubt, and no one in fact has ever contested it. So there is no need to dwell on this. But if their good faith is not disputed, might not the mystics have been deceived in the interpretation of their experience? Would not a theistic interpretation be due to previous dogmatic belief, with the result that the Christian saint spontaneously interprets in a Christian sense, namely, according to a determined conceptual apparatus, an experience that in its original purity would be beyond, or fall short of, any intellectual definition? And indeed this would seem to be confirmed by the fact that all the great religions seem to possess their own mystics. There is a Hindu mysticism, a Buddhist, a Mohammedan mysticism. Each has lent itself to a particular religious interpretation according to the religious doctrines already accepted.

That a religious doctrine already held may influence the interpretation which a mystic subsequently gives to his experience, that it can even color that experience to a certain extent insofar as it is given a meaning—all this is probable enough. Man is always wholly present in all his existential experiences. But this, we suggest, is no serious argument against the objective value of the mystic's testmony, and for the following reasons:

1. We are assured by a complete and unanimous agreement among mystics that their testimony is in no way an interpretation after the event, but a scrupulously faithful account of the experience itself in all its uniqueness and immediacy. The mystic professes to *experience* the presence of God; this experience seems to him significant in itself and not in virtue of any conceptual superstructure that may be added to it after the event.

In every mystic, no doubt, there is a philosophical or religious conception that *pre-exists* the mystical experience. Otherwise it would be hard to see how such an experience could ever have a meaning for the subject, or acquire the quality of an answer or an encounter. Every answer presupposes a question and every encounter a certain expectation. The mystical experience comes to "fulfill," in some sort, a question and an expectation. But it does so in a manner that surpasses expectation. For the mystic, it is the answer itself that is of value; so much so that the previous expectation, the pre-existing concept of the religious mystery, appears henceforth in his eyes as a remote adumbration, a wavering shadow, compared with the reality experienced and made manifest. That is why mystical theology is essentially negative; why the mystic finds himself powerless to translate into words the inexhaustible and unutterable riches of the mystery itself that he himself has been enabled to *touch*. Not that he considers these previous religious concepts to be false, but they are no longer anything beside the reality. St. Thomas broke his pen when he knew the mystery of God as an object of infused and experienced contemplation. As Simone Weil was to say later: "Of two men, neither of whom have experienced God, the one who denies Him may well be the nearer to Him." [22]

2. Nor should the difficulty be exaggerated that there is a certain kind of mysticism that tends to pantheism. In the first place it is a remarkable fact that even in the most orthodox of Christian mystics there are plenty of expressions that border, at first sight, on a pantheist idea of the world. We have only to think of the term "transforming union." Was it not St. Augustine, too, who said that God dwells

in us more intimately than we do in ourselves: *intimior intimo meo?*
One would suppose, for the mystic, there is nothing else but God.
But there is pantheism and pantheism. Genuine pantheism diminishes divinity: what it amounts to, essentially, is saying that God is
not God, does not become consciously divine, except through the
medium of the human consciousness. Without man, God would still
be no more than a blind urge, a great Unconscious. But if there is
one thing that mystical experience contradicts it is just this idea of
a God Who becomes realized as such through the mediation of any
human reality. If certain mystics speak as though man disappeared
in God, none ever suggests that God disappears in man, that God
without man would cease to be God. After all, it is not surprising
that the soul, swallowed up in the abyss of the divine, should become
as it were oblivious of its existence, since God has become for it the
unique reality. If, in these circumstances, the mystic should speak
as if there were nothing but God, it is very understandable. But this
is not pantheism in the common and accepted use of the term;
nor does it imply that in the mystical experience all human consciousness has truly ceased to exist, or that the human "I" has really
been annihilated. Otherwise, how are we to explain the mystic's
describing his experience? How comes it that he can experience the
transforming union as the supreme good of all? Without existence
it is impossible to experience anything. Finally, how are we to explain
the fact that this absorption of the soul in God is spontaneously
transformed into indefatigable action? [23]

3. But there is a third reason—and this not the least—for giving an
objective value to the testimony of the mystics to the existence of a
personal God. The interior experience we have spoken of is confirmed in an almost tangible and experimental manner by the fact
that God's love for His saints is manifested even in the very texture
of the material and sensible events that make up their existence.
What is generally called the miraculous is the most expressive sign
of this providence of God for His saints. The significance of the
miraculous is that of a divine language: thanks to this it becomes
abundantly evident that God is neither a blind urge nor an impersonal consciousness, but *Someone* who hears and gives an answer to
prayer.

Here, above all, it is important to look facts squarely in the face, to let them speak for themselves. What is commonly called the *language of facts* is nothing else than the manifestation of a meaning, and every meaning is a manifestation of order, a play of relations that constantly react one upon the other. This means that the miraculous, as a sign from God, must be regarded as a whole endowed with meaning. Our attention must therefore be directed to the structure of this *whole with a religious significance*.

What do we understand by the miraculous?

The miraculous as a religious phenomenon is a converging number of marvelous facts that are presented to us, by reason of their religious context, as a tangible response by God to human faith, as the sure and certain sign that God is with His saints.[24]

Taken in isolation, or rather considered in its mundane and physical significance, as an event among others, a miracle is an exceptional and marvelous fact: it is outside the ordinary ways of nature and surpasses what nature achieves, or is capable of achieving, in normal circumstances.

The margin that separates the miraculous from the ordinary behavior of nature may be wider or narrower. Hence we talk of major and minor miracles. Some miracles, regarded as supernatural, are very like certain exceptional cases that are encountered outside any religious context, or like certain strange phenomena that are due, it would seem, to an unusual but by no means supernatural influence of the psychical on the physical. It is a well-known occurrence in hospitals for an abrupt change to take place, at a particular moment in the course of an illness, without anyone being able to tell how or why. As to the effect of the psychical on the physiological, here, as everyone knows, science is still groping in the dark. But there are also major miracles: the multiplication of loaves, more or less instant restoration of destroyed tissues, the sudden stilling of a tempest at command, the raising of the dead. Here the element of the exceptional, namely, the distance between the exceptional event and what nature ordinarily effects or seems capable of effecting, is very great indeed. The greater this distance, the greater the astonishment that the event arouses and the more it provokes us to seek out the mysterious power that produced it.

Yet if the miracle were simply an isolated event, outside the regular order, it would have no meaning for us; it would be without intelligible significance. For a miracle to be understood, for it to be able to assume the appearance of a sign, it must stand out from the general groundwork of events and be seen as a whole with religious significance; it must be set in its concrete context, so that it can be observed whether, as such, it conveys any meaning. To understand a miracle, as a miracle, involves no exception to the general law that governs human intelligence. To understand is to establish relations, to discover a unity of order or significance. For external facts to have any meaning for us there must be, on the one hand, a regular recurrence of the facts in accordance with the same order; on the other hand, this order must correspond to a certain expectation in us— whether notional, affective, or existential—in company with which we go to meet the facts. Hence the importance of the hypothesis in science: and hence, speaking generally, the need for a pre-existing question before any response, as such, can be given. In short, understanding is the result of a double encounter: the encounter of the facts in such a way as to become totalities endowed with meaning, and the encounter of the facts with the human mind in quest of meaning and values.[25]

Consider the miraculous, now, in the light of these remarks.

The miracle is an exceptional event, but it is not an isolated event. In their very exceptionality and irregularity, miracles show their own characteristics and unique regularity: they are inserted in a religious context which establishes a certain relationship between them; they converge together and form a totality with a religious significance.

This significance is that of a divine language: the miraculous appears in the religious history of humanity as a sensible answer by God to human faith, or to repeat the quotation we gave above, as *the visible manifestation of divine Providence for His saints.*

Let us consider rather more closely the religious context that allows the miraculous to appear as a significant whole, as a whole endowed with structure, containing a vast number of significant totalities. For this is how in fact it does appear. To begin with, the existence of Christ makes in itself a vast and imposing totality; the life of every saint is a new one; the same can be said of the cult of certain saints, particularly of the Blessed Virgin; finally all these totalities converge and combine to make a single whole, one unique and very important fact.

If the Gospels allow us to form for ourselves any image of Christ it is surely that of the saint appearing in this world as a man of God. The existence of Christ, as it appears in the testimony of the evangelists, is a whole tissue of marvelous events, culminating in the Resurrection. Christ uses miracles, as we do gestures, to emphasize the spoken word. His prayer is all-powerful with God. "The words I speak to you are not My own words. . . . If you cannot trust My word, when I tell you that I am in the Father, and the Father is in Me, *let these powerful acts themselves be My warrant*." [26]

But the miraculous existence of Christ is not an isolated phenomenon, a kind of celestial apparition in the margin of human history, unconnected with anything that went before and leaving no trace afterwards. If it were so, our faith in Christ would be harder to justify, the Gospels far less comprehensible. If after a lapse of twenty centuries the miracles attributed to Jesus are so credible, it is because they are continued under our very eyes: the miracles of today illuminate and confirm the Gospel marvels, and vice versa. And in fact among the many miracles for which Jesus is famed, the greatest of all was not accomplished in His own lifetime: "Believe me when I tell you this," He continues, in the passage from St. John we have just quoted, "the man who has learned to believe in Me will be able to do what I do; nay, he will be able to do greater things yet" (John 14:12). "You therefore, must go out, making disciples of all nations . . . and behold I am with you all through the days that are coming, until the consummation of the world" (Matt. 28:19-20). Here then is the miracle of miracles, that which embraces all the rest: God was to remain with the apostolic community which would continue the work of Christ in His name; God's providence for His Messiah was to extend to all true believers, to all who should seek to find the kingdom of God and His approval: "Do not fret over your life, how to support it with food and drink; over your body, how to keep it clothed. . . . Make it your first care to find the kingdom of God, and His approval, and all these things shall be yours without the asking" (Matt. 6:25, 33).

Now here is a remarkable thing: this bold promise of Christ, covering at a single stroke whole centuries to come, has been amply fulfilled and goes on being fulfilled every day. The life of every saint fulfills it point by point. If there is one constant element in the fact of sanctity, one thing that forms its essence and its deepest secret, it is this: the saint is one who takes the Gospel seriously, discovers once again the original purity of the evangelic faith; and thereupon, instantly, the Gospel promises come to be fulfilled: not only are the beatitudes made a reality (namely, the inner religious experience we have spoken of); not only is the apostolic influence shed abroad— that faith which, according to St. John, is "the triumphant principle which triumphs over the world"; [27] but the miraculous element whch we find in the Gospel also appears once again in all its splendor, as though by sensible and objective signs to mark the fact that God is always with His Gospel. And all this continues to happen today.

The Curé d'Ars is not far removed from us (1786-1859). There was nothing in the least esoteric about his life; it was lived in broad daylight before thousands of witnesses who came daily to Ars to receive counsel of one who clearly sought only truth and appeared to be a man of God. What is then the secret of this life full of wonders? It was the same that had accounted already for the astonishing life of a St. Bernard, a St. Francis, a St. Vincent Ferrer, and so many others: Seek first the kingdom of God and all the rest will be yours without the asking; or, in other words, an absolute and continuous faith in divine Providence: that faith of which poverty and mortification are simply the outward sign and necessary instrument, since it is impossible to serve two masters at once. The Curé d'Ars believed in God with all a child's simplicity and purity, and God became his Providence. The Curé d'Ars laid open the most secret recesses of the human soul, foretold the future, and healed the sick, and under his hand the loaves were multiplied.

The life of Louis-Marie Grignon de Montfort (1673-1716), recently canonized by the Church, is no less significant: the same total surrender to God in absolute poverty, the same sensible presence of God foreseen by the Gospel. Grignon de Montfort restored sight to the blind, multiplied loaves, commanded the raging sea. No less well known are those two Italian saints, heroes of the boldest self-abandonment to Providence: Cottolengo (1786-1842) and Don Bosco (1815-1888). The life of each is a continual prodigy. They fed and housed some thousands of poor orphans, abandoned children, society's outcast and rejected youth: and all without any other capital than trust in God. It might happen, not once but time and again, that food and money would be lacking; there would be nothing to provide the next meal or pay the impatient creditor at the door. And then at the last moment, as by a veritable *deus ex machina*, the whole difficulty would be settled: an unknown stranger would turn up, in the nick of time, with a wagon laden with sacks of flour; another would deposit the sum required in the letter box; it would even happen that a bag of gold coins, exactly the sum that was needed, would suddenly be found in a drawer that had previously been searched in vain, even in the saint's own pocket, empty a moment before. Nearer to us still, we have little Thérèse of Lisieux (1873-1897). She had predicted that she would spend her life in heaven doing good on earth: the miracles associated with her cult are past counting. In 1936 there died in the suburbs of Paris a former chaplain of the 1914-1918 war, Father Daniel Brottier. He was the head of a huge orphanage known as the *Oeuvre des Apprentis d'Auteuil*. On the day of his funeral Cardinal Verdier declared that his life had been what he called "a permanent miracle." Here too had been the same confidence in God and in His saints. Father Brottier had a boundless faith in the Blessed Virgin and in Thérèse of the Child Jesus. Sensible proofs abound that God was with him and with his work. Perhaps the most remarkable of all is the following. Father Brottier had conceived the daring idea of building a chapel, that would cost him millions of francs, in honor of the saint of Lisieux. He possessed nothing at all, but there were providential signs that his project was pleasing to God; and he had the faith that moves mountains. Ignoring the advice of his friends, who considered his "imprudence" on this occasion was beyond all limits, he set about the work. Well, this is what happened (it is the saint's assistant, the bursar of the orphanage, who tells the story): Until the main work of the chapel was completed, that is for about two years, Father Brottier found a thousand-franc note every day, either in his mail or in the chapel offertory box or brought from an anonymous donor by the hands of an intermediary. Sometimes the "usual thousand note" was late in coming, but every day it turned up, even if not till the Father was making ready for bed.[28]

Those are a few facts among thousands; but to quote four or five names is really nothing when we think of the unending line of saints that the wisdom of the Gospel has produced in the course of the twenty centuries that separate us from Christ. Seen from a distance, it all doubtless merges into legend, and when confronted with legend it is easy to construct hypotheses: human imagination is fertile enough. But to look at the matter from a distance is to take refuge in the abstract and forego reality. For anyone who is willing to seek a basis in the concrete, to examine things in detail, assess the countless testimonies he has at his disposal and the infinite array of facts—for anyone, in short, who is willing to approach the saints— there is something here that is quite simply irresistible. The life of every saint is a revival of the Gospel faith, in an authentic and wholly original manner, and of the promises that Christ attached to that faith. That is why the miraculous, as we have defined it, appears like an imposing whole, unimpeachable and endowed with meaning: it is like a vast golden chain descending from Christ to ourselves and mounting from us to Christ; it is the certain sign that there is a God, and that God is no vague and impersonal reality, but a Father "Who sees what is done in secret . . . and knows well what your needs are before you ask Him" (Matt. 6:6,8). One might quote a significant remark by Anatole France: "Mentally deficient as no doubt believers are, it is curious that these exceptional forces, re-vealed in the miraculous, never work for any but these mental de-fectives!" [29] It is indeed very curious.

In the face of all this, the classic objections to the miraculous look very anemic. Moreover they proceed from a dogmatic rationalism which has not even the advantage, just now, of being fashionable.

The miraculous, it has been said, is *unknowable:* to decide what transcends the laws and possibilities of nature it would be necessary to know these laws and possibilities. In one sense that is true, but in any case it is beside the point. In the first place, it is not necessary to know everything in order to know anything: it is not necessary to have penetrated the mystery of nature to know that two and three make five, and that five loaves do not feed a multitude. But above all, recognition of the sign as a sign must not be confused with the science of physico-chemical elements that enter into the constitution of the sign, insofar as it is one among a number of physical facts. No knowledge is required of physiological or biological laws governing the play of muscular contractions before a child can recognize his mother's smile; or, for that matter, before any of us can find the *meaning* of a gesture or a word. The miraculous is *wholly endowed with meaning*, and as such it belongs to the order of language.

It has even been suggested that a *miracle is impossible*, because God could never derange the order He has Himself established; or again that a miracle is *unscientific*, since science establishes rules and laws, and therefore its task is to include within order all that, at first sight, would seem to be outside it.

It is presumptuous on man's part to think to decide exactly what God can or cannot do. That mania for dogmatizing! But it must be pointed out that the miraculous no more upsets the laws of nature than does the daily play of our personal liberty. So far from disturbing the determinism of physical laws, human liberty actually presupposes it at every moment; otherwise it could never function and perform its own work, which is to establish and further meanings and values. The various declarations of war that took place in the years 1939-1940 effected no alteration in the laws of physics; yet at this moment the whole face of the physical world is different from what it would have been if no war had taken place. How much energy, physical and chemical, has been squandered, which otherwise might have been kept in reserve or utilized for peaceful purposes; how many human lives (in physiological language: protoplasmic structures) have been dislocated, which might otherwise have still been in full vigor today! Every act we perform, every gesture we make, utilizes and turns to a definite direction the physico-chemical energy of our bodies and, to some degree, of the whole universe as well, without the laws of that universe being any whit disturbed. But, if this is the case, what is there surprising that God should be able to utilize, without disturbing, the energy-structure of the world we know, so that we may receive a sensible sign of His presence?

References

1. L. Feuerbach, *L'Essence du Christianisme* (Paris, 1864), p. 119. The reduction of the higher to the lower must be considered here as applying to ultimate and metaphysical explanation. Elsewhere, from the point of view of civilization, for instance, it is the lower that is explained by the higher, since it is man who supplies the ultimate meaning of history.

2. M. Heidegger, *What is Metaphysics?* French translation, *Qu'est que la métaphysique?*, by H. Corbies (Paris: Gallimard), p. 24, and *The Essence of*

Truth, French translation, *De l'Essence de la Verité*, with commentary by
A. De Waehlens and W. Biemel (Louvain: Nauwelaerts, 1948), p. 89.

3. Claude Bernard has well observed: "In the experimental method, experiments are made only to *see* or *prove*, namely, to *check* and *verify*. The experimental method, as a scientific method, rests wholly on the experimental verification of a scientific hypothesis." *Introduction à l'étude de la médicine expérimentale* (Geneva: Constant Bourquin, 1945), p. 409.

4. Empirical psychology does not succeed, of course, in eliminating completely the internal psychic fact, but it reduces it to an objective event among others, neglecting (as we shall see later) the "meaning" and "value" it has for consciousness.

5. Jean Rostand, *Pensées d'un biologiste* (Paris: Stock, 1939), p. 96.

6. *Ibid.*

7. Cf. Franz Gregoire, *Aux sources de la pensée de Marx: Hegel, Feuerbach*, Louvain, ed. (Institut supérieur de Philosophie, 1947), pp. 147ff.

8. Karl Marx, *Contribution à la critique de la philosophie du droit de Hegel, Oeuvres*, Vol. I (Paris, 1920), 84.

9. Jean Rostand, *op. cit.*, p. 112.

10. *Ibid.*, p. 37.

11. Albert Camus, *La Mythe de Sisyphe* (Paris: Gallimard, 1942), p. 15.

12. G. Marcel, "Position et approches concrètes du mystère ontologique," Appendix to *Le Monde Cassé* (Paris: Desclée, 1933), p. 291.

13. Dr. Alexis Carrel, *La Prière* (Brussels: Ed. Universitaires, 1944), p. 34.

14. René Le Senne, *Obstacle et Valeur* (Paris: Fernand Aubier, 1934), p. 5.

15. Hence positive science ignores the problem of freedom, because freedom takes us straight into the world of *meanings* and *values*. A man who acts freely gives a meaning to his actions and deliberately accepts this meaning, thereby making his actions his own, becoming their author.

16. To exist as an "I" is to experience existence as *for-the-self* and therefore as *value*. To exist with-others is to be capable of appreciating the other for himself, as *end-in-himself*. Even in science we hold this basic existential situation, which makes us appear to ourselves as I-and-others-in-the-world, since science is the pursuit of truth in common. But positive science itself does not take this existential aspect of its activity as an explicit subject matter for its investigations. It considers only the object, which is why it is called "objective."

17. *Op. cit.*, p. 27.

18. Claude Bernard, *La science expérimentale* (Paris: J. B. Bailliere & Fils, 1878), p. 126.

19. F. Engels, Introduction to the English edition of *Socialism, Utopian and Scientific* (Chicago: C. H. Kerr and Company, 1900).

20. A very typical example of the unfortunate confusion between positive science and metaphysics is that slogan of Engels, so frequently met with in Marxist materialist literature: "Our evolutionary conception of the universe allows no place at all for a creator" (Engels, *ibid.*). As if belief in God had anything to do with the evolutionist conception of life! The same could be said of Comte. Such a statement, which in itself simply proclaims the soundness and convenience of the positive *method*, takes on, with him, an *ontological* meaning. So it is in the following sentence: "The positive theory of the affective and intellectual functions must consist henceforth in the study of the phenomena of inner sensibility proper to the cerebral ganglions, and this is only a continuation of physiology" (*Cours de philosophie positive*, Lesson 45).

21. *Op. cit.*, p. 190.

22. Simone Weil, *La pesanteur et la grâce* (Paris: Plon, 1947), p. 151.

23. There is the same ambiguity about the word "passivity," so much used by the mystics. According to them the soul does nothing in mystical experience. But this does not mean that it sinks to the level of an inert object. On the contrary, it lives with eminent intensity.

24. Obviously this is to be understood in the wide sense. We have not in mind only miracles worked by saints in their lifetime; some take place in connection with the cult of the saints or generally within the framework of the evangelical community, founded by Christ and called the Church.

25. In simpler but less exact terms, this amounts to saying that intelligence is necessary to discover the intelligible.

26. John 14:10, 11-12.

27. 1 John 5:4.

28. Yves Pichon, *Le Père Brottier* (Paris: Oeuvre d'Auteuil, 1938), p. 128.

29. Cf. M. Claeys-Bouuaert, "Raisons personnelles de croire," *Nouvelle Revue Theologique* (February, 1933), p. 134.

CHAPTER 17

Foundations

of the Faith

JEAN DANIÉLOU

Our responsibility to assert our faith in the presence of the men of our time is a singular one. For what we assert is really something improbable; and it is normal for us to come up at first against an attitude of incredulity. What I mean by that is that the assertions required of us by our faith, namely, that the destiny which is ours goes beyond the frontiers of this life, since we are called by God to an eternal destiny; that the essential event of human history has already taken place; that never will any revolution or any amount of scientific progress bring us anything so important as the resurrection of Jesus Christ—these are affirmations of singular audacity.

They therefore confront us with a heavy intellectual responsibility. These assertions—have we the right to make them? Have we the right to involve the full responsibility of our liberties with them? Is the question here one simply of our preaching a view of the world which seems congenial to us; or, instead, do we really have the right, and the duty, to declare to every man, no matter who he is, that he will one day be judged by Jesus Christ, and that this trial is the only one of ultimate importance in any and every human life? Have we the right and duty to say to some Marxist associate of ours: "Because I really love you, I am obliged to tell you that one day you are going to be judged by Jesus Christ." For this is what we mean by "believing." That is to say that Christianity is not one philosophy side by side with a number of other philosophies, but the ultimate truth

The Scandal of Truth, by Jean Daniélou, S.J., W. J. Kerrigan, trans. Helicon Press, Baltimore, Maryland, 1962.

about man's destiny. Well, does Christianity really mean that for us? And doesn't the feebleness of our testimony come from our perhaps not having faith?

So, before thinking of giving the faith to others, we have to examine ourselves to determine whether we have it ourselves. Now one sure thing is that the way most of us conduct ourselves gives others the impression that we do not have faith. For, watching us, they say to themselves: "If it were really true what they say, then it ought to show up in their lives in some much more striking way." And often, in fact, we give unbelievers the impression that we are attached to Christianity, of course, as a way of looking at life that happens to suit us best, but not that it is *the* truth, period, that is, the only sense there is to man's life, a meaning that is God's plan and that every man must face up to. This is not a question of dogmatism; it is not a question of our wishing to impose our views on other people. In fact, it is not a question of our views at all. The faith is not something I adhere to because it is a world view that pleases me. We do not pick out our faith as we pick out a hat. I was recently talking with a young woman who said to me: "My husband tells me that by nature he is more Protestant than anything." The problem is not to determine whether Protestantism suits me best, or whether Buddhism suits me best, or whether Catholicism suits me best. One is not a Protestant because he has a taste for a certain liberty; one is not a Catholic because of whatever imaginable connivance with authority. One is a Catholic because he thinks Catholicism is true. And whether that suits me or upsets me, pleases me or displeases me, puts me at ease or makes me ill at ease, I am obliged to profess it— as true for myself and for other people.

Thus all this is a serious matter. Speaking of the faith is a grave responsibility. It is a responsibility which we assume in the presence of other people. We must therefore determine what this means. What I should like to do is just to examine myself to see what the faith means, what its nature is, and what its claims are. Have I really the right to believe all these things, in all intellectual honesty? Have I the right to stake my intelligence on the word of Jesus Christ? Have I the right to assert that it is the final answer to man's fate, to the riddles which it poses?

The first thing to be done is to determine what realm faith is in. There is in most men a religious sense. Atheism is a modern phenomenon in the first place, and in the second place, a phenomenon ultimately less widespread than people think. Recently I heard the pastor of a large Paris parish tell me that the more contact he had with the working-class circles the more he noticed how ready they were to receive the Christian message; and he added: "More, alas, than in middle-class circles." It is sure that there is in every human soul an openness to the sacred, to mystery, to the world beyond, and that what in Jaspers' language are called "limit situations"—confrontation of suffering, love, death, liberty—put man in the presence of realities which he is quite well aware transcend him. And, from this point of view, it may be said that the religious sense is a part of human nature. I myself think that its disappearance constitutes a maiming of human nature, and that a man in whom there is not openness to God is a man mutilated in an essential part of himself.

Of this quest for God it may be said that "religions" are the expression. And, in this sense, all religions have their truth, and we must give them their due as representing what I shall call man's quest for God. Men have always sought for God. And each religion is the way in which men of one age or of one land have given this quest life. We have only to read some of the religious books of India (I am thinking of the Bhagavadgita), certain poems by the great Moslem mystics (I am thinking of Al-Hallaj, whose wonderful mystical poems Louis Massignon has published), we have only to be in contact with the African world to grasp what a wealth of deep religious values are to be found in all the civilizations of the world. This constitutes what I shall call the "religious world," which is not yet the world of the faith. One may wonder whether, in our time, the crisis within this religious world is not like an obstacle preliminary to the wakening of faith. But what concerns me for what I am trying to define here is that we are not yet at this moment in the actual realm of faith. It is not necessary to be Christian in order to believe there is a God. All human civilizations have this religious aspect. It may be said that religions are part of the patrimony of the human race and represent one of its essential riches.

In the domain of faith we reach quite another order. Belief does not mean believing there is a God; it means believing that God intervenes in human life. The object of faith is an event, or a series of events. Belief means, in effect, believing that God spoke to Abraham, freed the people from Egypt, became flesh in the womb of Mary, raised up from among the dead the humanity to which He was united, and is present in the midst of us in the Holy Eucharist. And that is the supreme paradox. For men in fact do allow that we acknowledge, in a higher world, a divinity which surpasses us. But that God intervenes in the course of human life, and that in the midst of us there are divine operations going on—this seems absolutely scandalous. This latter in fact is what the greater part of men reject. They reject the supernatural.

Now that is exactly what the faith asserts. The sacred book of Christians is not some or other treatise of religious philosophy, it is a history—Sacred History. To believe means to accept the Bible, the Old and the New Testament. Now, what the Old and New Testaments contain is history. But there are two histories. There is the history of the great things men have done since the beginning, the history of the great cultures, the history of science, the history of discoveries and inventions, and political history; and this history is real history; it is the story of the great works of man; and it gives glory to man. We, however, we believe that there is another history, more profound. That is to say, there are things which are not man's work, but God's, and these works of God are infinitely greater than the greatest works of man. They surpass, that is, as Pascal put it, the works of man in proportion as the order of charity surpasses the order of intelligence and the order of physical bodies. To be a Christian, then, is to believe that there are divine operations in our midst, and that these divine operations are what constitute the greatest thing in the world. To be a Christian is to believe that a Thérèse of Lisieux in her Carmelite convent is more important in the hierarchy of values than the greatest of political figures or the greatest of scientists. For her importance is of another, and greater, order.

And to be a Christian is to believe that these divine operations are not merely past events, but that we are living in the full tide of sacred history, that we are living in a world in which God continues to act, and that, as the Protestant exegete Cullmann has so beautifully put it, the sacraments are the continuation into the time of the Church of the great works of God in the Old and in the New

Testaments. This is the magnificent proclamation which it is ours to make. This one thing we have to say to the Marxists, to the atheistic humanists, namely, that they miss perceiving the most profound dimension of human existence, which is the one which God brings about in man; ultimately, then, we reproach them with being superficial—with reaching, that is, only the surface of man, and failing to plumb the abysses of existence.

The more I study Marxism, what strikes me most is this same shockingly superficial quality. There may be found in it some things that have validity on the level of the world of appearances, on the level of the dialectic of economic life for example; but it leaves untouched what constitutes man's most essential side. And this is why we are so keenly aware, in rejecting Marxism, that what we are defending is not only God, but man. It is man in the fullness of his dimension, in his threefold relationship, that is, to the world, to other people, and to God. And that is why we shall never desist from our assertion of the divine dimension of human existence, because it seems to us a constituent of the only integral humanism, the only one that gives full justice to the dignity of human nature.

But let us turn directly to the substance of the act of faith. To believe means to believe that the Word of God was made flesh in the womb of Mary. You see the insolence of such an assertion. In the presence of a Marxist, of an atheist, of a scientist, we know what it will provoke. We can imagine what they will begin to say. If we do not dare to take the responsibility for our faith in all its paradoxicalness, if we let it be understood that it might be only a more or less mythological representation of some or other subjective phenomenon, then we have already begun to lighten the ship, and from that moment on have charted a career of betrayals. To be a Christian, in contrast, means insisting that nothing more nor less than this divine irruption into human life is exactly the joyous news, the magnificent, the splendid message that we proclaim. But being a Christian also means being capable of justifying this assertion in our own eyes and in other people's eyes, and our claim to the right to make it.

Regarding the object of faith I should like to make the final point that, since it bears on a divine event, it can only be one and universal. It is not the expression of the religious sensibility of one people or of one race. There is no worse betrayal of the Gospel than to be willing to make it out to be the religion of the West. Christianity is not one certain vision of the world. It is not a system which we accept because it suits us. The one and only problem is to determine whether something did happen. There is no other question. Did Christ rise from the dead or not? If so, this is of absolute interest for any and every man. We are not talking about a symbolization or projection, but about a real event. The question, then, is determining whether this event is real. If I am not persuaded that it is so, then I do not have the faith. I may have a Christian sensibility, I may be desirous that the spiritual values which are those of the Gospel will remain those of the free world, and that civilization will be inspired by the liberal principles I call the Christian mystique rather than by the socialist doctrine of the "people's democracies." But from that moment on, what I am defending is not the faith; it is some liberty or other, which does not come very high anyhow, of whose lesser worth I am aware, and which, like many of my contemporaries, I take advantage of while I have it, but with the vague feeling that it is not worth a whole lot of bother to defend.

We think we have the right to express the affirmations of our faith; we have the right to express them to everyone; and in particular we have the right to tell them to our atheist associates; and, if we have the right, we have necessarily the duty to do so. For if we express it, it is not as a personal opinion, such as we might hesitate to force on other people, but as a fact, one that forces itself upon us, whether it is agreeable to us or disagreeable, whether it follows the line of our own thinking or runs counter to it, whether we find consolation in it or, instead, it is something that balks our determination to run our lives as we please. For me, one of the least satisfactory proofs for the existence of God is the following: "I have a desire for happiness. But no earthly object can fully satisfy this desire. Therefore, God exists." Were I an unbeliever, this reasoning would immediately arouse my suspicions. I should already have a deep-seated impression that God is only the projection into infinity of a certain emotional need of mine and that it was I who was fashioning Him in my own image. No, I experience the fact that He exists because I run up against Him and because, if ever it were I that had fashioned Him, I should certainly have made quite a different job of it. As it is, I am obliged to accommodate myself to Him. I am obliged to take

Him just as He is. No, I never made Him, in my image. I am the one who finally has to come down to doing things His way. And there's the rub that makes me know I am in contact with the real: when I feel, that is, something which resists me, that I have no control of, and that, on the contrary, I must finally end up by adapting myself to, making way, giving up against my will, and while dragging my feet. But there is no way out. This is the way it is, and I have to put up with it. Thus am I aware, in sober fact, that I am in the presence of something real, and no creation of my imagination or of my sensibility.

But for all that, it remains true that affirmation of the faith is an extravagant assertion all the same. The assertion—in the twentieth century—of the Resurrection of the body; the assertion—in the twentieth century—of the Incarnation of the Word in the womb of Mary—all this is outstanding insolence. Do I have the right, in all intellectual honesty, and with all due rigor of thinking, to make these assertions to everybody? To so-and-so, who is a professor at the university? To so-and-so, the great medical specialist? To so-and-so, the great political figure. To . . . [Mao Tse-tung]? To Nasser? Well, what my friend La Pira usually does, when he meets some statesman, is to tell him, right off, that God exists, and that the statesman will be judged by Christ. Only then can their conversation begin. The question is ineluctable. The way so many Christians today put their Christianity in their pocket and consider Christ as something optional is a singular delusion. For the question is to determine whether in fact Christ did arise from the dead. If He did, that fact must determine everything else. Christianity is not a matter of private life. If there is anything in the world that is public, that is official, it is Christianity! For it is something that concerns the ultimate destinies of the whole human race and which for that very good reason has to be taken into account by everybody. This is all that I am saying. And this is the weighty interrogation that we are sitting down to. And that is why we must test the solidity of the bases which are the foundations of our faith, so that it will not be, among us, simply the inheritance of a tradition, sentimentally dear to us, or the expression of a certain bent within our own sensibilities, but will be, after having passed through the sieve of a pitiless criticism, something that continues to hold up, so that we may hold to it in the fullness of an adult existence.

Otherwise, there would always exist in us a more or less bad conscience. Faith, for most of us, is something we received from our families, from our circumtances of life. And it is a great grace to have received it in that way. But we reach an age when we have to embrace it in a personal manner, and embrace it as instinct with difficulties and beset by others' claims and questions. It must not fear critical examination. Criticism of this kind has a very great value, so long as it be remembered that its function is not to destroy, not to undermine (as some of our contemporaries think its function to be), but on the contrary, to test things in order to see whether they stand up. Thus, the business of criticism is to reinforce what is solid and to unsettle what is not; or if you prefer, looking at the matter in a different way, criticism is useful only when it is the expression of love—when it is not, that is, primarily a desire to destroy, but the will to edify in truth.

Now, there is no escaping the fact that if we take a look at the foundations of our faith, there comes at once to mind a host of questions—too many for treatment in this book, but the main ones of which I should like to call to mind, for at this point we reach the essential elements of conscious thought. Among scientists the difficulty is in effect that the intellectual instruments proper to them, of established accuracy in the domains for which they were made, are not utilizable for data in the domain of faith. Whence derives an impression, quite often, of not being on solid ground, of being confronted with a language where meanings are not hard and fast, of being in a field where anybody can say just about anything, since there is no way of determining the truth of anything. As a fellow taxi passenger said to me not very long ago, "It comes to this: Christianity can equally be proved true and be proved not true." The remark is very interesting. If you insist on—this man was a biologist—methods that are proper to physiology, it is plain that you will have no instrument which will allow you to discern, on the level of the data of faith, what is to be retained and to say what is true and what is not true. Whence that feeling on the part of many scientists that in that realm one can say what one likes, and that ultimately—I have heard great scientists say this—you make your choice on purely sub-jective grounds.

Here is something quite grave, first of all because if one chooses for purely subjective reasons, this means that one waives both justifying one's faith in one's own eyes and justifying it in other people's eyes. For, if it is only my feeling, well, then, I have no right to impose my feeling on other people. That would be intellectual imperialism indeed. I have the right simply to propose what I think. But having faith does not mean that at all. Having faith does not consist in saying: "I believe, for my part, that I think . . . anyhow, I just feel that Christianity is truth. . . ." Christ sent me forth into the world, and sent you my readers, whether priests or laymen, not to say, "My feeling is that . . . ," but to proclaim the truth, and not my truth or your truth, but truth, period.

Granted, there remains this great difficulty for scientific minds, namely, admitting that there can be evidence as rigorous in the order of testimony as in the order of positive sciences. This, I need not say, reveals a certain lack of any mind for metaphysics, a deficiency which by the way poses a very great problem from the point of view of scientific humanism. The problem of the scientists preoccupies me a great deal these days. I admire them very much. I think that the future belongs to them. But I think that the big thing they are going to need is the balance of a humanistic education such as their uni-versity unfortunately does not succeed in giving them and for which, consequently, they must look elsewhere. Here is a very great prob-lem. Scientists are called upon to play a decisive role in the world of tomorrow. It is absolutely indispensable that they be furnished with instruments of thought and expression that are really philo-sophical, based on methods just as rigorous as the methods of posi-tive sciences, but which require, as scientific methods do, a formal training.

I confess that I am constantly saddened upon seeing, at various conventions, men who are very great scientists or very great tech-nicians, who are strictly logical and exact when speaking about their specialty, but who, as soon as the talk turns to problems of civiliza-tion, are satisfied with the most lamentable vagueness about "spiritual values"—terms which cover no one has the sightest notion what, and among which reigns the most total confusion. And yet it would seem clearly necessary to know that, when one speaks of "liberty," this can mean five different things at least—and that, in this order, one can have quite as great precision as in the order of scientific problems. There is a rigor of philosophic thought that in its order is absolutely as valid as the rigor of scientific thought.

The problem of testimony arises for men of letters, yet in a different way. The difficulty here is that speech has been so much abused that, finally, one's word is simply no longer taken. The abuse of their word is a characteristic of literary men. A scientist is often someone who has something to say and who is not capable of saying it; a literary man. . . . This is grave. Our world is such an intelligent one! When you sit down with your weekly or monthly review, you have to marvel at the "refinements," the subtleties of modern-day intelligence—at its astonishing capacity to understand everything and to believe nothing. For that is precisely the definition of an intelligent man, according to one brand of intellectuality today. In this view, the exercise of intelligence is the very purpose of intelligence. And the quality of the language is a more serious matter than any content of the writer's word. To believe in truth reveals in these people's eyes a medieval mentality which is the stamp of only a few old-fashioned minds. This raises very serious questions.

This is the great problem, and it is grave. For it is on a person's word in the very first instance that human relationships rest. For a world where people no longer believe other people's word is a world where any trust becomes out of the question. And it may be wondered whether this spirit of distrust is not poisoning personal relationships among men today. Is there not a kind of doubting-sickness at work at the core of men's souls and destroying even the possibility of communication? And on the level even of our faith do we not harbor a low-grade infection of doubt, such as to make us wonder whether we have ever made an act of theological faith in the full sense of the word, that is, one in which our intelligence is engaged in totally eliminating every reserve, every evasion. I am speaking not of some kind of bet, but of an act totally involving our intelligence with the Word of Christ, without reserving anything to ourselves. And is there not, in this last bit of reserve which we keep so often in connection with faith itself, a certain determination on the part of our intelligence to depend exclusively upon itself, a certain difficulty in giving in, particularly under that pre-eminent form of surrender which is the surrender of the intelligence. This surrender we must never make easily; yet are there not cases where we have the right to make it? Here we reach the rock bottom of the reason why it is so hard for men of today to understand how an act of faith is possible and, even [when] they admit it as possible, to make that act of faith in the full sense of the word. The very idea of being able to speak of absolute truth as based on testimony seems inacceptable.

Now, staying on the human level, without speaking here yet of the testimony of the Gospel directly, we must say that testimony is a way of reaching certitude, a way as valid, in its order, as scientific demonstrations and experiments are in their order. Moreover, this way is the only one which affords access to one certain order of reality. This order of reality is nothing less than the order of persons. Now, if the universe of persons has infinite ascendancy over the order of the natural world, we must declare that the higher we go in the hierarchy of beings, the more does testimony, and not experimentation, become the means of knoweldge.

I shall explain these matters further. Experimentation has to do essentially with the order of things which are inferior to man. It bears upon objects. But someone else's person is something of which we can never make an object. We can know another person only to the extent that he chooses to reveal himself to us. And he can reveal himself to us only by giving us his word about himself. This is tantamount to saying that ultimately it is on another's word that we must rely in order to know him. And consequently, on this level, the testimony of someone's word is the sole means of communication among persons. How, then, if God is personal in a pre-eminent degree, and if even on the human level we cannot know the secret of others' persons except to the degree they choose to reveal it to us, how, I say, could we ever know the secret of God otherwise than in the measure in which God chooses to reveal it to us?

Testimony, then, appears as the mode of knowledge which corresponds to higher objects, and furthermore as a means of knowledge which is susceptible, in its own order, of a rigorousness quite equal to that of physical or mathematical demonstrations in their order.

This is obvious enough when we turn to historical sciences. No one would dream of questioning the existence of Napoleon or of Julius Caesar. Yet we do not know these men except through others' testimony. In the order of human relations, I do not know the love of another except through his own avowal. The problem is to determine whether I can place my trust in his word. Now, there are cases where I have, not only the right, but even the duty, to trust in this word, and where it would be absurd not to do so. Inability to trust others is one of the maladies of intelligence in our day.

It is therefore legitimate under certain conditions to credit testimony as true. Are these conditions verified in the case of the testimony given by Christ? Here we are at the heart of the problem which we must undertake to solve. There is one preliminary question. It is really not worth delaying with; still, reference must be made to it, for even in this day and age we still meet people who ask it. It is the question of the historicity of Christ. It puts us in the area of historical sciences in the most commonplace sense of the word: Have we the right to consider the Gospels, St. Paul's Epistles, and the Acts of the Apostles as documents of a historicity sufficient to warrant our reliance on them for our assertion that a Jesus of Nazareth actually existed, and lived in Galilee? There is no doubt about it in the mind of any scholar of standing. And discoveries during recent years (I am thinking especially of the Qumran finds, with which I am personally occupied) in fact confirm the validity of the data presented to us in the Gospels.

But this brings us, as a second step, beyond the Apostles' assertion about Christ, to what constitutes the very foundation of our faith—Christ's own assertion about Himself. Here the problem is to determine whether Christ is so reliable a witness that when He tells us that He is God come among men (an assertion, we repeat, in itself incredible), we have a right to believe Him—not only a right, but a duty. We have to be able, I mean, to say to our associates: "If you examine the problem objectively, you will be led to submit to the truth of what I am telling you; this is not a subjective opinion, but a reality which, I can honestly assure you, anyone in good faith will be brought to agree with."

What are the data in question? There is one thing that by and large the whole Gospel testifies to; that is that Christ presented Himself not simply as a man, but as coming from God, and as being of the same order as God. That He did so is a primary fact, scientifically established. We are not here taking His discourses as evidence, for if it were a question of these alone, they could always be called into question, and parts pointed to as interpolations; no, we are taking the whole of Christ's behavior, during His entire life. What we are saying is that the life of Christ is inexplicable if He was not claiming for Himself divine nature and divine authority. What I mean by that is that the public life of Christ was one long, constant conflict with the Jews. Now, the sole motive of the Jews' hostility toward Christ was the accusation of blasphemy brought against Him. This accusation is the great witness to the divinity of Christ, because it was rendered by His adversaries, the testimony given by an adversary always being less suspect of complicity.

This accusation of blasphemy, which the Jews never stopped bringing against Christ, reveals in effect that one thing is certain, namely, that Christ never stopped claiming for Himself an authority equal to God's. Two or three examples of this claim will suffice here. In the Sermon on the Mount Christ said: "You have heard that it was said, An eye for an eye and a tooth for a tooth. But I tell you that you should not offer resistance to injury." Have heard that it was said by whom? By Yahweh, who had given the Decalogue on Sinai. Christ, therefore, was claiming for Himself an authority equal to Yahweh's. Some years ago a rabbi said something to me which I have often quoted since: "You see, there is just one thing that we Jews have against Christ, and that is that he altered the Law. For the Law was given by God. And only God can alter what He has set forth." My response was: "You could say nothing that would please me more. I shall borrow your whole argument. The Law was set forth by God; only God can alter what was set forth by God. Therefore, if Jesus believed He had a right to alter the Law, it must be that Jesus considered Himself to be God." The rabbi was giving me one of the most striking demonstrations of the divinity of Christ, or at least was giving me iron-clad proof that there is one thing absolutely certain, and that is that Christ represented Himself to be God.

Well, then, there are three solutions possible. One, He was a visionary, a mystic of some sort lost in the clouds and fancying Himself God among men. Two, He was a liar; this thesis was sustained once, in the eighteenth century. Or, three, He was telling the truth, and extraordinary though it seem, had the right to call Himself the Son of God. Just three attitudes may be taken toward Christ as presented in the Gospels: putting Him down as a madman, or else as a liar, or acknowledging, with all the improbability of the claim, that He was right. The tragedy of the Jewish people was that they had no other possible choice than to believe in Him or to condemn Him to death. For if Christ had not the grounds for calling Himself the Son of God, He was a monster of pride. And from the Jewish point of view He committed the worst of transgressions, a sacrilege which, no less for us today, is the greatest of all sacrileges, a man's ambition to make himself God. The greatness of Judaism, like the greatness of Islam, lies in its denouncing idolatry, in its insisting that "God alone is God," in its denouncing man's every pretention to make himself God. The only problem is to determine whether there is not *one* case, a unique case, when a Person Who was a man had the right to say that He was God.

Now, is it possible to say that Christ was a madman, or a liar? There is one thing on which all men are in agreement, whether Christians, Jews, Moslems, Hindus, or even atheists, and that is that Jesus represents, at the very least, one of the very highest peaks of human nature. There are few men who do not love Christ. Gandhi considered Him the greatest figure in human history. Mohammed, in the Koran, assigned Him an elevated place, and saw in Him the greatest of the prophets. The Jewish writer Edmond Fleg has given us an admirable work representing Jesus as seen by the wandering Jew. And numerous are the Jews today who consider Christ one of the most marvelous men whom the race of Israel has produced. A socialist like Barbusse wrote a book presenting Christ as one of the most admirable figures in the brotherhood of mankind. Thus, all men without exception are united in saying that Christ represents one of the peaks, and doubtless the highest peak, of human history. Is it possible to say at the same time that this man was a liar or a madman?

Since it is absolutely certain that on the human level Christ represented Himself as being God, and since it is absolutely certain that on the human level He was one of the most admirable figures in human history, then this problem confronts every man: That Christ was God is perhaps improbable; yet it would be a serious matter to reject Christ's testimony. If I refuse to accept His testimony, then no human witness is worthy of belief. For if I have no right to believe Christ, whom have I grounds for believing? And I therefore do have the right, in all conscience, with clear mind and with full intellectual rigor, to say: "What Christ said is in fact improbable; and yet I must consider that He seems to me a witness of such genuineness that I have the right, on grounds of faith in His testimony, to believe the improbable."

I must add that up to this point I have restricted myself to a field accessible, not only to a Christian, but also to a Jew, a Moslem, or any man. In what I have said until now, I have included nothing which calls faith into play, nothing that cannot be accepted by any just man. Thereafter comes the final and decisive step, whereby I shall see in Christ not only human testimony such as appears to me a guarantee of credibility, but the very word of God made man. The adherence of my intelligence in its supreme expression will rest upon God's very word as upon an absolutely unshakable rock. At that moment I shall make my act of faith, commit my intelligence absolutely on the testimony of Jesus Christ, and have found an unshakable position from which I can confront all difficulties, all objections, and all doubts.

I shall add, finally, that Christ has given as a mission to His Church the transmitting of this testimony from generation to generation. The Church is nothing other than a group of men officially delegated by the Trinity with the duty of announcing perpetually, to all men, without exception, the coming judgment and the salvation given by Christ to enable them to do penance. The Church in particular speaks to . . . Mao Tse-tung . . . to Nasser, to the chiefs of state of all the world. The Church has the duty, perpetually, to tell all men what concerns every man without exception. And this testimony, when we have studied it throughout the 2000 years during which we have seen it developed, when we have seen its permanence throughout all the vicissitudes of the individuals who have borne it, when we have seen its fecundity in the souls of the saints, will then appear, itself, something so solid that we cannot fail to acknowledge in it the work of God nor to feel that we have an absolute right to place trust in it.

We are not here preaching our own ideas. We are simply saying to those around us: "I give you my assurance that here is something real, something to which you ought to be attentive, something which is truly essential in a man's life. And this I tell you because I love you and because I sincerely desire to see you share the discovery which has been mine." In such a case, the witness we bear has nothing about it of any sort of propaganda, or of any sort of intrusion into the lives of others; it is simply the desire to share the evidence of what we live by, the ultimate certitude which we possess ourselves.

I shall conclude by answering a final objection. I recall a meeting where once upon a time an eminent professor of the Sorbonne told us: "What puts me off about the faith is a certain comfortableness, something a thought middle class, something a shade like having arrived as regards one's thinking." Is it absolutely sure that what kept that man from being a Christian was the fear of comfort? Is it an absolutely sure thing that it is more comfortable to be Christian than to be not Christian? As for me, I am not persuaded of that at all. What I am convinced of, in contrast, is that the condition of a Christian, to the extent that being a Christian means agreeing to be at the disposition of someone else, is something extraordinarily uncomfortable! And you know it very well. When it comes right down to it, what puts you off is that once you set the wheels rolling you don't know how far you're liable to go. No, this, we know very well, is what keeps those without faith from having faith. And it is also what keeps those who do have faith from having more faith. We know, as Rivière put it so well, that "love involves staggering complications." We are always taking something upon ourselves when we introduce somebody else into our life, even from the human point of view. We know that no longer shall we be altogether our own man. Therein lies the adventuresomeness of human love as well as the self-sacrifice involved in it. When it comes down to it, if a man wishes to be undisturbed, he just has to give up the notion of marrying. Well, then! To allow Christ to enter our life is a terrible, terrible, terrible risk. What will it lead to? And faith—is precisely that.

So, no one will ever bring me to believe that faith is some kind of comfort. To take Christ seriously means allowing the irruption into one's life of Absolute Love, and allowing oneself to be led on to heaven knows what point. And this very risk is at the same time a deliverance, for, when all is said and done, we know very well that we ultimately desire just one thing—absolute love—and in the final tally, if it despoils us of ourselves, it leads us to what is better than ourselves. This means—and this is what seems to me essential—that faith is not a way of landing on one's feet at the end of intellectual adventures, a sort of quiet one rewards oneself with after intellectual turmoil. Faith is not an end. It is a beginning. It introduces our intelligence into the most marvelous of adventures, into what is *its* real destiny, namely, one day to contemplate the Trinity. It is a magnificent act in which, sensing the limits of our own understanding, we allow the uncreated Word of God to seize our intelligence and elevate it above itself to enable it to breast its highest hills.

Nor will this adventure ever have an end. The Church is magnificently optimistic enough to hold that the faith will seize us to wrest us from our individual slaveries and catch us up in an adventure which will fill our eternity and will consist in the ever more astonished discovery of the living God. How this is supposed to have some kind of taint of middle-class life or of comfortableness I just can't say.

BIBLIOGRAPHY

Part One

Abernathy, George L., and Thomas A. Langford, *Philosophy of Religion*. New York: The Macmillan Company, 1962.

Buber, Martin, *Good and Evil*. New York: Charles Scribner's Sons, 1953.

Farrer, Austin, *Love Almighty and Ills Unlimited*. Garden City, N.Y.: Doubleday & Company, Inc., 1961.

Lavelle, L., *Evil and Suffering*. New York: The Macmillan Company, 1963.

Lewis, C. S., *The Problem of Pain*. New York: The Macmillan Company, 1944.

MacGregor, Geddes and J. Wesley Robb, *Readings in Religious Philosophy*. Boston: Houghton Mifflin Company, 1962.

Petit, Francois, *The Problem of Evil*, Christopher Williams, trans. New York: Hawthorn Books, Inc., 1959.

Pike, Nelson, *God and Evil*. Englewood Cliffs, N.J.: Prentice-Hall, Inc., 1964.

Part Two

Collin, Rémy, *Evolution*, J. Tester, trans. New York: Hawthorn Books, Inc., 1959.

Corte, Nicholas, *The Origins of Man*, Eric Earnshaw, trans. New York: Hawthorn Books, Inc., 1959.

De Fraine, Jean, *The Bible and the Origin of Man*. New York: Desclée Co., 1961.

Dobzhansky, Theodosius, *Evolution, Genetics and Man*. New York: John Wiley & Sons, Inc., 1955.

Fothergill, P. G., *Evolution and Christians*. New York: David McKay Co., Inc., 1961.

Greene, John C., *Darwin and the Modern World View*. Baton Rouge: Louisiana State University Press, 1961.

Hutchings, Edward M., Jr., ed., *Frontiers in Science*. New York: Basic Books, Inc., 1958.

Huxley, Julian, *Essays of a Humanist*. New York: Harper & Row, Publishers, 1964.

————, *Evolution: The Modern Synthesis*. New York: Harper & Row, Publishers, 1942.

Mascall, Eric L., *Christian Theology and Natural Science*. New York: David McKay Co., Inc., 1961.

Nicholl, Donald, *Recent Thought in Focus*. New York: Sheed & Ward, 1952.

Noger, Raymond J., *The Wisdom of Evolution*. Garden City, N.Y.: Doubleday & Company, Inc., 1963.

Ong, Walter J., ed., *Darwin's Vision and Christian Perspectives*. New York: The Macmillan Company, 1960.

Simpson, George G., *The Meaning of Evolution*. New Haven, Conn.: Yale University Press, 1949.

Symposium on Evolution. Pittsburgh: Duquesne University Press, 1959.

Tax, Sol, ed., *Evolution after Darwin*, Vols. II and III. Chicago: University of Chicago Press, 1960.

Teilhard de Chardin, Pierre, *The Phenomenon of Man*, Bernard Wall, trans. New York: Harper & Row, Publishers, 1961.

Part Three

Asimov, Isaac, *Intelligent Man's Guide to Science*. New York: Basic Books, Inc., 1960.

Bondi, H., and others, *Rival Theories of Cosmology*. New York: Oxford University Press, Inc., 1960.

Exploring the Universe, American Foundation for Continuing Education. New York: McGraw-Hill Book Company, 1963.

Gamow, George, *The Creation of the Universe*. New York: New American Library of World Literature, 1952.

Heim, Karl, *The World: Its Creation and Consummation*. Philadelphia: Fortress Press, 1962.

Hoyle, Fred, *The Nature of the Universe*. New York: Harper & Row, Publishers, 1960.

Koestler, Arthur, *The Sleepwalkers*. New York: The Macmillan Company, 1963.

Lovell, A. C. B., *The Individual and the Universe*. New York: New American Library of World Literature, 1959.

Lyttleton, R. A., *The Modern Universe*. New York: Harper & Row, Publishers, 1956.

Mascall, Eric L., *Christian Theology and Natural Science*. New York: David McKay Co., Inc., 1956.

Munitz, M. K., ed., *Theories of the Universe*. New York: Free Press of Glencoe, Inc., 1957.

Pfeiffer, John, *From Galaxies to Man*. New York: Basic Books, Inc., 1959.

Smart, J. J. C., ed., *Problems of Space and Time*. New York: The Macmillan Company, 1964.

The Universe, editors of Scientific American. New York: Simon and Schuster, Inc., 1957.

Part Four

Allport, Gordon W., *Becoming*. New Haven, Conn.: Yale University Press, 1955.
Asimov, Isaac, *Intelligent Man's Guide to Science*. New York: Basic Books, Inc., 1960.
Biot, Rene, *What is Life?* Eric Smith, trans. New York: Hawthorn Books, Inc., 1959.
D'Arcy, Martin C., S.J., *Death and Life*. New York: David McKay Co., Inc., 1948.
————, *No Absent God*. New York: Harper & Row, Publishers, 1962.
Farrer, Austin M., *The Freedom of the Will*. New York: Charles Scribner's Sons, 1960.
Flew, Antony, *Body, Mind, and Death*. New York: The Macmillan Company, 1964.
Jung, Carl G., *Modern Man in Search of a Soul*, W. S. Dell and Cary F. Baynes, trans. New York: Harcourt, Brace & World, Inc., 1950.
Mascall, Eric L., *Christian Theology and Natural Science*. New York: David McKay Co., Inc., 1956.
May, Rollo, ed., *Existence*. New York: Basic Books, Inc., 1958.
New York University Institute of Philosophy, *Determinism and Freedom: In the Age of Modern Science*, Sidney Hook, ed. New York: The Macmillan Company, 1961.
Pontifex, Mark, *Freedom and Providence*. New York: Hawthorn Books, Inc., 1960.
Scher, Jordan M., *Theories of the Mind*. New York: Free Press of Glencoe, Inc., 1962.
Stern, Karl, *The Third Revolution*. New York: Harcourt, Brace, & World, Inc., 1954.
Strasser, Stephan, *The Soul in Metaphysical and Empirical Psychology*. Pittsburgh: Duquesne University Press, 1957.
Teilhard de Chardin, Pierre, *The Future of Man*, Norman Denny, trans. New York: Harper & Row, Publishers, 1964.
White, Victor, O.P., *Soul and Psyche*. London: Collins and Harvill Press, 1960.
Wiener, Norbert, *Cybernetics*. Cambridge, Mass.: MIT Press, 1961

Part Five

Eliade, Mircea, *Patterns in Comparative Religion*, Rosemary Sheed, trans. New York: Sheed & Ward, 1958.
Freud, Sigmund, *Moses and Monotheism*. New York: Alfred A. Knopf, Inc., 1955.
————, *Totem and Taboo*. New York: W. W. Norton & Company, Inc., 1952.

Herskovits, Melville J., *Man and His Works*. New York: Alfred A. Knopf, Inc., 1951.

Hoebel, Edward A., *Man in the Primitive World*. New York: McGraw-Hill Book Company, 1958.

Karl Marx and Friedrich Engels on Religion. Intro. by Reinhold Niebuhr. New York: Schocken Books, 1964.

Karrer, Otto, *Religions of Mankind*, E. I. Watkin, trans. New York: Sheed & Ward, 1936.

Kaufmann, W., ed., *Religion from Tolstoy to Camus*. New York: Harper & Row, Publishers, 1961.

Lessa, William A., and Evon Z. Vogt, *Reader in Comparative Religion*. New York: Harper & Row, Publishers, 1958.

Lissner, Ivan, *Man, God and Magic*, J. Maxwell Brownjohn, trans. New York: G. P. Putnam's Sons, 1961.

MacGregor, Geddes, and J. Wesley Robb, *Readings in Religious Philosophy*. Boston: Houghton Mifflin Company, 1962.

Malinowski, Bronislaw, *Magic, Science and Religion, and Other Essays*. Garden City, N.Y.: Doubleday & Company, Inc., 1954.

Philp, Howard L., *Freud and Religious Belief*. London: Rockliff, 1956.

Schmidt, Wilhelm, *Origin and Growth of Religion*, H. J. Rose, trans. New York: The Dial Press, Inc., 1931.

Yinger, John M., *Religion, Society, and the Individual*. New York: The Macmillan Company, 1957.

Zilboorg, Gregory, *Freud and Religion*. Westminster, Md.: Newman Press, 1958.

Part Six

Bouquet, A. C., *Comparative Religion*. Baltimore: Penguin Books, Inc., 1941.

Conze, Edward, *Buddhism: Its Essence and Development*. New York: Harper & Row, Publishers, 1959.

Daniélou, Alain, *Hindu Polytheism*. New York: Bollingen Foundation, 1964.

Daniélou, Jean, *God and the Ways of Knowing*, Walter Roberts, trans. New York: Meridian Books, 1960.

D'Arcy, Martin C., *The Mind and Heart of Love*. New York: Holt, Rinehart & Winston, Inc., 1947.

Dechanet, Jean M., *Christian Yoga*, Roland Hindmarsh, trans. New York: Harper & Row, Publishers, 1960.

Dumoulin, Heinrich, *A History of Zen Buddhism*. New York: Pantheon Books, Inc., 1963.

Gard, Richard A., ed., *Buddhism*. New York: George Braziller, Inc., 1961.

Gardet, Louis, *Mohammedanism*, William Burridge, trans. New York: Hawthorn Books, Inc., 1961.

Graham, Aelred, *Zen Catholicism; a Suggestion*. New York: Harcourt, Brace, & World, Inc., 1963.

Hardon, John, *Religions of the World*. Westminster, Md.: Newman Press, 1963.

Jurji, Edward J., *The Great Religions of the Modern World*. Princeton, N.J.: Princeton University Press, 1946.

Koestler, Arthur, *The Lotus and the Robot*. London: Hutchinson & Co., Ltd., 1960.

Kraemer, Hendrik, *World Cultures and World Religions; the Coming Dialogue*. Philadelphia: Westminster Press, 1960.

Lemaître, Solange, *Hinduism*, John F. Brown, trans. New York: Hawthorn Books, Inc., 1959.

McKain, David W., ed., *Christianity: Some Non-Christian Appraisals*. New York: McGraw-Hill Book Company, 1964.

Macnicol, Nicol, ed., *Hindu Scriptures*. New York: E. P. Dutton & Co., Inc., 1938.

Mascaró, Juan, trans., *The Bhagavad-Gita*. Baltimore: Penguin Books, Inc., 1962.

Neil, Stephen, *Christian Faith and Other Faiths*. London: Oxford University Press, 1961.

Noss, John B., *Man's Religions*. New York: The Macmillan Company, 1963.

Parrinder, Geoffrey, *Comparative Religion*. London: George Allen and Unwin, 1962.

———, *Upanishads-Gita and Bible*. London: Faber & Faber, Ltd., 1962.

Percheron, Maurice, *Buddha and Buddhism*, Edmund Stapleton, trans. New York: Harper & Row, Publishers, 1957.

Renou, Louis, ed., *Hinduism*. New York: George Braziller, Inc., 1961.

Smith, Huston, *The Religions of Man*. New York: New American Library of World Literature, 1959.

Tillich, Paul, *Christianity and the Encounter of the World Religions*. New York: Columbia University Press, 1963.

Zaehner, Robert C., *At Sundry Times*. London: Faber & Faber, Ltd., 1958.

———, *The Comparison of Religions*. Boston: Beacon Press, Inc., 1962.

———, *The Concise Encyclopedia of Living Faiths*. New York: Hawthorn Books, Inc., 1959.

———, *Hinduism*. London: Oxford University Press, 1962.

———, *Matter and Spirit*. New York: Harper & Row, Publishers, 1963.

Part Seven

Abelé, Jean, *Christianity and Science*, R. F. Trevett, trans. New York: Hawthorn Books, Inc., 1961.

Abernathy, George L., and Thomas A. Langford, *Philosophy of Religion*. New York: The Macmillan Company, 1962.

Baille, John, and Hugh Martin, eds., *Revelation*. London: Faber & Faber, Ltd., 1937.

Borne, Étienne, *Atheism*, S. J. Tester, trans. New York: Hawthorn Books, Inc., 1961.

Camus, Albert, *The Myth of Sisyphus and Other Essays*. New York: Albert A. Knopf, Inc., 1955.

Colodny, Robert G., ed., *Frontiers of Science and Philosophy*. Pittsburg: University of Pittsburg Press, 1963.

Daniélou, Jean, *God and the Ways of Knowing*, Walter Roberts, trans. New York: Meridian Books, 1960.

D'Arcy, Martin C., *Death and Life*. New York: David McKay Co., Inc., 1948.

————, *The Nature of Belief*. New York: Sheed & Ward, 1931.

Dondeyne, Albert, *Contemporary European Thought and the Christian Faith*. Pittsburgh: Duquesne University Press, 1958.

Flew, Antony, and Alasdair Macintyre, *New Essays in Philosophical Theology*. London: SCM Press, Ltd., 1955.

Hartshorne, Charles, and William L. Reese, eds., *Philosophers Speak of God*. Chicago: University of Chicago Press, 1953.

Hick, John, ed., *The Existence of God*. New York: The Macmillan Company, 1964.

Hoyle, Fred, *Man and Materialism*. New York: Harper & Row, Publishers, 1956.

Huxley, Julian, *Essays of a Humanist*. New York: Harper & Row, Publishers, 1964.

Jolivet, Regis, *The God of Reason*, Mark Pontifex, trans. New York: Hawthorn Books, Inc., 1958.

Joly, Eugene, *What is Faith?* Illtyd Trethowan, trans. New York: Hawthorn Books, Inc., 1958.

Lepp, Ignace, *Atheism in our Times*. New York: The Macmillan Company, 1963.

MacGregor, Geddes, and J. Wesley Robb, *Readings in Religious Philosophy*. Boston: Houghton Mifflin Company, 1962.

Newman, James R., ed., *What Is Science?* New York: Simon and Schuster, Inc., 1955.

Ramsey, Ian T., ed., *Prospect for Metaphysics*. New York: Philosophical Library, 1961.

Rapport, Samuel, and Helen Wright, *Science, Method, and Meaning*. New York: New York University Press, 1963.

Robinson, John A. T., *Honest to God*. Philadelphia: The Westminster Press, 1963.

Shapley, H., ed., *Science Ponders Religion*. New York: Appleton-Century-Crofts, 1960.

Taylor, Frank S., *Concerning Science*. London: Macdonald, 1949.

Van Melsen, A. G., *Science and Technology*. Pittsburgh: Duquesne University Press, 1961.

Whitehead, Alfred North, *Science and the Modern World*. New York: The Macmillan Company, 1925. (Also published in paperback.)